The Layman's Dictionary of Psychiatry

Everyday Handbooks

The Layman's Dictionary of Psychiatry

James A. Brussel, M.D.

George La Fond Cantzlaar

Barnes and Noble, Inc.   New York

Booksellers & Publishers   Since 1873

To

AUDREY SCHUMAN BRUSSEL

and

MAYME BASSETT CANTZLAAR

Acknowledgments

A dictionary does not spring from the minds of its authors alone. As Kipling wrote:

> When 'Omer smote 'is bloomin' lyre,
> He'd 'eard men sing by land an' sea;
> An' what he thought 'e might require,
> 'E went an' took—the same as me!

The authors of *The Layman's Dictionary of Psychiatry* would feel it remiss not to mention the works they consulted to strengthen their belief in the need to include certain terms, to avoid chance duplications of existing definitions, and to seek areas where improved definitions were most needed. We referred most often to the following:

DICTIONARIES

A Psychiatric Word Book, ed. Hutchings (7th ed.; N.Y.: States Hospital Press, 1943)

Dorland's Illustrated Medical Dictionary (24th ed.; Phila.: Saunders, 1965)

Gould's Medical Dictionary, eds. Brownlow and others (5th ed.; Phila.: Blakiston, 1941)

Psychiatric Dictionary, eds. Hinsie and Campbell (3rd ed.; N.Y.: Oxford University Press, 1960)

Stedman's Medical Dictionary, eds. Asimov and others (20th ed.; Baltimore: Williams & Wilkins, 1961)

Webster's New International Dictionary of the English Language, Unabridged (3rd ed.; Springfield: G. & C. Merriam., 1961)

ENCYCLOPEDIAS, HISTORIES, AND GUIDES

A History of Medical Psychology, Zilboorg & Henry (1st ed.; N.Y.: W. W. Norton, 1941)

A *History of Medicine*, Major (1st ed.; Springfield: Thomas, 1954)

Physician's Guide to Psychiatric Tests and Terminology, Schering Corp., 1958

REFERENCE BOOKS

Abnormal Psychology, Coville and others (1st ed.; N.Y.: Barnes & Noble, 1960)

Clinical Neurology, Wechsler (8th ed.; Phila.: Saunders, 1958)

Clinical Psychiatry, Noyes (4th ed.; Phila.: Saunders, 1953)

Outline of Psychiatry, Cammer (1st ed.; N.Y.: McGraw-Hill, 1962)

Principles of Internal Medicine, Harrison and others (4th ed.; N.Y.: McGraw-Hill, 1962)

Psychosomatic Medicine, Weiss and English (3rd ed.; Phila.: Saunders, 1957)

We wish to pay special tribute to Dr. Laurence F. Hawkins formerly of the Barnes & Noble editorial staff. His critical approach to many of our definitions as they were originally phrased and his scrupulous insistence on the *mot juste*, contributed much to the clarity of the book. To Dr. Samuel Smith, editor-in-chief, goes our deep appreciation for his encouragement of our effort. We are also grateful to Mr. Louis Mindell for his expert and painstaking review of the proofs.

JAMES A. BRUSSEL
GEORGE L. CANTZLAAR

About the Authors

JAMES ARNOLD BRUSSEL, M.D., is Assistant Commissioner of Mental Hygiene for the State of New York. A graduate of the University of Pennsylvania School of Medicine, Dr. Brussel took advanced studies at Columbia University and the New York State Psychiatric Institute. He is a practicing psychiatrist and neurologist, holding American Board certifications in both specialties. He has served as director of New York State's After-Care Program for the mentally ill and was a pioneer in the development of the Interstate Mental Health Compact. In World War II, while chief of neuropsychiatry at Fort Dix, Dr. Brussel introduced the Rorschach Psychodiagnostic Method into military psychiatry. An associate editor of *The Psychiatric Quarterly*, Dr. Brussel has made many contributions to encyclopedias, dictionaries, and professional journals. He also serves as consultant to the New York City Police Department and the city courts. Dr. Brussel is the author of *The Layman's Guide to Psychiatry*, a Barnes & Noble Everyday Handbook.

GEORGE LA FOND CANTZLAAR has been active in the field of mental health for more than three decades. A graduate of Colgate University, he has been assistant editor of the *The Psychiatric Quarterly* and editor of *Mental Hygiene News*. He was the first director of public relations for the New York State Department of Mental Hygiene. Mr. Cantzlaar assisted the late Dr. Richard Hutching in revising *A Psychiatric Word Book* and worked closely with Drs. Edward Weiss and O. Spurgeon English in the preparation of two editions of *Psychosomatic Medicine*. He has served as a director of the Mental Health Society of Southwestern Florida and was editor of the Proceedings of the second and third Psychosurgical Conferences conducted by Columbia University and the National Institute of Mental Health. Mr. Cantzlaar is the author of *Your Guide to the Weather*, a Barnes & Noble Everyday Handbook.

Note to Reader

The reader is counseled to avoid a hasty application of descriptive psychiatric terms to particular persons and circumstances. It is wise to bear in mind that the key to the mental or emotional state of an individual is not to be found in a single behavior pattern or psychosomatic syndrome. Even the trained psychiatrist hesitates to affix labels to a patient on the basis of a few observations or interviews, and he never attempts an interpretation or a diagnosis without a thorough study of the fullest possible account of the patient's life history.

Many psychiatric terms describe reactions which have both normal and abnormal manifestations. For example, the word *ablutomania* is properly used when an individual is an abject slave to the impulse to wash himself almost continuously. But this does not mean that a certain amount of attention to personal cleanliness, even when carried to some extreme, is to be regarded as a sign of mental disturbance. Another area where this caution should be heeded is that of –*phobias*, –*philias*, and –*manias*, all combining forms indicating extreme dislike (fear), affection for, and reaction to, respectively. The reader may be inclined to ask whether fear of snakes (*ophidiophobia*), for example, is not a normal reaction. In reply, the reader's attention is directed to the entry *phobia*, where the criteria for *phobia* in the psychopathologic sense are stated.

Next, the authors wish to point out that only a few of the myriad combining forms of the above are in this dictionary. Indeed, the reader could, on his own, construct such terms to suit innumerable phenomena and situations. Most of them, however, would only describe circumstances in which other, more basic, reactions were involved. Those listed here are the more frequently encountered conditions. The reader may note that many –*phobias* have counterparts; thus, *gerontophobia*– *gerontophilia* or *pyrophobia*–*pyromania*. The reader may be tempted to conclude that for every *phobia* there is an antonymous –*philia*, but clinical experience does not support this notion. If the converse forms are not found in the dictionary, the chances are that they are not commonly used in psychiatry. There are other combining forms which are used with other Latin and Greek prefixes and suffixes. For example, the prefix *a*– will be recognized as meaning "without" or "having a negative force," whereas *dys*– will be interpreted as "faulty" or "partially disturbed." For example, *alexia*, inability to read; *dyslexia*, impairment of reading ability.

Not a few words in the psychiatric idiom have been shortened, and the shorter forms are in common usage, such as *neurosis* for *psychoneurosis* and *analysis* for *psychoanalysis*. In most cases, both forms are given, with variant spellings and synonyms and related terms. Some of the words listed may strike the reader as being plain-language, nontechnical words; other words are used popularly even though they are derived from the language of psychiatry and psychology. These latter words usually have a more precise definition as psychiatric terms than they do when they are used otherwise. *Censorship*, thus, has a very particular significance in psychoanalysis; *affect*, as a noun, is used in a special sense as well.

As these terms are used, and, as they become more familiar to the reader, he will be able to extrapolate from one usage of a combining form to another of the same form, and, at least superficially, recognize the meaning. Most readers will already know such combining forms as *para*–(resembling), *pseudo*–(false), *homo*–(of or toward the same kind), *hetero*–(of or toward other kinds), and so on. Other forms are less well known, and the authors believe that the following list of these combining forms, approached through ordinary English words, will be useful to most readers. Those listed here provide the roots for nearly 40 percent of the words defined in this dictionary, and this figure probably represents their incidence in psychiatric language.

Ordinary word	Combining form	Examples
appetite	*or*	acoria, anorexia
body	*soma*	somatogenic, psychoso- matic, somatotype
brain	*ceph, enceph*	cephalgia, encephalitis, brachycephalia
disease, disorder	*path*	pathergasia, sociopathy
drinking, thirst	*dips*	dipsomania, polydipsia
eating	*phag*	geophagia, scotophagia
energy	*erg*	erg(as)iophobia, merergasia
excitement	*mania*	kleptomania, necromania
expression of ideas	*phas*	aphasia, heterophasia, logophasia
fear of	*phobia*	batophobia, keraunophobia, ichthyophobia
feeling	*phoria*	euphoria, haptodysphoria
fondness	*philia*	epistemophilia, ophidio- philia, pedophilia
hatred of	*mis*	misogyny, misopedia
hearing	*acous*	acousma, hyperacousia
love	*erot*	erotomania, autoerotic
lust	*lag*	coprolagnia, lagneuomania
memory	*mnem*	amnesia, anamnesis
men	*andr*	andromania, androgyny
mind, mental	*psych*	allopsychic, psychosis, psychopathology
movement	*kin, prax*	kinesthesia, hyperkinesia, eupraxia
pain	*alg*	algolagnia, haphalgesia, psychalgesia
people	*anthrop*	anthrophobia, hippanthropy
pleasure	*(h)edon*	algedonics, hedonophobia
reading	*lex*	bradylexia, dyslexia
seeing, being seen	*op, scop*	amblyopia, micropsia, scopolagnia
sensation	*esthes*	estheticokinetic, anesthesia, hyperesthesia
sleep, sleeplike	*hypn*	hypnolepsy, parahypnosis
smell	*os*	anosmia, osmodysphoria, osphresiolagnia
speaking	*lal, log*	glossolalia, tachylogia, logorrhea
	phras, phem	embolophrasia, heterophemia

Ordinary word	Combining form	Examples
standing	*stas*	dystasia, astasia
taste	*geus(t)*	cacogeusia, ageustia
touch	*aph, haph, hapt*	anaphia, haphalgia, haptodysphoria
understanding	*gnos*	acroagnosis, abarognosia
walking	*bas*	abasia, basiphobia
will	*b(o)ul*	ab(o)ulia, bulimia
women	*gyn*	gynecomania
writing	*graph*	dermatographic, palingraphia

abaissement. Janet's term for the weakening of the ego's ability to ignore or resist a powerful demand from the id. It occurs temporarily in such states as exhaustion, fever, severe emotional upset, intoxication, and normal sleep. It persists in neurotic and schizophrenic depression.

abarognosia, -sis. Loss of ability to appreciate weight or pressure. Syn. *baragnosia, baroagnosis.* Cf. *barognosis.*

abasia. Lack of proper muscular coordination in walking, seen in Sydenham's chorea, general paresis, hysteria, and several neurologic disorders. Cf. *astasia, astasia-abasia, dysbasia.*

ablutomania. Obsession with washing, regarded psychiatrically as the outward expression of unconscious feelings of guilt. Cf. *hand-washing complex.*

abnormal. Deviating from a measured average or a generally accepted norm. The term is popularly used in a derogatory sense to mean "unusual and inferior (or undesirable)." Strictly speaking, what is superior is also abnormal. With respect to mental health, abnormality ranges from mere transitory inability to cope with a stressful situation to persistent bizarre or destructive behavior or total disorientation and withdrawal from the stream of everyday life. The criteria for abnormality vary with the environment and with a particular situation in the same environment; they also undergo change with the passage of time.

aboulia. *abulia.*

abreaction. A mental process occurring under everyday conditions and in psychoanalysis by which the patient relives an

1

experience the memory of which was repressed because of its painful or humiliating nature. The memory, along with the original emotional content, breaks into the conscious level in a masked form. Cf. *catharsis, desensitization, ventilation.*

absent state. 1. According to Freud, a transient loss of consciousness sometimes observed in severe emotional outbursts and at the peak of sexual gratification. 2. Temporary loss of consciousness, as in epilepsy.

abstinence delirium. Delirium provoked by withdrawal of an addictive agent. See also *withdrawal syndrome.*

abstraction. According to Jung, "the drawing out or isolation of a content from a connection, containing other elements, whose combination as a totality is something unique or individual, and therefore inaccessible to comparison." Abstraction can be achieved by feeling, intuition, sensation, and thinking.

abulia. Absence of will power; inability to take action or make decisions, even very simple ones (e.g., whether to pass through a doorway, though no risk is involved). Seen in an anxiety reaction, it is due to feelings of insecurity; in schizophrenia, to lack of motivation or of interest in the real world. Cf. *hypobulia.*

acalculia. A form of aphasia in which the subject has lost the ability to perform even the most elementary arithmetic computations.

acanthesthesia. A paresthesia (false sensory reaction) characterized by the sensation commonly called "pins and needles." It may have a neurologic origin.

acarophobia. Exaggerated fear of mites, worms, etc., often with the delusion that one is infested with them. Cf. *helminthophobia.*

acatamathesia. *aphasia.*

acathexis. Absence of emotional attachment to or response toward some person, thing, situation, or concept which would normally be important to the individual. Cf. *cathexis.*

acathisia, akathisia. Anxiety over sitting down or remaining seated, though no danger is involved. Syn. *kathisiophobia.*

accident proneness. A person who has a history of repeated, usually preventable accidents is said to be "accident prone." Some psychiatrists believe that such series of accidents are brought on by the subject's unconscious motivation for self-punishment growing out of an emotional conflict, usually one in which guilt feelings are involved; it is as if the individual deliberately and repeatedly places himself in jeopardy. Others have seen in this reaction evidence of a strong unconscious death wish. Still others have suggested that the accident-prone person harbors a poorly repressed self-directed hostility.

acculturation. See under *Sullivan.*

acetylcholine (ACh). A compound of choline and acetic acid found in most animal tissue; it is parasympathomimetic in action. Many investigators feel that overproduction of acetylcholine may be responsible for severe psychiatric conditions such as schizophrenia, and for this reason drugs which retard acetylcholine production are used in association with psychotherapy.

acidosis. Increased hydrogen ion concentration in the body due to the accumulation of acid or loss of base (the nonacid part of a salt). It can be generated by severe and prolonged emotional stress.

acoasm. *acousma.*

acoria. 1. Bulimia. 2. Failure to be satisfied after eating.

acousma. A simple auditory hallucination, such as a hum, a buzz, or a tinkling. Syn. *acoasm.*

acousmatagnosis. *word deafness.*

acoustic agraphia. See under *agraphia.*

acousticophobia. Unreasoning fear of any sound.

acrasia. Lack of self-control.

acratia. *adynamia.*

acroagnosis. Loss of sense perception in an extremity; its origin may be organic (as in tabes dorsalis) or functional (as in hysteria).

acroanesthesia. Loss of sense of temperature, touch, and motion in the extremities, seen in both psychogenic and somatogenic disorders.

acroataxia. Incoordination of muscles of the fingers and toes, seen in certain neuropathic states.

acrohypothermia, -my. A sensation of unusual coldness, especially of hands and feet, often encountered in marked degree in persons of asthenic habitus and in schizophrenia.

acrokinesia, -sis. Excessive, often purposeless, motion seen in hysteria, in chorea, and occasionally in the manic phase of manic-depressive psychosis.

acroparesthesia. 1. Any perversion of sensation in the extremities, whether due to neurologic disorder or to hysteria. 2. A psychoneurotic state, observed chiefly in middle-aged women, in which the predominant manifestations are tingling or crawling sensations in the hands and/or feet, extreme sensitivity and pain in the fingers or toes, coldness, and color changes in the skin ranging from pallor to bluishness.

acrophobia. A morbid dread of being at high places. Cf. *bathophobia, batophobia.*

ACTH. *adrenocorticotropic hormone.*

acting-out. An aberrant behavior reaction due to a developmental defect in personality and manifested as a personality or character disorder; misconduct replaces subjective experiences such as anxiety, or emotional or psychiatric disorders. Acting-out is not only socially unacceptable, but, like psychic illness, is equally unacceptable as an unconscious compromise.

acute brain syndrome. See *brain syndrome.*

acute hallucinosis. *alcoholic hallucinosis.*

adaptation. Alteration of one's responses to meet the demands of new situations or conditions. Cf. *adjustment.*

addiction. Compulsive use of alcohol or a narcotic drug. By extension of meaning, one may be said to be "addicted" to smoking, eating, or any kind of self-indulgent behavior when these acts become excessive and persistent. The significant characteristic of any addiction is the severe reaction of the addict to withdrawal of the substance to which he is addicted. See also *alcoholism, narcotism.* Cf. *habituation.*

Addison's disease. A disease caused by tuberculous or malignant destruction or by atrophy of the adrenal (suprarenal) glands, first described by Thomas Addison, English physician (1793-1860). The disorder is characterized by weakness, emaciation, dehydration, and nervousness, and, occasionally, by psychiatric disturbances.

adenopathy. Malfunction or disease of a gland.

adiadochokinesia, -sis. Inability to perform alternating movements in quick succession. Cf. *dysdiadochokinesia.*

adiposogenital dystrophy. A condition associated with mental retardation. It is marked by obesity, underdevelopment of genital organs, with reversal of secondary sex characteristics, and unnaturally white, delicate skin; by visual changes; and by other organic pathology. Syn. *Laurence-Moon-Biedl syndrome.*

adipsia. 1. Exaggerated, unreasoning avoidance of fluid intake. 2. Absence of thirst under conditions in which it would be expected. Syn. *aposia.*

adjustment. Equilibrium between the individual and his environment or between the individual and an unconscious conflict that he harbors. The word has a relative significance. A patient may be said to be "adjusted to his illness," as in a *psychoneurosis.* In another sense, a mentally ill person may be said to be "socially adjusted" if, while still showing some signs of a *psychosis,* he is able to carry on reasonably well in the community. The ability to attain satisfactory adjustment varies with the degree of adaptability of the individual. Cf. *maladjustment.*

adjuvant therapy. See *psychotherapeutic adjuvant.*

Adler, Alfred. Austro-American psychiatrist (1870-1937), originally a follower and friend of Freud, who later broke with him and founded the school of *individual psychology.*

adrenal gland. The endocrine gland located above each kidney. The medulla (central portion) of each gland secretes epinephrine, a hormone that constricts blood vessels and stimulates the heart. The adrenal cortex (outer layer) secretes several hormones that are important in reproduction and the regulation of metabolism. Syn. *suprarenal gland.*

Adrenalin. Trade name for epinephrine.

adrenochrome. An oxidation product of epinephrine, capable of producing hallucinations.

adrenocorticotropic, -trophic hormone (ACTH). A hormone, secreted by the pituitary, that stimulates the growth, nourishment, and activity of the adrenal cortex.

adrenogenital syndrome. An endocrine disorder due to over-production of hormones in the cortex of the adrenal glands, manifested in a child by accelerated sexual and physical development, heterosexual drives, and general prematurity in attitude and ideation. Cf. *cerebral gigantism, pheochromocytoma, precocious matronism.*

advantage through illness. See *secondary advantage.*

adynamia. Psychodynamic weakness; lack of drive. Syn. *acratia.*

aeroneurosis. A psychoneurotic condition peculiar to aviators, characterized by various bodily complaints, nervousness, restlessness, and anxiety.

aerophagia, -gy. A compulsive act in which the patient repeatedly swallows air and belches violently. A similar compulsive act, accomplished per anum, is called *rectal aerophagia.*

aerosialophagia, -gy. A compulsive habit of constantly swallowing air and saliva.

affect. (af'ekt) *n.* A psychiatric term nearly synonymous with but more comprehensive than *emotion* or *mood.* It refers to the whole complex of ideas and feeling-tone of one's reactions. See also *displacement of affect, fading of affect, inversion of affect.* Cf. *psychic energy.*

affective reaction. Any one of a group of exaggerated emotional responses the consequences of which are serious maladjustment and incapacitation. Included are: involutional psychosis, manic-depressive psychosis, and neurotic depression. See also *affect, emotion.*

affectivity. Responsiveness to emotional stimulation.

affektepilepsie. *hysterical epilepsy.*

affirmation. The stage, during autosuggestion, in which the subject begins to cooperate with the therapist, in contrast to his previous muteness or reluctance to respond.

after-hearing. Persistent awareness of a sound after the stimulus producing it has ceased. It may be seen in a psychoneurosis.

âge critique. The menopause.

âge de retour. Senility; "second childhood."

ageusia, -stia. Loss or impairment of the sense of taste. It is usually due to organic causes, but it may also have an emotional origin. Deeply depressed patients, who show little interest in their environment, frequently claim they do not "taste" what they are eating. Cf. *dysgeusia, hypogeusia, parageusia, pseudogeusia.*

aggression. In psychiatry, the drive for mastery in response to unconscious feelings of inferiority or frustration. It is expressed in resentful or hostile behavior, speech, or attitude. Some persons, being insufficiently aggressive, are oversubmissive; others are supercharged with aggression, in particular those who suffer *sociopathic personality disturbances.* Various kinds and degrees of aggression play a role in many mental disorders.

aggressive personality. A *sociopathic personality disturbance* in which the individual reacts, even to minor frustrations, with outbursts of temper, irritability, and violent or destructive behavior, usually to his own disadvantage. See also *aggression.*

aging and mental acuity. In 1963 the National Institute of Mental Health, at Bethesda, Maryland, studied a large group of healthy elderly men ranging in age from 65 to 92 and found that they differed little in mental acuity from a group of younger men with a mean age of 21. These older men were mentally flexible and alert and also "vigorous, and interested and deeply involved in everyday living." They were found to be "significantly superior" to young men in verbal intelligence. The Institute predicted that with the promise of control of the now common metabolic diseases of later life and continued advances in the area of personality development, there will be "more individuals who are old in years but functionally young by present standards."

agitated depression. The extreme form of a depressed state, characterized by marked anxiety, restlessness, weeping, and wringing of the hands. It is usually accompanied by ideas of unworthiness or guilt and thoughts of or attempts at suicide.

agitolalia, agitophasia. Marked rapidity of speech, with words slurred, distorted, or muted, usually occurring under the stress of excitement.

aglutition. *aphagia.*

agnosia, -sis. Total or partial loss of the ability to recognize familiar objects and persons. The condition may prevail in any of the five principal senses, and thus is termed, *auditory, visual, gustatory, tactile,* or *olfactory* agnosia. *-agnosia, -sis* also appears as a combining form, as in *acousmatagnosis.*

agoraphobia. An unreasoning fear of open places. The fear may be experienced at the mere prospect of leaving an enclosed space (as a room, a house, an elevator), which represents a form of protection for the sufferer. Syn. *cenophobia, kenophobia.* Cf. *claustrophobia, hodophobia.*

agrammaphasia, -matism. Loss of the ability to express oneself satisfactorily. Normal word order is transposed, or parts of speech, tense, or other linguistic principles, formerly mastered, are badly misused.

agraphia. A form of aphasia due to a disorder of the nervous system or to hysteria, characterized by loss of the ability to write. It is called *absolute* when the subject cannot even form the individual letters of the alphabet; *acoustic* when he cannot write from dictation; *amnemonic* when he can write words but not a sentence; *cerebral* when he is unable to express an idea in writing; *congenital* or *developmental* when, though there is no organic defect or serious impairment of intelligence, he is unable or at great pains to learn to write; *verbal* when he cannot write words. Cf. *anorthographia, -phy.*

agromania. A compulsive desire to be alone in isolated surroundings, commonly encountered in schizophrenia or in schizoid individuals.

agrypnia. Insomnia. Syn. *ahypnia.*

agyiophobia. Morbid fear of being on or crossing a street.

aichmophobia. Exaggerated fear of sharp or pointed implements or other objects, or of being pointed at or touched with a finger or a pointed object. Syn. *belonephobia.*

ailuromania, -ophilia. An excessive fondness for cats. The term is applied to the schizoid or schizophrenic recluse whose libido is concentrated on cats picked up on the street and kept at home. Syn. *galeomania, galeophilia, gatomania, gatophilia.*

ailurophobia. Morbid fear of cats. Syn. *galeophobia, gatophobia.*

airsickness. See under *motion sickness.*

air-swallowing. *aerophagia.*

akathisia. *acathisia.*

akinesia, -sis. Total loss of voluntary motor function in a muscle or group of muscles. In conversion hysteria it may be limited to one group of muscles (a patient may complain that he is unable to move his fingers) or it may be total paralysis. Akinesia is often seen as complete immobility, as in catatonia. Akinesia is also seen in general paresis. *Cerebral akinesia* is paralysis due to brain damage as in a stroke. Cf. *dyskinesia.*

akinesia algera. A symptom of hysteria wherein pain is produced by any kind of movement.

akinesthesia. Loss of the sense of one's own muscular activity or movement.

akinetic epilepsy. A form of *petit mal* epilepsy characterized by sudden postural loss, sometimes only by nodding of the head. The subject may fall to the floor, but will get up promptly.

akoasm. *acousma.*

alalia. *aphonia.*

alcohol and behavior. Although alcoholic beverages are commonly thought of as stimulants, they are really depressants. With their first drink or two, most drinkers tend to become more lively and express themselves more freely. This is due, however, to depression of the mechanism that normally inhibits the individual's actions rather than to stimulation *per se*. Emotions which the drinker would ordinarily suppress come to the surface and he says and does things contrary to his usual behavior. The shy and retiring individual may become "the life of the party," and the usually reticent person may become boisterous and belligerent. How and where in the brain alcohol exerts its influence depends on the degree to which alcohol is concentrated in the blood. It first acts on the cortex of the brain, where restraint and judgment are controlled. The higher the concentration of alcohol, the deeper its effects reach into the subcortical areas of the brain, where they interfere with both physical and mental performance.

alcoholic deterioration. *chronic alcoholism.*

alcoholic hallucinosis. Extreme excitement marked by hallucinations of a terrifying nature, illusions, and, very often, rage, frequently seen in a person who is intoxicated by alcohol. The psychoemotional component is short-lived, usually disappearing as the effects of the alcohol wear off.

alcoholic paranoid state. The condition of an alcoholic who is irritable, sullen, and suspicious. It is suggestive of a strong homosexual component in the subject's personality. See also *paranoid personality.*

alcoholic personality. Although research has failed to uncover a typical "alcoholic personality," alcoholics do have certain general traits in common: emotional immaturity, preoccupation with self, insecurity, and feelings of guilt—traits which are also seen in persons with problems of maladjustment other than alcoholism.

alcoholic psychoses. An all-inclusive term covering mental disorders such as: acute hallucinosis, alcoholic paranoid state, chronic alcoholism, delirium tremens, and Korsakoff's syndrome or psychosis. The more accurate term is "psychoses associated with addiction to alcohol" (APA nomenclature, 1952 revision).

alcoholism. An ill-defined, though commonly used term, whose meaning ranges from proneness to indulge in periodic drinking bouts to the most devastating forms of addiction and alcoholic psychosis. No definition is completely satisfactory, but two of the best follow: (1) "A chronic behavioral disorder manifested by repeated drinking of alcoholic beverages in excess of the dietary usages of the community and to the extent that it interferes with the individual's health or his social or economic functioning." (Mark Keller) (2) "An alcoholic is one who is concerned about how activities interfere with his drinking instead of how drinking interferes with his activities." (World Health Organization)

Alcoholism is a syndrome which encompasses body, mind, and character. It has come to be widely recognized as primarily a psychiatric problem rather than a judicial or even a pharmacologic one. With rare exceptions, the personality dynamics of alcoholics resemble those seen in schizophrenia and, less commonly, manic-depressive psychosis. A characteristic common to alcoholics is an increasing reluctance to eat (in some instances amounting to abhorrence of food) as the addiction to alcohol deepens. Most alcoholics will admit that preparation or consumption of the simplest meal would interfere with their drinking program. Thus, they consume more and more alcohol and less and less of the substances they require to maintain a state of good nourishment. Psychiatrically speaking, they have embarked on a campaign of gradual suicide through malnutrition.

aldolase. See under *Tay-Sachs' disease.*

Alexander, Franz. Hungarian-American psychoanalyst (1890-

1964) who, with Thomas French, founded the Chicago Institute for Psychoanalysis. Alexander, as co-leader of the "Chicago school," rejected Freud's insistence on intensive, long-term psychotherapy.

alexia. A form of aphasia in which, although vision and intelligence are not impaired, the patient cannot acquire or has lost the ability to read printed or written matter. It is *motor* alexia when the patient understands the printed or written word but cannot read it aloud. Syn. *logagnosia, logamnesia, visual aphasia, word blindness.*

algedonics. The science concerned with the dynamics of pleasure and pain.

algesia, algesthesia. Painful sensation.

algolagnia. Inducing or increasing one's sexual pleasure by inflicting or experiencing pain; a manifestation of sadomasochism. *Active* algolagnia is sadism; *passive,* masochism.

algophilia. *masochism.*

algophobia. Obsessive fear of pain and suffering; observed in emotionally and mentally disturbed persons who suffer intense feelings of guilt.

alienist. A psychiatrist. Nowadays the term is used almost exclusively by attorneys and journalists.

allergy. Selective hypersensitivity to a substance that stimulates abnormal body reactions. It is seen commonly in psychoneurotic individuals or those having a strong psychoneurotic tendency. Many studies of patients with allergies have demonstrated the coexistence of disturbed personality reactions with allergic disorders.

allocheiria, allochiria. A distortion of sensation observed in persons suffering tabes dorsalis, who sometimes locate feeling in the wrong hand.

alloerotism, alloeroticism. In psychoanalytic nomenclature, the outward flow of libido. Freud stated that alloerotism does not manifest itself until the individual becomes aware of his genitalia (phallic stage); he also stressed the child's direction of libido flow to its parents as the first external objects. Jung, on the other hand, claimed that even in this early period libido flows toward all objects: persons, things, even concepts. See also *extraversion*.

allopsychic. Pertaining to mental processes when they relate to the outside world (i.e., to other persons or things or to the environment in general).

allotriogeusia. Any perversion of the sense of taste, whether due to organic or to psychic factors.

allotriophagia, -agy. 1. *pica.* 2. Appetite for substances not ordinarily thought of as food.

alogia. Speechlessness due to a brain lesion.

alpha rhythm or waves. The electroencephalographic tracing produced by the brain in normal activity. The interval is 8 to 12 waves per second with the subject at rest. Also called *Berger rhythm.* Cf. *beta rhythm, delta rhythm, gamma rhythm.*

alteregoism. Direction of libido toward persons in the same situation as oneself; empathy.

alternating personality. See *multiple personality.*

altrigenderism. In social development, the emergence, usually late in infancy, of attraction to persons of the opposite gender, without reference to sexual impulses. Cf. *heterosexuality.*

alysmus. The disquietude and morbid state of mind that accompany physical illness. It is supportive of the theory that all illness has both somatic and psychologic features. See also *psychosomatic.*

Alzheimer's disease. A variety of presenile psychosis with sclerosis, described by Alois Alzheimer, German neurologist (1864-1915). It is characterized by progressive mental deterioration, marked by memory impairment, apraxia, and speech disorders such as paraphrasia and logoclonia. Other symptoms include extreme depression, restlessness, anxiety, visual disorders, fainting and convulsive seizures, and paralysis of the face. It occurs in middle life and is seen more frequently in females. The course of the disease is rapid and fatal.

amaurotic family idiocy.   See *Tay-Sachs' disease.*

amaxophobia.   Morbid fear of riding in any kind of vehicle.

ambisexual.   Pertaining to or possessing emotions and feelings that can be ascribed to either sex. See also under *homosexual.* Cf. *bisexual.*

ambivalence, -cy.   The coexistence of opposed trends and feelings (pleasure-pain, love-hate, tenderness-cruelty) toward another person, an object, or an idea.

ambiversion.   Jung's term for the coexistence of the two fundamental forms of personality reaction, *introversion* and *extraversion.* A person in whom this coexistence is found is called an *ambivert.*

amblyopia.   Dulled vision without organic basis. It is called *toxic amblyopia* when encountered in alcoholism, drug addiction, and poisoning by chemicals such as nicotine. It may also be the normal result of extreme fatigue.

amentia.   An obsolescent term for severe congenital or acquired mental retardation.

aminia.   Inability to use or understand gestures or signs properly.

amnemonic.   Pertaining to impairment or loss of memory.

amnemonic agraphia.   See under *agraphia.*

amnesia.   Loss of memory, total or partial, caused by physical or psychic trauma. Amnesia is *anterograde* if the lost memories are of events that occurred after the precipitating incident (e.g., brain damage, stressful experience); *retrograde* if the patient cannot recall incidents or data experienced before the precipitating incident. Criminals often feign amnesia, but this is readily detected by tests such as the Rorschach Psychodiagnostic Method and by examination under the influence of amphetamine. See also *amnestic aphasia.* Cf. *blackout, dissociative reaction, ecmnesia, lapsus memoriae.*

amnestic aphasia. Loss of memory of the sound-images for words. For example, the subject cannot name a familiar object, but may be able to tell, in broken speech or only by gesture, the use of the object. It is often seen in psychosis with cerebral arteriosclerosis, senile psychosis, and cerebrovascular accidents. Syn. *dysnomia, nominal aphasia.* Cf. *amnesia.*

amnestic syndrome. A condition characterized by anterograde or retrograde amnesia, or both, retention defects, disorientation, and attempts to fill in memory gaps with confabulations. It is seen in organic brain disorders. Cf. *Korsakoff psychosis.*

amok. See *lata(h), piblockto.*

amor lesbicus. *lesbianism.*

amorphinism. *withdrawal syndrome.*

amphetamine. A sympathomimetic chemical substance which stimulates the central nervous system. It is used in psychiatry as a psychic energizer. The stimulating effects of the drug have led to its abuse. Addiction to the drug is becoming quite common in the United States. It is often used injudiciously to overcome sleepiness and fatigue and as an appetite depressant.

amphierotism. According to Ferenczi, the state in which the individual can visualize himself as either masculine or feminine or both.

amphigenetic. See *bisexual.*

amphimixis. Term introduced by Ferenczi for the integration of libidinal impulses associated with the urethra, the oral cavity, and the anus into the complex of genital erotism.

amusia, sensory. *tone deafness.*

amychophobia. Unreasoning fear of being scratched or bitten by an animal.

amyoesthesia, -sis. Loss of the sense of weight, position, and motion, whether due to neurologic or emotional causes.

amyostasia, -sis. Difficulty in standing, owing to muscular tremors, often observed in tabes dorsalis.

amyotaxia, -taxy. Ataxia due to lesions of the spine or cerebellum, as in syphilis of the central nervous system.

anaclitic object choice. Bestowal of libido on another person, thing, or idea which one feels will gratify his desires, and on which he feels dependent. The sense of dependency may be motivated by hunger, desire for security, erotic needs, or a yearning for approval. The object choice is usually changed with the passage of time and unfolding of the personality (parent, teacher, hero, employer, clergyman, lover, spouse). Cf. *ego ideal.*

anacroasia. *word deafness.*

anadipsia. Insatiable thirst, commonly observed in the manic phase of manic-depressive psychosis. It is usually seen in certain pituitary diseases, but may also be psychogenic in origin. The individual, owing to intense excitement, may lose much of his body fluid (through perspiration, urination, etc.) and yet, even though the fluid is replaced, continues to insist that he is very thirsty.

anagogic. Pertaining to the idealistic, moral, or spiritual content in psychic experience, as opposed to the instinctual or self-gratifying content.

anal character. In psychoanalytic terminology, the adult personality pattern retaining certain features of the toilet training period of infancy: parsimony, greed, perfectionism, punctuality, and extreme neatness and orderliness. These traits are regarded as pathologic only when they dominate the personality in adulthood. Cf. *oral character.*

anal erotism, anal eroticism. According to Freud, libidinal pleasure associated with bowel function, prominent in the first year of life and often reflected in later years in certain personality traits, such as overscrupulosity and miserliness.

anal sadism. A psychoanalytic concept referring to the expression of aggressive motivation colored by the sadistic features of anal eroticism. See *sadism.* Cf. *oral sadism.*

anal stage. According to Freud, the period of infancy in which, because toilet training is emphasized, the individual's attention is concentrated on bowel function. It is regarded as a critical determinant of the ultimate personality pattern, since for the first time the infant must modify his behavior according to the demands of the environment (mother or nurse). See also *anal character, sublimation, taboo.*

analeptic. *adj.* Restorative; strength-giving. *n.* 1. A tonic. 2. A drug which stimulates the central nervous system, such as amphetamine sulfate.

analgesia, analgesthesia, analgia. Insensitivity to pain while conscious. It may be due to emotional or psychiatric disorder, neurologic disease, or the effect of a drug. Some profoundly neurotic regressive and masochistic patients are able to stick pins into themselves without experiencing pain.

analysand. Patient undergoing psychoanalysis.

analysis. Shorter term for psychoanalysis.

analyst. Shorter term for psychoanalyst.

analytic(al) psychology. Jung's modification of psychoanalysis in which he stressed life goals, the role of *introversion* and *extraversion* in personality development, and the influence of the *collective* or *racial unconscious.* Jung minimized the role of sexuality—one of the differences between Freud and Jung that led to the split between the two. See also *anima, animus, archetype, extraversion, introversion, persona.*

anamnesis. The patient's history as recounted to the physician or social worker by the patient, or his relatives or friends, or obtained from other sources. Cf. *catamnesis.*

ananabasia. Inability or unwillingness, because of fear, to ascend to high places. Cf. *acrophobia, bathophobia.*

anancastic. Descriptive of obsessive-compulsive activity.

anandria. ("lack of maleness") Sexual impotence.

anaphia. Loss or dysfunction of the sensation of touch, due to neurologic or emotional disorder.

anaphrodisia. Absence or impairment of sexual desire. Cf. *frigidity.*

anaphrodisiac. *adj.* Tending to suppress sexual drive. *n.* Any drug that diminishes sexual appetite.

anarthria literalis. *stammering.*

anasarca hystericum. Transient swelling, usually of the abdominal cavity, in the absence of physiologic cause, found almost exclusively in hysterical individuals. Emotional stimulation of the sympathetic nervous system may give rise to the condition.

androgen. A male sex hormone governing the appearance, growth, and maintenance of male sex characteristics.

andromania. *nymphomania.*

androphobia. Unreasoning or unnatural fear of men, manifested by a woman or by a man with a strong homosexual component in the personality. Cf. *apandria.*

anemophobia. Unreasoning fear of wind or drafts.

anepia. Inability to speak, seen in neurologic conditions such as brain tumor, in emotional disorders such as hysterical aphonia, in severe mental retardation, and in catatonic schizophrenia.

anergasia, anergastic reaction. 1. Absence of functional activity. 2. Meyer's term for any mental illness due to brain damage or disease.

angioneurosis. A psychoneurotic reaction associated with symptoms of heart and blood vessel disorder. See also *cardiac neurosis, pseudoangina.*

angioneurotic edema. A physiologic manifestation of neurosis expressed as a disturbance of blood vessels in which normal dilation and contraction activity is disturbed. The most common sign is accumulation of fluid in tissue spaces (edema). It is often precipitated by allergic reactions to specific foodstuffs. Syn. *Quinke's disease.*

angophrasia. The hesitant, slurred, choking speech commonly encountered in general paresis.

anhedonia. Loss of interest in pursuits formerly pleasurable to an individual. Cf. *hebetude.*

anima. 1. According to Jung, the soul, the innermost personality. 2. In Jung's analytic psychology, the female component of the male personality. Cf. *animus, persona.*

animal magnetism. See *mesmerism.*

animatism. Personalization of animals and inanimate objects; normal in children, exaggerated in some psychotic patients.

animus. In Jung's analytic psychology, the male component of the female personality. Cf. *anima.*

anlage. (ahń lah-geh) An element in the personality representing the opposite sex which, Jung said, normally reposes in the personality at the unconscious level. Thus, a man has a female anlage, a woman a male anlage. Cf. *anima, animus, persona.*

anomia. Nominal aphasia.

anoesia, anoia. Severe mental retardation.

anoetic. 1. Of or pertaining to anoesia. 2. Semiconscious.

anorexia nervosa. Loss of appetite or aversion to food, a psychoneurotic disorder. It is seen more commonly in young unmarried females, but also occurs in older women and in men. In *false anorexia* (pseudoanorexia), the patient insists she does not eat but does so secretly.

anorgasmia, -my. Failure to achieve orgasm, whether from organic or psychic causes. Cf. *frigidity, impotence.*

anorthographia, -phy. The inability to write correctly because of motor incoordination, as opposed to agraphia due to brain damage. Syn. *motor agraphia.*

anosmia. Loss or impairment of the sense of smell, whether organic or psychic in origin.

anosognosia. Inability or refusal to admit that one is physically or mentally ill or handicapped, as seen often in paralytics.

Antabuse. A trade name for tetraethylthiuram disulfide, which is used to combat chronic alcoholism. An alcoholic beverage taken after a dose of Antabuse results in nausea and vomiting. The drug is effective provided the patient takes it each morning. It is not a cure, but it does render the individual more amenable to psychotherapy.

anterograde amnesia. See under *amnesia.*

anthophobia. An unreasoning or morbid dread of flowers, either upon coming into contact with them or upon being exposed to their fragrance, or contemplating or anticipating these experiences.

anthropophagia, -gy. While this word literally means "the eating of human flesh," in psychiatry it refers to a type of sadistic sexual perversion that embraces strong tendencies toward mutilation, rape, and cannibalism.

anthropophobia. Morbid fear of people.

anticathexis. *counterinvestment.*

anticonvulsant, -sive. *adj.* Preventing or terminating a convulsion. *n.* Any drug used to prevent or terminate a convulsive seizure.

antidepressant. In psychiatry, any drug that counteracts the mood of depression.

antifetishism. According to Hirschfeld, an unconscious mechanism in which a person with strong homosexual tendencies seeks to conceal from himself his erotic attachment to his own sex by exhibiting aversions to certain atypical physical features in the opposite sex. For example, a man may express revulsion at the appearance of hair on a woman's upper lip or at the sight of a flat-chested woman. The expression of distaste serves to veil what is really an attraction to the masculine features. Cf. *fetishism.*

antihistamine. Any sympathomimetic preparation having effects opposite to those of histamine. Antihistamines are used to control such psychosomatic conditions as asthma and various allergic reactions caused in part by emotional factors.

antihormone.   A substance produced by the body that counteracts the action of a particular hormone.

antihypnotic.   A chemical agent used to prevent sleep.

antinarcotic.   Any substance (e.g., coffee) or procedure (e.g., "cold turkey") that serves to prevent or terminate narcosis or to counteract the effects of a narcotic drug. Cf. *antihypnotic.*

antisocial reaction.   Seen in a *sociopathic personality disorder,* characterized by rejection of and refusal to comply with the obligations and restraints of society. Cf. *dyssocial reaction.*

antlophobia.   Morbid, unwarranted fear of floods. Cf. *thalassophobia.*

anxiety.   A painful state of fear and uncertainty over the immediate or remote future. In various contexts the word describes a symptom, a diagnostic category, or, in appropriate circumstances, a normal state. Anxiety is seen in a majority of ordinary emotional and mental reactions and in physiologic events such as the menopause. As a psychiatric symptom anxiety is encountered in the form of a generalized reaction to an imagined or impending situation. Since the motivation for the reaction originates in the unconscious, the subject is not aware of the source of his apprehension, and may offer a superficially reasonable explanation for it. As a diagnostic entity, it is called *anxiety reaction* (formerly anxiety neurosis). The word is also used as an attributive in such terms as "anxiety dream" and "anxiety state." Freud believed that anxiety begins at birth; Rank elaborated on this opinion. Recent research has suggested that various stimuli, including the pregnant woman's emotions, can precipitate anxiety in a fetus as early as the fifth month, thus lending some indirect support to the concept of "maternal impressions." See also *basic anxiety, free-floating anxiety, neurotic anxiety, objective anxiety.*

anxiety dream.   See under *dream.*

anxiety reaction.   See under *anxiety.*

anxiety state. A form of psychoneurosis in which the predominant (often the sole) manifestation is episodic or chronic anxiety with or without a precipitating stimulus in the environment. A common example is the person who "worries when he has nothing to worry about."

APA. American Psychiatric Association. See *classification of mental disorders.*

apallesthesia. Inability to sense vibration. While usually due to involvement of the sensory nerve apparatus, it is also seen in mental states, particularly catatonia and certain psychoneuroses, where vibration, along with other environmental stimuli, fails to elicit a response. Cf. *analgesia.*

apandria. In a female, aversion to males. Cf. *lesbianism.*

apastia. Self-starvation, as seen in some mental disorders. See also *anorexia nervosa.* Cf. *apocarteresis.*

apeirophobia. Morbid fear of infinite space and time. Cf. *astrophobia.*

aphagia. Inability to swallow, whether organic or psychic in origin. Syn. *acataposis, aglutition.* Cf. *dysphagia, globus hystericus.*

aphalgesia, -sis. In hysteria, the experiencing of pain or revulsion upon contact with a harmless substance which has a symbolic unconscious significance for the individual. Syn. *haphalgesia.*

aphanisis. A term originated by Jones to signify the complete extinction of *sexuality* in an individual, due to emotional factors. Cf. *frigidity.*

aphasia. Disease or injury of brain centers may result in defect or loss of the power to express thought and feeling by the spoken, written, or printed word, or by gesture; or the inability to understand the spoken, written, or printed word. Syn. *acatamathesia.* There are literally dozens of varieties of aphasias, which may exist alone or in combination; in the latter case, the term is *combined aphasia.* The following list presents the most common forms:

Also known as:

acoustic a.	auditory a.
amnemonic a.	anomia, dysnomia
amnesic a.	amnestic a.
anosmic a.	
central a.	paraphasia
functional a.	
global a.	cortical a., expressive-receptive a.
mixed a.	
motor a.	ataxic a.
nominal a.	
periphrastic a.	
sensory a.	impressive a., receptive a.
semantic a.	
syntactical a.	jargon a.
total a.	combined a. (*see definition above*)
visual a.	word blindness, optical alexia

apheixia. 1. Apathy, inattention, or indifference to environmental stimuli. 2. Absent-mindedness.

aphemia. A form of aphasia in which the sufferer can move his lips but is unable to carry out the coordinated movements required for speech. It is most usually due to destruction of a portion of Broca's area in the brain. It often coexists with agraphia. Cf. *aphonia.*

aphephobia. Morbid fear of brushing against or being touched by other persons. Syn. *haphephobia, haptephobia.*

aphonia. A form of aphasia marked by inability to speak. It may be organic in origin but often occurs as a phenomenon of conversion hysteria in response to a frightening experience; in the latter instance, it is assumed that the speechlessness is a reaction to an unconscious emotional conflict. Syn. *alalia, anaudia.*

aphrasia. A form of aphasia marked by the inability to utter or understand phrases, although the subject can pronounce and understand single words. Cf. *ataxiaphasia, dysphrasia.*

aphrodisiac. *adj.* Characterized by, or tending to create sexual excitement. *n.* Any substance that induces or heightens sexual excitement.

aphrodisiomania. *erotomania.*

aphronia.   Psychoanalytic term for lack of practical judgment.

aphthenxia.   A form of aphasia in which speech sounds are imperfectly uttered.

apiphobia.   Exaggerated fear of bees, even when only thinking about them.

apocarteresis.   Suicide by starvation; the extreme form of apastia.

apodemialgia.   Wanderlust generated by hatred for, or uneasiness in, the home environment.

apoplexy.   "Stroke," so-called because its onset resembles a sudden blow. It is brought on by hemorrhage or blockage of an artery in the brain, which results in loss of consciousness usually followed by paralysis. It may be instantly fatal, or the patient may die within hours or days. Many persons suffering paralysis from a stroke become so depressed that they may even refuse to eat.

apopnixis.   *globus hystericus.*

aporrhipsis.   Casting off of clothing or bed covers by persons in disturbed mental states. Cf. *carphology.*

aposia.   *adipsia.*

appersonation, appersonification.   *identification.*

approximate answers, syndrome of.   *Ganser's syndrome.*

apraxia.   Inability to perform purposeful movements although there is no paralysis. It is due to damage in the cortex of the brain. Cf. *pseudoapraxia.*

aprosexia.   Inability to concentrate, due to preoccupation, excitement, or apathy.

aquaphobia.   Morbid fear of water. Cf. *antlophobia, hydrophobia.*

arachnephobia.   Morbid dread of spiders.

arachnoid.   The middle of the three coverings of the brain and spinal cord. See *meninges.*

archaic. Descriptive of any phylogenetic inheritance of the unconscious. See also *collective* or *racial unconscious.*

archaism, archaicism. According to Jungian analytical psychology, unconscious reflection (i.e., survival) of phylogenetic psychic features; in Jung's words, "the ancient character of psychic contents and functions." See also *autochthonous ideas, collective unconscious.*

archetype. According to Jung, a primordial, phylogenetic idea or trend of thought in the form of unconscious drives, moods, and concepts derived from the experience of the human race.

arctic hysteria or madness. *piblockto.*

Argyll Robertson pupil. A pupil that accommodates to distance but not to light. It is seen in general paresis and, less commonly, in several other conditions. Named for Douglas M. C. L. Argyll Robertson, Scottish physician (1837-1909).

arithmomania. Obsessive preoccupation with numbers and numerical relations, often manifested in a compulsion to count persons or objects.

arterenol. *norepinephrine.*

arteriosclerosis. See *cerebral arteriosclerosis.*

asemia, asemasia. An aphasia in which the patient cannot use or comprehend words, gestures, or symbols. Syn. *asymbolia.*

assimilation. Jung's term for the incorporation of new mental experiences into one's existing pattern of thought content.

association. A mental mechanism in which a sense impression or an image evokes the memory of another image or idea previously related to the former.

association centers. See under *cerebral cortex.*

association, controlled. Summoning up repressed memory in response to a therapist's or an analyst's suggestion.

association, free. Voluntary summoning up of a repressed memory by a patient without the therapist's or analyst's suggestion.

association tests. Psychological inquiries to determine the subject's ability to respond to key words which are intended to unearth repressed material. The reaction time is also regarded as a revealing factor.

associative reaction. A reaction in which the response is withheld until the idea presented has suggested an associated one.

astasia. Inability to stand. Its cause may be functional or organic. Cf. *abasia, ananastasia, astasia-abasia, ataxia.*

astasia-abasia. Inability to stand or walk. It is neurotic in nature (as in conversion hysteria). Cf. *abasia, astasia, ataxia.*

astereognosis. A form of agnosia in which the individual has lost the ability to recognize objects by the sense of touch (stereognosis). It may be due to brain damage, profound fatigue, or alcoholism, and is seen in the extreme states of certain psychoses and psychoneuroses. Cf. *atactilia.*

asthenia. In psychiatry, lack of dynamic force in the personality. Syn. *adynamia.* Cf. *effort syndrome.*

asthenic delirium. *exhaustion delirium.*

asthenic habitus or type. According to Kretschmer, a constitutional type characterized by slender build and long limbs. Persons of this type who become mentally ill are most often schizophrenics or have schizoid personality patterns. Cf. *ectomorph.*

asthenophobia. Morbid fear of weakness, in one possessed of normal or superior strength.

asthma. See *bronchial asthma.*

astraphobia, astrapophobia. *keraunophobia.*

astrophobia. Morbid fear of celestial phenomena. Syn. *siderophobia.* Cf. *apeirophobia.*

astyphia, astysia. Inability to achieve penile erection.

asyllabia. An aphasia; a reading and writing disability in which syllables cannot be formed, though the letters are recognized and properly identified. See also *agraphia, alexia, aphasia.*

asymbolia. *asemia.*

asyndesis. The use of unconnected phrases, sometimes displayed by schizophrenics and patients suffering brain damage. Cf. *word salad.*

asynergia, -gy. Lack of complex motor coordination, often caused by damage to the cerebellum.

asynodia. 1. Lack of sexual harmony. 2. Sexual impotence.

atactilia. Loss of the sense of touch, due either to disturbance of the central nervous system, or to the extreme regression of a psychosis. Occasionally it is seen as a feature of hysteria. Cf. *astereognosis.*

ataractic. *n.* tranquilizer. *adj.* Having the effect of a tranquilizer.

ataxia. Muscular incoordination. As a symptom of hysteria it is called *astasia-abasia.* Cf. *hemiataxia.*

ataxiaphasia. An aphasia characterized by the inability to form complete sentences. Cf. *aphrasia.*

ataxic gait. A disturbed gait in which the foot is raised high and the sole is slapped sharply on the floor or ground, commonly encountered in tabes dorsalis. Syn. *tabetic gait.*

ataxophemia. Incoherence in speech.

ataxophobia. Morbid fear of losing control of muscular coordination.

atelia, ateliosis. Arrested mental and/or physical growth. Cf. *infantilism.*

atephobia. Vague fear of impending ruin or doom. See also *anxiety.*

athetoid. Resembling *athetosis.*

athetosis. A neurologic disorder manifested by recurring slow, involuntary wormlike movements of the digits, usually seen in children, and due to brain damage. It is observed commonly in cerebral palsy and in chorea following *hemiplegia.* See also *gout, juvenile.* Cf. *chorea, pseudoathetosis.*

athletic habitus or **type.** A constitutional type, according to Kretschmer, marked by well-proportioned, muscular physique. Mentally ill persons of this body type commonly exhibit paranoid reactions. Cf. *mesomorphy.*

athymia. 1. Absence of emotional response. 2. Absence of the thymus gland.

atonia, -ny. Lack of normal muscle tone.

atopognosia, -sis. 1. Inability to localize touch sensations, owing to neurologic disorder. Cf. *atactilia.* 2. Failure to respond to external stimuli, seen in hysteria or in the profound regression of a psychosis.

atremia. Although this word literally means "without trembling," it is used to describe a psychoneurosis in which the patient complains of unusual pains and other sensations in the head and back whenever he is not lying down. Syn. *Neftel's disease.*

attention, disturbances of. See *aprosexia, hyperprosexia.*

attonity. Stupor with partial to complete immobility, encountered in psychotic depression and catatonia.

audimutism. Muteness without deafness.

audioepilepsy. See under *reflex epilepsy.*

auditory agnosia. See *agnosia.*

auditory center. See under *cerebral cortex.*

aulophobia. Fear or uneasiness upon seeing, handling, or playing a wind instrument (clarinet, oboe, etc.) that might serve as a phallic symbol.

aura. A premonitory sensation preceding an epileptic seizure, especially of the grand mal type. It may take the form of a paresthesia that begins in an extremity or in the abdominal viscera and rises to the head; sensations of light, sounds, or odors; giddiness; or a general feeling of unreality.

aura cursoria. An aura in which the patient runs about aimlessly. Syn. *cursive epilepsy.*

autarchy. *magic omnipotence.*

autemesia, -sis. Vomiting at will, as an expression of anger or fear.

autism. Persistent indulgence in fantasy and daydreaming. Syn. *dereism, infantile schizophrenia.*

autistic child. A child whose extreme introversion, preoccupation with rhythmic, mechanical movement, and dedication to fantasies suggest either mental retardation or the early development of a schizoid personality, if not schizophrenia.

autoanalysis. *self-analysis.*

autocatharsis. A technique used in psychotherapy, in which the patient writes freely of his mental or emotional troubles and later reviews what he has written, thus gaining a degree of insight proportional to his ability to regard himself objectively. It is a form of self-analysis.

autochthonous ideas. Mental impressions originating within the psyche independently of external stimulation. Jung suggested that many autochthonous ideas are derived from the collective or racial unconscious. Cf. *archaism.*

autodepilation. *trichologia.*

autoerotism. This term has several interpretations in psychoanalysis and psychiatry. It is used by some as synonymous with masturbation. Others give it the broader meaning of narcissism. Still others mean by it an individual's introversion of libido when the environment fails to provide a love object. Freud, in his description of psychosexual development, called the first 18 to 36 months of life the "autoerotic period," which he divided into the oral stage and the anal stage.

autofellatio. Mouthing one's own penis.

autogenic, -ous. Self-generated, arising without external influence (e.g., instinctual drives such as hunger and desire for sleep).

autographism. *dermatographia.*

autohypnosis. Self-induced hypnosis. Syn. *idiohypnosis.* Cf. *autosuggestion.*

automatism. Seemingly involuntary activity, as seen in sleep-walking, hysterical states, and certain types of epilepsy. Cf. *fugue, oneirism.*

automatization. An unconscious enslavement of the psycho-neurotic or psychotic individual, whereby he is compelled to act at the command of his infantile impulses.

automysophobia. Morbid fear that one is physically unclean or that one exudes an unpleasant odor.

autonomasia. An aphasia in which the subject is unable to recall nouns although he has fair control of other parts of speech.

autonomic (vegetative) nervous system. So called because it acts more or less autonomously, that is, independently of conscious control. The autonomic nervous system governs the fundamental life processes (heart action, breathing, digestion, etc.) and metabolism (conversion of food and other ingested substances into tissue, energy, and substances to be eliminated), and helps to produce emotional tone by its activation of hormone secretory activity. There are two divisions: the *sympathetic* and the *parasympathetic.* The sympathetic is instinctive and emotionally motivated. The parasympathetic, also known as the *craniosacral division,* is concerned with nutrition and reproduction (race preservation) and copes with the environment. A comparison of their effects is presented in the accompanying table.

Sympathetic	Organ or System	Parasympathetic
Constricts	Blood vessels of the brain	Dilates
Dilates	Pupil of the eye	Constricts
Inhibits, occasionally stimulates secretion	Salivary glands	Stimulates secretion
Raises blood pressure	Carotid sinus	Lowers blood pressure
Accelerates	Heart action	Decelerates
Depresses	Peristalsis	Stimulates
Contracts	Anal sphincter	Releases for defecation
Retards excitation	Prostate and seminal vessels	Promotes ejaculation
Stimulates	Endocrine glands	Depresses

autopathic. *idiopathic.*

autophagia, -gy. Eating or biting oneself, as in profound anxiety or depression, or in advanced schizophrenia.

autosuggestion. Suggestion that arises from within the individual as opposed to that coming from others.

autotomia. Self-mutilation. From the psychiatric point of view, the subject seeks to rid himself of an offending part or organ with regard to which he has unconscious feelings of guilt.

avocalia. An aphasia in which the subject loses the ability to sing on key or to produce valid musical sounds vocally; a motor form of *amusia.*

awareness. *conscious.*

ℬ

Babinski reflex or sign. Reflex extension of the toes when the sole of the foot is stroked lightly. Joseph F. Babinski, French neurologist (1857-1932), discovered that in normal infants and in adults afflicted with certain diseases of the nervous system (e.g., multiple sclerosis), the reflex extension of the toes is accompanied by spreading of the digits.

bacillophobia, bacteriophobia. Morbid and unreasonable fear of germs. In some psychoneurotic persons this may reach the extreme of refusal to touch a doorknob without first covering the hand. Syn. *microbophobia.* Cf. *mysophobia, parasitophobia.*

ballism(us). Jerky leg and arm movements, as those seen in chorea. Cf. *hemiballismus.*

baragnosia, -sis. *abarognosia.*

Barany's pointing test. *past-pointing test.*

barbital. A habit-forming drug (diethylbarbituric acid), the basis of many sedatives known as barbiturates.

barbiturates. A group of sedatives prepared from barbital, the most commonly used being phenobarbital.

barbiturism. A toxic state resulting from overdosage of a barbiturate. It is characterized by ataxia, delirium, and coma, and is fatal if treatment is not promptly instituted. Patients with personality disorders, particularly those with passive-dependent personalities, seem to constitute the majority of barbiturate users. The motivation to use barbiturates seems to be a search for oblivion rather than for a state of euphoria.

baresthesia. Sense of weight or pressure.

baroagnosis. *abarognosia.*

barognosis. Ability to appreciate weight or pressure.

barophobia. Morbid concern over the force of gravity, manifested by a sensation of weightlessness and a fear that one will fall into space.

barylalia. Thick, indistinct speech sometimes observed in organic lesions such as general paresis.

basal metabolism. A measure of the minimal degree of bodily activity required to sustain life. A test of basal metabolism may be used to rule out organic factors in several emotional disorders. It is, however, being replaced by more exact procedures, such as the serum protein-bound-iodine test.

Basedow's disease. *hyperthyroidism.*

basic anxiety. Horney's descriptive term for the emotional reaction of a child who develops "a profound insecurity and vague apprehensiveness" owing to parents who are "dominating, overprotective, intimidating, irritable, overexacting, overindulgent, erratic, partial to other siblings, hypocritical, indifferent, etc." As a result, Horney claimed, the child does not develop a feeling of belonging.

basiphobia, basophobia. Morbid fear of walking, usually associated with fear of collapse or fainting. Cf. *stasibasiphobia.*

bathophobia. Morbid fear of falling from a high place. Syn. *hypsophobia.* Cf. *acrophobia, ananabasia, batophobia.*

bathyesthesia. Sensibility to pain or pressure in areas beneath the surface of the body; "deep" sensation.

batophobia. Uneasiness when passing among very high places or objects. Cf. *claustrophobia.*

battarism(us). *stammering, stuttering.*

Bechtereff, -ev. See *Bekhterev-Mendel reflex.*

Bedlam. Corruption of the name *Bethlehem,* referring to the Hospital of St. Mary of Bethlehem in London, established as a priory in 1247 and opened as an "asylum for the insane" in 1402. The word has been popularly used to indicate wild disorder.

behavior disorders. A group of sociopathic personality reactions in children characterized principally by perverse sexual activity, criminality, running away, cruelty, truancy, fighting, destructiveness, lying, and disobedience. The child feels no remorse or guilt. These reactions are generally attributed to parental hostility toward and rejection of the child.

Bekhterev-Mendel reflex. In a person suffering disease of the pyramidal tract (motor nerve pathway from the brain to the spinal cord) percussion of the back of the foot causes reflex flexion (bending) of the second to the fifth toes. Normally, the response is one of extension.

belle indifférence. Janet's term for the attitude of some hysterical persons toward their neuroses. The patient may state that his condition is "terrible" or "unbearable," but his facial expression and manner present a picture of complacency.

belonephobia. *aichmophobia.*

Bender Visual Motor Gestalt Test. One of several tests for special function, aptitude, and interest, having as its object the discovery of weaknesses in concept formation and abstract thinking. The subject is shown nine standardized cards in sequence, each having a geometric design printed on it and is asked to copy each design on a sheet of paper; some examiners prefer that the subject reproduce the designs from memory after each card is withdrawn. The test, devised by Lauretta Bender, American child psychiatrist, is useful for examining patients in whom brain damage is suspected, as well as schizophrenics. See *gestalt.*

Benzedrine. See *amphetamine.*

Berger, Frank M. Czechoslovakian-American physician and pharmacologist, known for his discovery of meprobamate in 1954, thus initiating a new variety of tranquilizers.

Berger, Hans. German neurologist (1873-1914) known for his descriptions of electroencephalographic recordings. See *alpha rhythm.*

beri-beri. A disease complex due to lack of thiamine (vitamin B_1) in the diet. The physical symptoms are often accompanied by mental deterioration.

Bernheim, Hippolyte-Marie. French psychotherapist (1840-1919) who made intensive investigations into suggestion as a therapeutic measure.

bestiality. Sexual intercourse between humans and animals. Cf. *sodomy.*

beta rhythm or waves. A pattern of brain waves recorded through encephalography occurring at the rate of 18 to 35 per second. The beta rhythm is more persistent in the frontal lobes and is a guide to the subject's brain activity so far as reception of sensory impulses and initiation of motor impulses are concerned. Cf. *alpha rhythm, delta rhythm, gamma rhythm.*

bhang. See *Cannabis.*

bibliokleptomania. Irresistible impulse to steal books. See *kleptomania.*

bibliomania. Compulsion to collect books, usually of a rare or curious nature, without any intention to make practical use of them.

bibliotherapy. A psychotherapeutic adjuvant in which the patient is induced to read certain books, under guidance, for various purposes: to correct erroneous ideas, to stimulate him to participate in discussions, to broaden his range of interests, etc.

Binet, Alfred. French psychologist (1857-1911) who, with Theodore Simon, created a series of intelligence tests. See *Binet-Simon Scale, tests.*

Binet age. *mental age.*

Binet-Simon Scale, Tests. Tests used to gauge intellectual capacity. They comprise a series of questions and problems, grouped for applicability to ages up to sixteen years; some are verbal, while others require only recognition of form and manual skills. The subject's performance is expressed in terms of mental age. The form of these tests now used in the United States is the *Terman (Stanford) Revision,* also called the *Stanford-Binet Test.* See also *intelligence quotient, intelligence tests.*

biopsychology. *psychobiology.*

bipolarity. *ambivalence.*

birth trauma. 1. Injury suffered at birth; it may involve damage to the brain, the spinal cord, or a nerve. 2. A psychoanalytic concept advanced by Rank, ascribing mental and emotional disorders to the severe psychic shock that he believed an infant experiences at birth. Rank emphasized the sudden, violent change from the safety and comfort of intrauterine life to the insecurity of the outer world as a pervasive and continuing influence on the formation of the personality.

Bis ether. *indoklon.*

bisexual. 1. Hermaphroditic; having gonads of both sexes. 2. Pertaining to engagement in both heterosexual and homosexual activity. Syn. *amphigenetic.* Cf. *ambisexual.*

biting period. In Freud's concept of psychosexual development, the second phase of the *oral erotic stage,* following immediately after the *sucking period.* It begins with the eruption of teeth (on the average in the seventh month of life). According to Freud, with dentition the infant finds that he has a new weapon with which to control his surroundings (oral sadism): the infliction of pain on the source of his frustration (the mother) or, in the absence of the source, on anything within reach.

bivalence, -cy. *ambivalence, -cy.*

blackout. A popular term for transient loss of visual function, with or without loss of consciousness, due to sudden reduction of blood supply to the brain. It is seen in fainting states and in alcoholic intoxication.

bladder training. See *toilet training.*

blepharism, blepharospasm. Continuous blinking. When seen in psychiatric disorders, as in catatonia, at intervals the lids are held closed, as if the patient were determined to shut himself off from the world about him.

Bleuler, Eugen. Swiss psychiatrist (1857-1939) who coined the term *schizophrenia* to replace *dementia praecox.* He worked extensively on dissociation phenomena in schizophrenia, which he described as a "molecular split," in contrast to Janet's principle of the "total split" of hysteria. He was especially concerned with symbolism. Bleuler originated the terms *autistic thinking, autochthonous ideas,* and *schizoid personality;* and he stated that ambivalence is the root of schizophrenic negativism.

blindness. See *word-blindness.*

blocking. Interruption of thought, unconsciously generated and often encountered in emotionally disordered patients during a psychotherapeutic interview. It results in retarded, arrested, or evasive responses. Psychoanalysts attribute it to the threatened emergence of a repressed idea into consciousness and the effect of the superego's attempt to keep it repressed.

blood protein-bound-iodine test. *serum protein-bound-iodine test.*

"blue velvet" addiction. A common drug addiction. The narcotic substance, taken orally or intravenously, is a mixture of paregoric (camphorated tincture of opium) and pyribenzamine (tripelennamine hydrochloride, a common antihistamine sold in the form of blue tablets). When used intravenously, this mixture may have harmful effects on the liver, blood, heart, blood pressure, and respiratory apparatus. An individual under the influence of "blue velvet" manifests reactions that are a combination of those seen in amphetamine usage and in opiumism.

BMR. Basal metabolic rate. See *basal metabolism.*

body type. See *habitus, somatotypes.*

borderline intelligence. See under *mental retardation.*

Bounak, V. V. Contemporary Russian psychologist (1886–). See *euryplastic.*

bowel training. See *toilet training.*

brachycephalia, -ism, -ly. Exaggerated broadness of the forehead. It is seen in extreme forms in certain types of mental retardation.

bradyglossia. Retarded speech, characterized by impairment of tongue control. Cf. *bradylalia.*

bradykinesia, -sis. Slow movement seen in depression and catatonia.

bradylalia. Dragging speech.

bradylexia. Retarded reading ability.

bradyphrasia. *bradylalia.*

bradyphrenia. Sluggish thinking, commonly observed in lethargic encephalitis, oversedation, and mental retardation.

bradypragia, -praxia. Retarded action and movement, as seen in various conditions such as senility, various paralyses, certain drug addictions (e.g., opiumism), depressive states, and catatonic schizophrenia.

bradyrhythmia. *delta rhythm.*

brain. That part of the central nervous system which is enclosed within the cranium, where it is bathed by a clear, colorless liquid (cerebrospinal fluid). It is further protected by membranes, the *meninges.* The principal divisions of the brain are: the *cerebrum, cerebellum, pons varolii,* and *medulla oblongata.* The average human brain weighs a little over three pounds, but size and weight are not gauges of intelligence. Aside from enabling man to engage in interpretation, judgment, recall, and creative thinking, the brain provides centers for the control of movement and balance, glandular activity, and emotional re-action, as well as for the regulation of heart action, respiration, and other fundamental bodily functions. See also *brain damage, brain, stem, brain surgery, brain syndrome, brain tumor, cerebral cortex, cerebrovascular accident, electroencephalography.*

brain centers.　See under *cerebral cortex.*

brain damage, injury, or **trauma.**　The brain is susceptible to two classes of injuries: those caused by *damage to the skull* and those arising from a *cerebrovascular accident.* Every blow on the head does not necessarily injure the brain. Skull fracture, with-out damage to the brain itself, is significant only if the broken bone pierces the scalp (compound fracture), owing to the possibility of infection to the brain or its coverings (meninges). A "depressed" fracture (one that leaves a portion of the skull indented) may produce bleeding just outside the dura mater, and this may increase the intracranial pressure. In any brain injury the victim suffers some loss of consciousness, ranging from momentary stupor to coma; the degree depends on the severity and extent of the injury. See also *cerebrovascular accident, post-traumatic syndrome, subdural hemorrhage.*

brain hemorrhage.　See under *cerebrovascular accident.*

brain rhythm.　See under *electroencephalography.*

brain stem.　The brain, other than the cerebral hemispheres and the cerebellum. It includes the pons varolii and medulla oblon-gata, along with the corpus callosum and other lesser parts.

brain surgery.　Surgery undertaken to repair damage to the brain or its blood vessels, or to remove tumors. Cf. *psycho-surgery.*

brain syndrome, acute and chronic.　A classification of mental disorders in which disturbance of mental function is caused or precipitated by a primary impairment of brain tissue function. A brain syndrome is called *acute* if it is a temporary condition from which the patient is expected to recover; it is *chronic* if the condition is irreversible, i.e., recovery is not expected. Among the acute brain syndromes are those associated with brain or systemic infections, injury (particularly to the skull), circulatory disturbances (e.g., cerebral arteriosclerosis), convulsive disorders (e.g., epilepsy), metabolic disorders (e.g., diabetes), brain tumor, psychosis due to drug or poison intoxication, and unknown causes. Among the chronic brain syndromes are those associated with congenital malformations of the skull, congenital spastic paralysis of all four limbs, Down's disease, prenatal maternal infectious disease, birth trauma, general paresis and other central nervous system infections (e.g., tuberculosis), intoxication by alcohol, drugs, or poison, head injury, and unknown causes.

brain trauma. *brain damage.*

brain tumor. Any new growth within the cranial cavity. A tumor of the brain exerts its damaging effects on behavior and thinking by pressure on brain cells and nerves, blockage of cerebrospinal fluid and blood pathways, and irritation of brain elements and/or coverings. For instance, a tumor that affects the *thalamus* impairs sensation and, by spreading to the neighboring *hypothalamus,* involves emotional centers, producing unprovoked weeping or laughter and other overt signs, as well as personality changes (psychoneurosis or psychosis). Symptoms of brain tumor vary widely in individual cases, but included are: headache, giddiness, lethargy, vomiting, and convulsions.

brainwashing. A colloquial term used to describe enslavement of the minds of prisoners of war by enemy captors. Although brainwashing is widely believed to include the use of drugs, hypnotism, and mechanical gadgets, the same effects may be achieved by such methods as sleep-deprivation and solitary confinement. Syn. *menticide.*

brain wave. See under *electroencephalography.*

breakdown. See *nervous breakdown.*

Breuer, Josef. Austrian psychiatrist and psychoanalyst (1842-1925). Freud's first co-worker, with whom he established the principle of the *unconscious* and the concepts of the *id, ego,* and *superego.* Breuer and Freud were pioneers in the use of catharsis as a psychotherapeutic approach to hysteria and this method eventually became the foundation of Freudian psychoanalysis.

Brill, Abraham A. American psychoanalyst (1874-1948), who, as Freud's first American student, introduced his mentor's doctrines into the United States, fostered their acceptance, and made the first English translations of Freud's writings.

Broca's area. The speech center in the prefrontal lobe of the brain, described by Paul Broca, French surgeon and anthropologist (1824-80).

Broca's aphasia. *motor aphasia.*

bromhidrosiphobia. Obsessive preoccupation with the idea that one is giving off offensive odors. It is usually accompanied by hallucinations of smell.

bromide or **bromine poisoning, bromidism,** or **brominism.** The pathologic state brought on by overdosage with or excessive use of bromides. It is characterized by lethargy, cold hands and feet, unpleasant breath, skin eruptions, and in some cases, diminution or cessation of sexual activity. A psychosis marked by hallucinations, delusions, disorientation, and disturbed behavior may ensue.

bromomania. Excessive craving for bromides, as seen in chronic addicts to proprietary medicines containing bromide. Also the psychotic state associated with bromide poisoning.

bronchial asthma. A chronic respiratory condition manifested by recurrent paroxysms of labored, wheezing respiration and a sense of constriction of the chest. Although it is recognized that asthma is a reaction to an allergen or to an infection of the nose, sinuses, or bronchi, most clinicians agree that, in the long run especially, emotional stress is a significant precipitating cause of an attack. Psychoanalysts go further, describing the asthmatic attack as unconscious rebellion against separation from the mother figure (similar to "breath-holding," a device which some children use as a rebellion against a frustrating situation). Many asthma sufferers exhibit signs of overprotective rearing, the asthma being a bodily expression of the emotional stress thus generated. See also *organ language.*

Brown-Séquard syndrome. A syndrome which follows a lesion on one side of the spinal cord. It is marked by paralysis on the same side of the body as the lesion and loss of sensation on the opposite side; named for Charles Edouard Brown-Séquard, Franco-British neurophysiologist (1817-94) who described it.

bruxism. Compulsive grinding of the teeth, most often observed during sleep, but also noted in an individual under severe physical or emotional strain. It is not uncommon in psychotic and neurotic patients. Syn. *odontoprisis, stridor dentium.*

bruxomania. Bruxism associated with generally excited behavior.

bufotenin. Dimethyl serotonin, a hallucinogen, thought by some investigators to be a factor in the causation of psychoses. See *serotonin.*

bulbocapnine. An alkaloid derived from the tubers of the herb *Bulbocapnus cavus.* It is used to control tremors such as those seen in certain organic disorders (e.g. parkinsonism, chorea).

bulimia. Compulsive eating, seen in certain psychotic states (e.g., hebephrenic schizophrenia) and in brain lesions. Syn. *acoria, hyperorexia, polyorexia, polyphagia.* Cf. *pica.*

cacesthesia, kakesthesia. Any morbid sensation. Cf. *cenesthopathy.*

cachexia. Malnutrition and general ill health, a common feature of anorexia nervosa.

cacodemonomania. *demonomania.*

cacogeusia. The experiencing of an unpleasant taste without eating or drinking anything objectionable. It may be due to organic or to psychogenic causes.

cacosmia. *bromhidrosiphobia.*

cainophobia, cainotophobia. *neophobia.*

callomania. Manic behavior in which the patient reacts with a display of exaggerated or inappropriate vanity to delusions of being inordinately beautiful or handsome.

camphoromania. Addiction to camphor fumes, or a desire to inhale them.

camptocormia. Forward bending of the trunk, a posture maintained by some sufferers from traumatic psychoneurosis, in which the condition has no organic basis.

Cannabis. Hemp, specifically the flowering tops of *Cannabis indica* in Asia, *Cannabis sativa* in the Americas. Its active chemical constituents are the basis of the intoxicant drugs called *bhang, churrus, hashish,* and *marihuana,* among other names. These drugs are antispasmodic, sedative and aphrodisiac in action.

cannibalism. Psychoanalytic term for a trend of thought in which a patient is obsessed with the idea of eating human flesh. The trend is sometimes encountered in schizophrenia. Cf. *anthropophagy.*

Cannon, Walter B. American physiologist (1871-1945), known as the "father of endocrinology." He was the first to demonstrate an active relationship between the endocrine glands and the emotions. In his theory of emotions he stressed the role of the hypothalamus and the interplay of the ductless glands and the autonomic nervous system. He further showed how the endocrine constitution of the individual acts to establish and maintain many personality traits, both normal and abnormal. The spreading acceptance of his theory and its demonstration in such disorders as thyrotoxicosis helped to lay the foundation for psychosomatic medicine.

Capgras' syndrome. An unusual type of misidentification, sometimes seen in a paranoid psychotic. The reaction was described by Jean Marie Joseph Capgras, French psychiatrist (1873-1950).

Although the patient recognizes the physical features and characteristic behavior of a person confronting him, he is unable or unwilling to identify him and insists that he is seeing a "double," or an imposter. Also called the *illusion of negative doubles*. This kind of negativistic, suspicious reaction is characteristic of the paranoid personality.

carbon dioxide therapy. A form of shock treatment introduced by Meduna in which a mixture of oxygen and carbon dioxide is administered with an anesthesia apparatus. The procedure enjoyed a brief period of popularity among psychiatrists, chiefly in the west and southwest of the United States, in the 1950's. The danger of asphyxiation led to its abandonment.

carbon monoxide poisoning. Psychotic symptoms are often observed following what appears to be recovery from carbon monoxide poisoning. If brain damage has been slight, the victim may exhibit confusion, aphasia, and/or apraxia, from which he will eventually recover. With severe or widespread brain damage, chronic mental deterioration may ensue.

cardiac neurosis. An anxiety state in which the patient, who is enjoying satisfactory, even excellent, physical health, nevertheless complains of shortness of breath, palpitation, and other symptoms referable to the heart, and expresses fear that he is suffering from severe heart disease Syn. *cardiophobia*. Cf. *angioneurosis*.

cardiophobia. *cardiac neurosis.*

cardiovascular neurosis. A symptom-complex similar to that of cardiac neurosis, with complaints concerning both the heart and the blood vessels.

carotid sinus syndrome. Dizziness, fainting, convulsions, decreased heart action, and lowering of blood pressure caused by excessive stimulation of the carotid sinus (a dilation of the carotid artery in the neck), which is concerned with control of blood pressure. This stimulation may occur spontaneously, as a result of pressure on the sinuses, or through unusual sensitivity of the sinuses (as in hardening of the arteries), or because of emotional shock. Syn. *vasovagal attack.*

carphology. Aimless plucking or picking (as at bedclothes), frequently seen in bedridden confused senile patients and patients in states of delirium or profound exhaustion. Cf. *aporrhipsis.*

castration complex. A psychoanalytic concept that attempts to describe the child's reaction to the sexual differences in the external genitalia and the consequences of this reaction in the evolution of the personality. In his delineation of the phases of psychosexual development, Freud speaks of the *phallic stage.* This is the period in infancy when the baby becomes aware of his phallus (penis) as a source of pleasure. Freud said that at this point the child's libido is concentrated on the genital region, resulting in a reaction to dim memories of fear reposing in the unconscious. A very young child cannot understand the physical differences in the sexes; when a boy discovers that a girl has no penis he may conclude that she once had a penis, but that it was cut off as a punishment. He may come to believe that if he continues to show sexual interest in his mother he, too, will be deprived of his penis as a punishment; this is one of the basic elements of the *Oedipus complex.* However, he finds release from this belief and fear through *reaction formation, sublimation,* and *substitution,* and the imagined or actual castration threats from the father cause him to identify with that parent and to set up in himself the father's prohibitions. In this way the castration complex is repressed, though it is reactivated in puberty. In the female the castration complex is not well defined. Freud said. "Nevertheless, we know that the female child is extremely sensitive about the lack of a sex organ equal to that of the male child." She comes to regard herself as inferior to the boy (penis envy) and from this springs a chain of reactions characteristic of the female; the girl feels that she was mutilated in infancy and blames the mother, and this reaction leads to the *Electra complex.*

castrophrenia. The delusion, sometimes observed in severe psychotic disturbances, that thoughts are being sucked from the mind by enemies. Syn. *nooklopia.* Cf. *ideas of influence.*

catagelophobia. Unreasoning and constant fear of being ridiculed, manifested by individuals who are overwhelmed by feelings of inferiority.

catalepsy. Prolonged maintenance of postural attitudes and immobility, due to psychogenic causes; it is synonymous with *flexibilitas cerea,* but the latter is customarily reserved to describe this muscular condition in schizophrenic catatonia. See also under *trance.* Cf. *cataplexy.*

catamnesis. The patient's history following the period covered by the *anamnesis;* sometimes used for "follow-up history."

cataphasia. *perseveration.*

cataplexy. Psychogenic immobility or loss of muscular tone, causing the patient to fall to the ground; usually accompanied by stupor. It is a hysterical reaction. Cf. *catalepsy.*

catathymia. A consciously expressed emotional reaction which is an outward reflection of an emotionally charged complex in the unconscious. Thus, inner hatred of the father may be manifested by strong resentment toward, and even actual assault upon, persons occupying the role of *parent figures* (supervisor, teacher, etc.).

catatonia. (Literally, "breakdown in tone.") A clinical subdivision of schizophrenia, the principal features of which are flexibilitas cerea, echolalia and echopraxia, negativism, and in the most extreme states, *stupor.* In the *active* form the patient displays impulsive, belligerent behavior and resists any manipulation or direction; in the *passive* form he maintains a fixed, bizarre grimace, remains immobile and mute, refuses food, and may be insensitive to pain Cf. *catalepsy.*

categorical demand. The psychoanalytic concept of an all-or-none, domineering supergo, seen in a person of rigid behavior, which effects its control inexorably and with total rejection of any compromise whatsoever.

catharsis. The consequence of a psychotherapeutic technique in which the patient is encouraged to speak freely and fully of his difficulties (*ventilation*). Repressed painful thoughts or experiences are brought to consciousness, whereupon their original significance is explained to the patient. With this insight regarding the unconscious basis of his anxiety and discomfort, he is relieved of the tension associated with the underlying conflict. Syn. *psychocatharsis.* Cf. *abreaction, autocatharsis, desensitization.*

cathexis. Concentration of emotion and mental energy on an idea, person, or experience. It is called *object cathexis* when libido is directed externally (alloeroticism); it is called *subject,* or *ego cathexis* when libido is directed inwardly (autoerotism). Syn. *investment.* Cf. *acathexis.*

catoptrophobia. Fear or anxiety upon encountering or approaching a mirror or other reflective surface. A person may, for example, feel uneasy upon seeing his reflection in a shop window.

cenesthesia. Awareness of normal functioning of the body's organs and systems; the nonspecific feeling that "all is well." Cf. *euphoria.*

cenesthopathy. A vague feeling that the body, or some part of it, is diseased or is not functioning properly. When the personality is dominated by this feeling, the general state is called *hypochondria.*

cenophobia. *agoraphobia.*

censorship. According to Freud, the psychic influence which prevents certain unconsciously maintained drives, desires, and memories from emerging into consciousness unless they are disguised to conform to the individual's moral standards. It is especially active in dreams. See also *repression, superego.*

centers, brain. See under *cerebral cortex.*

central nervous system (CNS). The brain, the spinal cord, and their sensory ganglia.

cephalgia, cephalalgia. *headache.*

cerea flexibilitas. *flexibilitas cerea.*

cerebellar gait. An irregular, careening gait seen in patients suffering certain lesions of the cerebellum.

cerebellum. ("little brain") A division of the brain situated behind the cerebrum. It is concerned principally with coordination of movements and maintenance of equilibrium. Impulses are received in the cerebellum from the skin, muscles, and joints; from nerve fibers in areas of the brain where optical and auditory impressions are received; and from the balancing elements within the inner ear. Thus, the cerebellum accounts for coordination between mind and muscle. A diseased or injured cerebellum makes it impossible to complete purposeful movements skillfully and smoothly.

cerebral agraphia. See under *agraphia.*

cerebral akinesia. See under *akinesia.*

cerebral arteriosclerosis. Hardening or thickening of the walls of the arteries of the brain. It may be mild and develop slowly, as a normal result of aging, and cause the individual no significant or obvious difficulty. In its more severe form it may produce throbbing headache, "ringing in the ears," dizziness, and fainting spells. The syndrome may be the forerunner of apoplexy. Psychosis may ensue, with confusion, memory failure that varies from time to time ("patchy memory defect"), difficulty in concentrating, and emotional instability; *perseveration* is not uncommon. It is often difficult to differentiate between cerebral arteriosclerosis and senile psychosis (see comparative table under the latter heading).

cerebral cortex. The outer layer of the cerebrum, consisting of cells known collectively as "gray matter," where the principal brain centers are located; these are the motor, sensory, visual, auditory, olfactory, and association centers.

The *motor centers* located in the forepart of the cerebral cortex, control voluntary movements of skeletal muscles on the opposite side of the body, and certain movements of the head and eyes. Damage to the motor centers causes convulsions, fainting, coma, or spastic paralysis affecting the opposite side of the body.

The *sensory center,* located in the lateral and posterior parts of the cerebral cortex, receives sensations from the thalamus which, in turn, has received these impulses from skin, muscles, joints, and tendons on the opposite side of the body. Destructive lesions cause impairment of sensibility (e.g., inability to localize, or to measure the intensity of, a painful stimulus) and a diminution in the various forms of skin sensation.

The *visual center* is located in the occiput (back of the brain). Damage to this center may produce visual hallucinations, while more extensive destruction may cause optical defects on the side opposite the lesion (e.g., a lesion of the left occiput will be reflected in disorder in the right side of each eye since sensory fibers from the eyes cross before reaching the cortex).

The *auditory center* is located in the temporal region; damage in this area usually causes only partial deafness. Total deafness from brain implication indicates involvement of both sides of the cortex.

The *olfactory center* is located on the frontal underside of the cerebrum. Damage in this center results in loss of the ability to detect smell. Irritative lesions may cause olfactory hallucinations characterized by sensations of peculiar odors (and sometimes peculiar tastes), often associated with a dreamy state. These hallucinations may be part of an epileptic aura.

The *association centers,* making up the remaining portions of the cerebral cortex, are linked with the various sensory and motor areas by connecting fibers. They are assumed to be of importance in maintaining the "higher" mental activities in man, though it has been impossible to localize any specific faculty or element of conscious experience. Alterations in speech function and comprehension (aphasias) and in the ability to correlate skin sensations, which enables the individual to recognize familiar objects by sense of touch while his eyes are closed, are examples of the effects of lesions of the association centers.

cerebral dominance. Functional predominance of one cerebral hemisphere over the other, demonstrated in motor activity such as handedness, and in visual acuity that is superior in one eye.

cerebral gigantism. A neuropsychiatric syndrome, reported by J. F. Sotos and his co-workers at Harvard Medical School. The condition is seen in children ranging in age from 1 to 10 years whose growth in infancy is markedly accelerated and who mature very early sexually (macrogenitosomia). Other symptoms include mental retardation, muscular incoordination, and, in some cases, hydrocephalus. There is a strong resemblance among these children, in their downward slanting eyes, prominent foreheads and jaws, large hands and feet, long arms, and arched palates.

cerebral hemorrhage. See under *cerebrovascular accident.*

cerebral impotence. See under *impotence.*

cerebral palsy (CP). 1. In a broad sense, any paralysis due to brain damage. 2. Little's disease.

cerebral thrombosis. Formation of a clot in a brain artery, eventually leading to occlusion of the artery. The psychic consequences are those of cerebral hemorrhage. See also *cerebrovascular accident.*

cerebromeningitis. See *meningitis.*

cerebrospinal axis. See under *spinal cord.*

cerebrospinal fever or **meningitis.** See *meningitis.*

cerebrospinal fluid. A colorless, odorless, tasteless fluid that pervades the brain and the spinal canal. It serves two purposes: to provide a cushion against shock for the nerve fibers in the spinal cord and for the brain, and to carry some of the nutrient substances required by brain cells. Small amounts of this fluid are sometimes drained from the spinal canal by hypodermic syringe for examination, to determine whether infectious organisms have invaded the central nervous system and for other diagnostic purposes.

cerebrotonia. 1. The motivational aspect of mental activity, somewhat analagous to the concept of muscle tone (tonus). 2. In Sheldon's classification of body types, the personality associated with an ectomorphic physique, characterized by hyperactivity, hypersensitivity, and intentness.

cerebrovascular accident (CVA). The occurrence of any of several conditions that result in hemorrhage within the brain, brought on either by the appearance of a clot in a blood vessel or by the escape of blood through a vessel wall that has been weakened by infection or degenerative disease. The term is *not* used to refer to hemorrhage caused by external force, as in skull fracture (see brain damage).

cerebrum.   That portion of the brain engaged principally in the voluntary mental functions. It comprises two hemispheres, a left and a right, each containing an outer layer of gray matter and an inner layer of white matter. The *gray matter* is the cerebral cortex, through which man controls speech, thought, and voluntary actions. The *white matter*, continuous with a similar layer in the spinal cord, provides a communicating system between the spinal nerves and the cerebral cortex. The serpentine folds of the cerebrum are known as *gyri* (sing., *gyrus*), the spaces between them as *sulci* (sing., *sulcus*). Each hemisphere is divided into lobes, which are identified as to their location adjacent to bones of the cranium: *frontal, temporal, parietal,* and *occipital.*

character.   The sum of individual traits reflecting the standards of and determined by the mores of society. See also *anal character, oral character.* Cf. *personality.*

character disorders.   *personality disorders.*

Charcot, Jean-Martin.   French neuropsychiatrist (1825-93), who is considered to be the originator of scientific psychotherapy. At first he believed that hysteria was organic in origin but later attributed it to psychological causes. He did much to foster acceptance of the theory and practice of hypnosis. Charcot was the first to call attention to the occurrence of hysteria in the male (previously it was thought to be an exclusively female condition). Freud was among his pupils.

cheimaphobia.   *psychrophobia.*

chemotherapy in psychiatry.   Because full understanding of the specific causes and the nature of mental afflictions is still lacking, treatment with chemical agents, both natural and synthetic, is directed principally toward eradication of symptoms. Nevertheless, there has been encouraging progress in the field. The tranquilizers, for example, have rendered many patients more amenable to psychotherapy. Continued research supports the suspicion that alterations in brain metabolism follow the administration of the tranquilizers, and that this may be what produces the sought-after results. It has also been suggested that certain drugs block the action of an enzyme whose function it is to metabolize the amines (derivatives of proteins) and possibly the histamines (substances regarded as facilitators or inhibitors of the transmission of nerve impulses), Syn. *pharmacotherapy.* See also *psychic energizer, tranquilizer.*

Chiarugi, Vincenzo. Italian physician (1759-1820) who was a pioneer in the custodial care of the mentally ill. It is alleged that he shares, with Pinel, the distinction of being the first European to forbid the use of fetters in an "insane asylum."

Chicago school. See *Alexander.*

child psychiatry. The study, diagnosis, and treatment of mentally and emotionally ill children. The child psychiatrist finds himself engaged mainly in the areas of personality or character disorders, special symptom reactions, mental retardation, and adjustment problems. Although many psychiatric conditions found in adults are not presented to the child psychiatrist, he must be aware of the degree to which the seeds of mental illness are sown early in life and alert to indications of developing neuroses and psychoses.

In general, the causes of emotional illness in a child are found in a disturbance in the equilibrium between his innate characteristics and present or past adverse environmental influences. Abnormal behavior in a child usually indicates that he is disturbed because of an unhealthy relationship to someone near him; parental rejection or overprotection and excessive parental demands are the commonest factors.

chionophobia. A morbid fear of snow.

chirablutomania. *hand-washing complex.*

chlorpromazine. A synthetic tranquilizer, known commercially as Thorazine. It is effective in reducing agitation, excitement, and anxiety. Chlorpromazine is useful in the management of mental and emotional disturbances and is often employed in the control of alcoholic conditions such as delirium tremens and alcoholic hallucinosis, and to alleviate the unpleasant aspects of the withdrawal syndrome.

cholinergic. Pertaining to or effecting the release of *acetylcholine* at nerve endings.

chorea. Any of several neurologic afflictions that are characterized by involuntary, jerky movements. See *Huntington's chorea, Syndenham's chorea.* Cf. *hemichorea, pseudochorea.*

choreic, choreiform. Resembling chorea.

choreo-athetoid. Characterized by a combination of choreic and athetoid movements.

chorionic gonadotropin. A hormone prepared from the urine of pregnant women. It has been employed by some investigators to change mood and personality disorders in autistic boys, who become more amenable to training after its administration.

chrematophobia. Unreasoning abhorrence and fear of touching or handling money because it is thought to be contaminated by evil influences or by deadly bacteria.

chromophilia. An abnormality of interpretation observed in some persons undergoing a Rorschach inquiry or an Organic Integrity tests. Form is interpreted as color. The condition is due to organic brain disorder.

chromophobia, chromatophobia. A morbid fear of or aversion to a certain color or colors.

chromosome. An element that can be seen in a cell's nucleus when cellular division occurs. Chromosomes carry genes (hereditary factors). See also *chromosome 21* under *Down's syndrome.*

chronic alcoholism. The terminal phase of progressively damaging addiction to alcohol. The patient has an abhorrence of interpersonal relations and of nourishment. In the beginning he misses meals in order to devote himself to drinking; ultimately he refuses all solid foods and nonalcoholic beverages. Malnutrition and general decrepitude mark the end of the road. The motivation appears to be that of deliberate self-destruction. Syn. *chronic intoxication.*

chronomania. Compulsive perfectionism in matters involving time.

chronophobia. Unreasoning anxiety over the passage of time.

chthonophagia. *geophagia.*

churrus. See *cannabis.*

circumstantiality. A common reaction in manic individuals. Answers to questions are replete with almost endless and often irrelevant details. See also *flight of ideas.*

cisvestism. Wearing clothes that are appropriate for one's sex but are strikingly at variance with one's age, occupation, or social position. In the fantasy play of children, certain cisvestic manifestations may be quite normal, as in the case of the little girl who dresses up in her mother's clothes. Cf. *transvestism.*

clang association. Repetitive reproduction of a speech sound by an excited manic-depressive or catatonic patient, uttering syllables or words that are associated in similarity of sound but not in meaning or appropriateness. The patient may say, "I have pain in the head . . . go to bed . . . maybe I'm dead." It is sometimes referred to as "rhyming mania."

classification of mental disorders. Throughout the nineteenth century, psychiatric terminology was under the influence of Kraepelin's diagnostic classifications and a tendency to ascribe moralistic values to mental disorders. Early in the twentieth century many changes in terminology were made in response to new diagnostic methods and varied clinical observations. The categories of *psychopathic personality* and *psychoneurosis,* among others, were introduced. The classification approved by the American Psychiatric Association in 1952 quite frankly recognizes the limitations of our knowledge of the nature of mental illness and is designed to allow for modification resulting from future discoveries. It establishes two general classes of disorders: those caused by or associated with impairment of brain-tissue function (organic), and those for which there is no clearly demonstrable physical cause (functional or psychogenic). The main subdivisions are:

Disorders caused by or associated with impairment of brain-tissue function
    acute brain disorders
    chronic brain disorders
    mental deficiency (retardation)
Disorders of psychogenic origin without clearly defined physical cause or structural change in the brain
    psychotic disorders
    psychophysiologic (psychosomatic) autonomic and visceral disorders
    personality disorders
    transient situational personality disorders

claustrophilia. Morbid desire to be alone coexisting with a fear of open places; *eremophilia* and *agoraphobia*.

claustrophobia. Morbid fear of being confined, or anxiety when in any closed space. Cf. *agoraphobia, batophobia*.

clavus. Headache described by a patient as one "like a nail being driven through my head."

climacophobia. Unreasoning, obsessive dread of using stairs or staircases.

climacteric, climacterium. A biologically critical period in life, roughly "middle age" (involution). From the psychiatric point of view the most significant signs are in the realm of exaggerated emotional responses: irritability and a tendency to depression and anxiety, with periods of weeping. These symptoms are interpreted as the consequences of increased or decreased activity of various endocrine glands and other organs and body systems owing to the aging process. The range of severity is very wide among individuals; in the case of females, there is often evidence that the subject's outlook on life has been influenced by old wives' tales about the menopause. A male climacteric has been observed, with the same pattern of behavior. See also *involution*.

clitoral stage. See under *genital stage*.

clitoromania. *nymphomania*.

cloaca theory. The notion held by many children and expressed by some neurotic adults that the infant emerges at birth from the anus.

clonic spasm, clonus. Muscular spasm in which contraction and relaxation take place repeatedly and at short intervals. It is an indication of certain neurologic disorders. It is also seen in grand mal epilepsy and in hysterical seizures. Syn. *clonism.*

clownism. Grotesque contortions and emotional outbursts, seen in some instances of hysterical epilepsy.

cluttering. Rapid, confused speech marked by omission of syllables and words; seen in organic diseases (such as advanced general paresis, alcoholism, and certain drug addictions) and in psychiatric disorders (such as regressed schizophrenia, mental retardation, and some instances of the manic phase of manic-depressive disorders). Cf. *asyndesis, glossolalia, word salad.*

CNS. *central nervous system.*

cocaine. A sympathomimetic alkaloid derived from the leaves of various species of the plant *Erythroxylon,* which has anesthetic and narcotic properties. See *cocainism.*

"cocaine bug." See *formication.*

cocanism. The condition that accompanies cocaine addiction. A single dose, taken orally or hypodermically, induces brief giddiness and slight headache, which are followed by a feeling of euphoria (usually with hallucinations), and delusions of grandeur and power (manic phase). This acute stage of elation is followed by generalized weakness of mental functioning, fatigue, incoordination, and tremulousness. In long-continued addiction the final picture is one of a morose, irritable, suspicious person who is totally unconcerned with domestic and occupational obligations.

cocainomania. Popularly, but erroneously, thought of as synonymous with cocainism. It refers specifically to the acute, excited phase of cocainism.

coitophobia. Morbid dread of sexual intercourse. The unconscious mechanism involves feelings of guilt and/or inferiority, or superficially repressed homosexual drives. The outward reaction to life in general is one of prudishness.

cold knife surgery. See *cryopsychosurgery.*

"cold turkey." A popular term for the pattern of symptoms in an addict who is suddenly and forcibly deprived of his drug. See also *withdrawal syndrome.*

colitis. See *mucous colitis.*

collective or **racial unconscious.** Jung's term for his concept of inheritance, through the brain structure, of primitive racial ideas and impulses which do not enter consciousness. Jung stressed the role of the collective unconscious in mental and emotional motivations hidden in the unconscious which manifest themselves in the form of ritualism, autochthonous ideas, archaic thinking, and primordial images. Cf. *personal unconscious.*

color taste. *pseudogeusesthesia.*

color hearing. See *synesthesia.*

coma. The profoundest degree of unconsciousness. There is no voluntary movement of any kind, and the patient cannot be aroused. It is believed that in coma the individual is unable to perceive pain, inasmuch as he does not react to stimuli such as pin pricks. Coma is seen in neuropsychiatric conditions such as profuse cerebral hemorrhage, severe head injury, and acute alcoholism. Cf. *stupor.*

coma vigil. Coma in which the patient's eyes are open. Sometimes seen in organic brain diseases. Coma vigil is commonly interrupted by periods of consciousness or semiconsciousness.

combat fatigue or **neurosis.** A World War II term (which replaced "shell shock" of World War I) describing a neurotic reaction to the stresses of combat or anticipation of it. The chief characteristic is *anxiety* persisting when danger no longer threatens or is remote. A full-blown psychoneurosis (e.g., conversion hysteria) or psychosis may ensue. The real or simulated (as in training) battle situation is regarded as a precipitating instead of an underlying cause.

combined degeneration. *subacute combined degeneration of the spinal cord.*

commissure. Transverse bands of nerve fibers that lead from the gyri of one cerebral hemisphere to those of the other and between the two sides of the spinal cord.

compensation. A defense mechanism that is used to make up for a real or fancied defect or inferiority by creating a real or fancied achievement or superiority. The commonest manifestation is an effort to achieve success in one field after failure in another. In this circumstance compensation is normal and useful provided that it does not assume exaggerated or antisocial forms. See also *overcompensation.*

complex. A system of repressed memories of emotionally charged experiences that may significantly influence the attitudes and behavior of the individual. See *castration, Electra, grandfather, hand-washing, inferiority, Jocasta, Oedipus, and superiority complexes.*

compromise, psychoneurosis as a. See under *psychoneurosis.*

compulsion. The motor expression of an obsession.

compulsive reaction. See *obsessive-compulsive reaction.*

computer diagnosis. Psychological testing through the use of digital computers. The patient marks his answers on punch cards with an electrosensitive pencil. The computer automatically scores the cards, furnishing a personality profile in 18 seconds. Computer assessment of personality is a swift and welcome aid to, but not a replacement for, human diagnostic skill.

condensation. The unconscious telescoping of several experiences, locations, objects, or persons into one, serving to mask an underlying conflict or unpleasant memory; one of the mental mechanisms that function in the dream.

conditioned fear. A fear arising from external sources (such as parental threats and warnings) in contrast to a *neurotic fear* which results from unconscious dread of a person or a situation, either of which may be the actual source or merely symbols of an emotional conflict. Cf. *phobia, phobic reaction.*

conditioned reflex. A response acquired through repeated association and training. The concept was firmly established by Pavlov's experiments in which a dog was presented with food and a bell was rung; eventually the sound of the bell alone produced salivation without the presence of food.

conduct disorders. *behavior disorders.*

confabulation. A symptom encountered in several mental disorders (sociopathic personality disorders, psychosis associated with cerebral arteriosclerosis, and Korsakoff's psychosis), in which the subject, in response to suggestion, relates imaginary experiences, often weaving together in great detail irrelevant and unconnected ideas and events. It frequently serves the patient in filling the gaps caused by memory loss. Syn. *fabrication.* Cf. *pathologic lying.*

conflict. In psychoanalytic parlance, a clash between the demands of the id and those of the ego and superego, or between the demands of the ego and the restrictions imposed by society (reality).

confusion. A symptom of certain mental conditions, notably organic psychoses (e.g., senile psychosis and psychosis associated with cerebral arteriosclerosis), manifested by inability to identify oneself or one's surroundings, relatives, or associates; disorientation; ignorance of the immediate circumstances; or inability to recognize objects and to tell their uses.

conscience. See *superego.*

conscious, the. In psychoanalytic usage, the level of mental functioning in which the individual is aware of his external surroundings, the circumstances to which he is reacting, and, to a greater or lesser degree, his own motivation. It is the medium in which purposive behavior and constructive thinking take place. Syn. *awareness.* Cf. *unconscious.*

consciousness, double See *multiple personality.*

constipation. Psychoanalysts interpret chronic constipation in emotionally and mentally disturbed persons as a reflection of infantile rebellion against and hostility toward a mother who failed to display tenderness and affection during her child's toilet training period. This is particularly true of the mother who is a precisionist and an authoritarian. She does not "give" love to her baby during the training era; in return, he will not "give" (feces) to her. In adulthood such a person may turn out to be unsympathetic, unyielding, and rigid. Faced with situations that demand some self-sacrifice, he stubbornly refuses to "give."

constitutional psychopathic inferiority. An old diagnostic term which has been replaced by *sociopathy.*

constitutional type. See *habitus.*

contamination. According to Freud, a form of condensation, in which the individual invents and utters combinations of two or more words. An example is "hapmer" (*hap*piness + *mer*riment). Cf. *neologism.*

content, latent and **manifested.** See under *dream.*

contrectation. Fondling; the excitative "play" preliminary to sexual intercourse. Syn. *foreplay.* See also *forepleasure.*

controlled association. See *association, controlled*

conversion. In its psychoanalytic sense, the expression through physical symptoms of a poorly repressed emotional conflict. The concept is a precursor of the psychosomatic approach to illness. See also *conversion hysteria, organ language.*

conversion hysteria. A psychoneurosis which, according to Freud, is a compromise by which a socially unacceptable conflict that cannot be overtly expressed is transformed into physical affliction, which is socially acceptable. In this way the mind (psyche) is relieved through the body (soma).

convolution. Any of the raised portions, or "folds," seen in a serpentine pattern over the surface of the brain and outlined by fissures (sulci). Syn. *gyrus.*

convulsion. A violent involuntary contraction of a voluntary muscle or set of muscles; a "fit" or "seizure." It can be demonstrated by electroencephalography that convulsions are brought on by a focal or generalized acute disturbance of brain function, but the precise cause is not always known. Convulsions are most commonly associated with brain damage and epilepsy, but they are also seen in many other conditions, such as brain tumor, withdrawal syndrome, infection, overdosage with a tranquilizer, and in certain shock therapies.

convulsive therapy.   Any of several procedures for the treatment of mental illness, in which convulsions are anticipated reactions, such as indoklon, insulin and electric shock therapy.

coordination, disorders of.   Conditions resulting from damage to the cerebellum or its pathways as a consequence of injury, infection, poisoning, cerebrovascular accident, or brain tumor. Lack or disturbance of coordination may also be the somatic expression of a psychoneurosis. Some common signs of inco-ordination are: adiadochokinesis, ataxia, chorea, dysarthria, dysmetria.

coprolagnia.   A perversion in which sexual pleasure is derived from the act of viewing, handling, speaking, or thinking of human excrement.

coprolalia.   Habitual use of obscene language, commonly encountered in regressed patients, especially schizophrenics. Syn. *eschrolalia.*

coprophagia, -gy.   *scatophagia, -gy.*

coprophemia.   Foul language as uttered constantly by some disturbed psychotic patients.

coprophilia.   Morbid fondness for or attraction to filth, especially excrement. It is not regarded as abnormal in infants who play with their excrement and daub their surroundings with it, but not infrequently it is seen in schizophrenia when the adult patient has regressed to the infantile level. Syn. *scatophilia.*

coprophobia.   Exaggerated fear of or revulsion toward excrement or, by extension, dirt. Syn. *scatophobia.* Cf. *mysophobia.*

coprophrasia.   Injection of extremely foul expressions into otherwise inoffensive speech by some psychotic persons.

cord.   See *spinal cord.*

cortex. See *cerebral cortex.*

cortical. 1. Relating to the outer coverings or layers of an organ. 2. Relating to the cerebral cortex.

cortical epilepsy. *Jacksonian epilepsy.*

corticospinal. Pertaining to, arising in, or affecting both the cerebrum and the spinal cord with reference to structure or to function.

cosmic identification. *magic omnipotence.*

counteraffect. *inversion of affect.*

counterinvestment. In psychoanalysis, the mental mechanism by which the individual masks the true, unacceptable character of an imperfectly repressed idea. For example, repressed desire to kill one's father may force its way into consciousness disguised as love for the father. Syn. *anticathexis.* Cf. *investment.*

countertransference. In psychoanalysis, the analyst's emotional involvement in the patient's psychic problem. It is due to arousal by the patient of repressed feelings in the analyst's unconscious. Cf. *abreaction.*

CP. *cerebral palsy.*

cranial nerves. The twelve nerves given off by the brain; a brief outline follows:

Nerve	Motor Function	Sensory Function
I Olfactory		Nasal mucous membrane
II Optic		Retina of eye (vision)
III Oculomotor	Muscles of eye	
IV Trochlear	Muscles of eye	
V Trigeminal	Muscles used in mastication	Face
VI Abducens	Muscles of eye	
VII Facial	Muscles of face	
VIII Auditory		Ear (hearing and balance)

Nerve	Motor Function	Sensory Function
IX Glossopharyn-geal		Tongue and pharynx
X Vagus	Larynx, lungs, heart, stomach, esophagus, abdominal viscera	Larynx, lungs, heart, stomach, esophagus, abdominal viscera
XI Spinal Accessory	Heart, muscles of neck and upper back	
XII Hypoglossal	Tongue, muscles of larynx and neck	

craniosacral. Pertaining to the parasympathetic nervous system, that part of the autonomic nervous system that ranges from the medulla and midbrain to the lowest part of the spinal cord in the region of the sacrum.

creeping paralysis. *tabes dorsalis.*

cremnophobia. Unreasoning dread of precipices, often experienced vicariously (as when seeing them in a television picture) or in fantasy.

cretinism. A form of severe mental retardation due to congenital hypothyroidism. The condition may be recognized in the first months of life. The cretin is apathetic and lethargic. He is physically underdeveloped, his tongue protrudes, and his facial features are coarse. Breathing is difficult, speech defective, and the subject has difficulty maintaining stability of posture and gait.

cri du chat. See *crying cat syndrome.*

crisis. See *girdle crisis.*

critical period. Freud tried to explain the development of psychoneuroses through a "critical period," implying that at one time in life there is a surge of primary or secondary personality development, and that factors influencing this period may account for abnormal behavioral responses later in life. The original concept of a critical period has been broadened to mean any time of heightened sensitivity that influences social, intellectual, emotional, and, perhaps physiologic development.

For example, early social deprivation is believed to render the individual unable to participate in group activities; he is timid, retiring, sexually incompetent, lacks useful defense mechanisms, and develops bizarre affectional and emotional reactions. Cf. *âge critique*.

cross-legged gait. *scissors gait.*

crying cat syndrome. A condition seen in early infancy, manifested by mental retardation, failure to thrive, microcephaly, spasticity of all four limbs, various anatomical defects, spasm of the larynx resulting in vocal sounds like a "crying cat," and the facial appearance as seen in *Down's syndrome.* Syn. *cri du chat.*

cryopsychosurgery. Destruction of brain tissue by application of extreme cold. The procedure, painless and bloodless, is used to eliminate the palsy, tremors, and rigidity of parkinsonism. Syn. *cold knife surgery, ice needle surgery.*

cryptomnesia. A disorder of memory in which the subject believes that he is undergoing a completely new experience when he is really recalling a forgotten experience. The reverse of this phenomenon is *déjà vu.* Cf. *eidetic imagery, paramnesia.*

culture and psychopathology. See *Horney; Sullivan.*

cunnilingus. A sexual act in which the female genitalia are stimulated orally or lingually.

cursive epilepsy. A form of epilepsy in which the patient runs forward, apparently oblivious of any obstacles he may encounter. Syn. *running fits.*

Cushing's disease or syndrome. A symptom complex due to hyperfunction of the adrenal cortex, first described by Harvey William Cushing (1869–1939), American pioneer in neurosurgery, also noted for his work in endocrinology. It is caused by excessive secretion of corticosteroid hormones and sometimes by a tumor of the anterior portion of the pituitary gland. In addition to high blood pressure, painful obesity of the trunk and face, bluishness of finger tips and lobes of the ears, and cessation of menstruation in women, there is emotional depression sometimes to the point of suicide. Syn. *pituitary basophilism.*

cycloid. Characterized by alternating feelings of well-being and of depression (mood swings).

cyclothymia. 1. The circular form of manic-depressive psychosis. 2. A personality type characterized by fluctuation of mood between depression and elation.

cyclothymic personality. A personality that is cycloid in nature, but in which the mood swings are often reflections of unconscious conflicts rather than being the results of environmental stimulation.

cynophobia. Morbid fear of dogs.

cypridophobia. Morbid fear of contracting a venereal disease.

cystathianuria. *homocystinuria.*

𝒟

deafness. See *mind deafness, word deafness.*

death instinct, death wish. A psychoanalytic concept advanced by Freud; the impulse, usually unconscious, for personal oblivion. Suicide or the attempt to commit suicide is not necessarily a consequence. Common expressions of the impulse are: *accident proneness, alcoholism,* withdrawal from the stream of life into the unreal world of *schizophrenia,* or *manic-depressive* or *involutional psychosis.* See also *Eros and Thanatos.*

decerebrate rigidity. Exaggerated spasticity in muscles normally required to maintain posture, owing to tumor in or injury to motor pathways that lead away from the cerebral cortex. See also *Tay-Sachs' disease.*

defemination. Dominance of masculine drives in a female. Cf. *effemination, eviration.*

defense mechanism. Any unconscious attempt to adjust to frustrations or assaults on the ego. Defense mechanisms are measures through which the individual preserves his self-esteem and softens the blow of failure, deprivation, or feelings of guilt. All defense mechanisms are forms of evasion or self-deception. Some (e.g., compensation, identification) may be used constructively. Others (e.g., regression, reaction formation), applied excessively, undermine the personality. The most common defense mechanisms are:

compensation	projection
condensation	rationalization
conversion	reaction-formation
denial	regression
displacement of affect	repression
fantasy	sublimation
identification	undoing

degeneration, combined. *Subacute combined degeneration of the spinal cord.*

degenitality. A psychoanalytical term for the outward, non-genital expression of unconscious sexual instinctive drives. Syn. *desexuality.*

dehypnotize. To rouse a subject from a hypnotic trance.

deintegration. Fragmentation of the personality, as seen in profound emotional and mental disorders.

déjà vu. A nonpathologic disturbance of time and space in which the subject has the false impression that he has previously encountered the same set of circumstances or surroundings that he is now experiencing. It is the reverse of *cryptomnesia.* Cf. *paramnesia, pseudomnesia.*

delirium. A psychic disturbance, usually due to toxic factors in certain drugs or diseases, marked by lowering of awareness of one's surroundings, illusions, hallucinations, excitement, restlessness and overactivity, and incoherence. It is usually of short duration. Cf. *dream state, fugue, subdelirium.*

delirium grandiosum. *megalomania.*

delirium mite.   (mit'-eh) *quiet delirium.*

delirium tremens.   An acute manifestation of alcoholic deterioration. It usually follows a prolonged drinking bout during which the patient has not eaten. Colloquially referred to as "the d.t.'s," this is the agitated state associated with visual hallucinations such as "pink elephants" or weird forms that "pursue" the patient. The emotional reaction, therefore, is one of abject fear. Physical effects are very severe and immediate treatment is concentrated on efforts to preserve life, since death from heart failure may ensue. The patient sinks into a deep sleep and awakens comparatively clear mentally but physically exhausted and with total amnesia for the episode. Syn. *oinomania.*

delta rhythm or **waves.**   In electroencephalography, a brain rhythm marked by less than 7.5 waves per second; 3-per-second waves, especially if they are "spiked,'" are specific indications of *petit mal* epilepsy. Syn. *bradyrhythmia.*

delusion.   A disorder of judgment in which the subject's false interpretation of a set of circumstances cannot be shaken even in the face of the most contrary evidence. The truly deluded person often displays errors of judgment that are bizarre. Systematized delusions are described under *paranoia.*

delusion, nihilistic.   The delusion of nonexistence, frequently encountered in schizophrenia and in the melancholic type of involutional psychosis. The patient may deny his own existence or the existence of his entire family, of all of mankind, or of the universe. It is the ultimate form of the *flight reaction.* Cf. *depersonalization, dissociation.*

delusion, somatic.   A delusion in which the patient believes that certain of his organs (or his entire body) are disintegrating, and that this is due to some vague external influence. Also any delusion that refers to the body or its components.

delusions of grandeur.   Delusions in which the patient imagines himself to be possessed of great wealth, power, or superior talents.

delusion of persecution.   Delusions in which the central theme concerns maltreatment by one or more persons. Usually the delusions are patently disorganized and general in their application. In true *paranoia*, however, they are highly organized and superficially plausible.

dementia. An obsolescent term, once used to designate many psychotic states.

demonomania. A delusional trend in which the patient believes himself to be acting under the influence of evil spirits. Syn. *cacodemonomania.* Cf. *diabolepsy.*

demonophobia. Fear of evil spirits.

demophobia. *ochlophobia.*

demorphinization. Gradual withdrawal of morphine in the treatment of morphine addiction. See also *withdrawal syndrome.*

demotivation. Loss of drive or abandonment of goal owing to regression in psychosis (e.g., in hebephrenia) or to psychoneurotic depression. Cf. *hypoboulia.*

denial. A defense mechanism whereby a person suffering a psychosis escapes the psychic pain or anxiety associated with reality by unconsciously rejecting reality. For example, the patient may persistently deny that his child has died, even in the face of irrefutable evidence (such as being shown the corpse). Cf. *negativism.*

depersonalization. A disorder of *affect* in which a patient is beset by feelings of unreality and of altered personality or identity. The patient may deny his own existence or that of the world about him. The reaction is commonly met in schizophrenia, in the severe depression of a manic-depressive psychosis, and in certain neuroses. See also *dissociation; delusion, nihilistic.* Cf. *derealization.*

depressant. Any chemical agent that reduces functional activity and vital energies, such as opium and some of the tranquilizers.

depression. An emotional reaction, characterized by feelings of sadness, loneliness, rejection, failure, or hopelessness, or a combination of them. It is regarded as indicative of mental illness when it is out of proportion to the circumstances or when it persists beyond a reasonable time and the subject makes no effort to rouse himself from the state or to cope with the circumstances that generated it. See also *agitated depression, neurotic depression,* and under *manic-depressive psychosis.* Cf. *melancholia.*

depressive reaction.   The phase of a manic-depressive reaction or psychosis in which the patient is assailed by feelings of unworthiness and futility and, in the more extreme state, entertains ideas of suicide. It is also characterized by decreased activity, speech, and thought. It may precede a manic phase, or may be the dominant pattern of the patient's reaction. Cf. *neurotic depression.*

derangement.   Another term for *psychosis,* obsolete in psychiatry but still used in some legal and popular writing.

derealization.   A feeling expressed by a profoundly depressed patient that people, things, even the entire world, are changing or are not as they should be and, therefore, are unreal. Cf. *depersonalization.*

dereism.   *autism.*

dermatographia, -phism.   A skin condition encountered in certain psychoneuroses. It is marked by extreme susceptibility to irritation; an elevation is produced by running a fingernail or a blunt instrument over the surface of the skin. Syn. *autographism, skin-writing.* See also *tache cérébrale.*

dermatoneurosis.   A psychosomatic condition whose symptoms are expressed through body tissue, e.g., skin disorders, such as hives, pains, or *paresthesias* in the skin or its appendages.

dermatophobia.   Morbid fear or revulsion at the sight or touch of dead or living skin, either of humans or of animals—even one's own skin. Cf. *doraphobia.*

dermatosiophobia.   An exaggerated fear of contracting a skin infection or disease.

dermo-.   See words under *dermato-.*

desensitization.   In psychotherapy, the procedure wherein the patient is urged to discuss fully and repeatedly the stressful experiences of his past. The procedure is effective in the elimination or reduction of such psychic symptoms as phobias and obsessive-compulsive reactions. Cf. *abreaction, catharsis, ventilation.*

desexuality. *degenitality.*

Dexedrine. A trade name for one of the amphetamines.

diabolepsy. The delusion of a paranoid patient that he posesses diabolic or supernatural powers.

diataxia. Ataxia on both sides of the body.

diathesis. Constitutional predisposition to disease.

diathesis, explosive. The tendency to commit impulsive acts of violence, seen most often in traumatic psychosis and catatonic schizophrenia.

Diethelm, Oskar. Swiss-born American psychiatrist (1879-), originator of distributive analysis.

diethylbarbituric acid. *barbital.*

Dilantin. A trade name for diphenylhydantoin sodium, an anticonvulsant that is particularly effective in controlling grand mal epilepsy.

diplegia. Partial or complete paralysis of both sides of the body.

diplegia, spastic *Little's disease.*

dipsomania. Periodic compulsive indulgence in alcoholic beverages.

direct psychoanalysis. A variation of Freudian psychoanalysis championed by several American psychiatrists who claim that conventional analysis overemphasizes the exploration of the individual's psyche, with the analyst playing the role of passive observer and commentator. Proponents of direct psychoanalysis place more stress on the active therapeutic responsibilities of the psychiatrist, who, they feel, must guide the patient as a parent guides the child. They also extend Freud's concept of early psychosexual development to parallel stages in adulthood.

Finally, they view the solution to an Oedipus situation (see Oedipus complex) as one of establishing a satisfactory relationship with a parent.

directive fiction. A term in Adler's individual psychology indicating the idea of superiority which a person adopts as compensation for his feelings of inferiority. Cf. *life goal, life lie, life plan.*

dirt-eating. *geophagia.*

discharge catharsis. Catharsis induced by an analyst in the course of a therapeutic session.

disease; disorder; disturbance. Nearly synonymous words, as used in the phrases "mental disease," "mental disorder," "mental disturbance." The first is concerned with the patient's mental illness as a pathologic process; the other two are descriptive of his aberrant thoughts, moods, and behavior. See also *mental illness.*

disorientation. Loss, or lack, of the ability to place oneself in relation to one's personal identity, one's surroundings, time, or interpersonal relationships; a common symptom of severe infections, delirious states, acute toxic states, several regressive reactions, some organic brain disorders, and following shock therapy.

displacement. A mechanism in the dream whereby persons, objects, situations, and ideas disturbing to the ego are replaced by less offensive ones. Cf. *distortion.*

displacement of affect. A defense mechanism in which a disturbing emotional trend is transferred from an object that is unacceptable to the ego to an acceptable one; or in which unacceptable thought content is expressed in an acceptable way. An example of the former, common in the dream, is the substitution of hatred toward some other person for hatred of parent, spouse, employer, teacher, or even oneself. An example of the latter is the self-righteous outburst of temper which acts as a substitute for a frank verbal expression of an unconscious hatred or aggressive trend. See also *manifest content* under *dream.*

disseminated sclerosis. *multiple sclerosis.*

dissociation. 1. An unconscious mental mechanism by which an idea or a group of ideas splits off from the main body of the personality and becomes inaccessible to the conscious mind. Cf. *depersonalization, nihilism.* 2. Bleuler's term for the basic phenomenon in schizophrenia.

dissociative reaction. A variety of psychoneurosis in which anxiety and tension are so distressing to the patient that he is driven to divorce himself from his own identity, for a time a least. One form of this reaction is a sort of Jekyll-Hyde paradox: one day the patient is reasonable, calm, and considerate; another day he is harsh, carping, hysterical, and demanding. The dissociation may be so severe that amnesia or fugue develops. Cf. *multiple personality.*

distortion. An unconscious mental mechanism that operates during the dream, by which the latent content is altered in order to mask the underlying motives and ideas that are either unacceptable to society or damaging to the ego. Cf. *displacement.*

distractibility. A disorder of attention characterized by a readiness to wander from a subject under discussion or a task in which one is engaged, in response to insignificant changes in the environment. It occurs in an exaggerated form in the manic phase of manic-depressive psychosis.

distributive analysis. Diethelm's question-and-answer technique, a dynamic application, in therapy, of the principles of Meyer's psychobiology. The queries are directed by the psychotherapist along lines suggested by the patient's symptoms, problems, attitudes, and fantasies, Syn. *dynamic therapy.*

Dix, Dorothea Lynde. American pioneer in mental hygiene (1802-1887), who began her campaign for prison and "insane asylum" reform in 1841 in Massachusetts, gradually extended her efforts to other states. Her reform movement spread through Canada, Europe, and Japan.

domatophobia. A variety of claustrophobia in which an emotionally or mentally disturbed individual dreads being in a house or an apartment.

dopamine. A chemical compound produced in the body and normally found in the brain. Experiments indicate that the absence of dopamine may be responsible for the development of parkinsonism.

doraphobia. Unreasoning fear of touching the skin or pelt of an animal, living or dead, for fear of contracting a dread disease. Cf. *dermatophobia.*

doubles, negative or positive. See *Capgras' syndrome.*

Down's syndrome or disease. (mongolism) A form of congenital severe mental retardation named for John Haydon Langdon Down, English physician (1828–96). It is a genetic defect sometimes due to a doubling of *chromosome 21.* Among the causes of this syndrome are: faulty functioning of the pituitary gland, failure of the mother to produce adequate and proper hormonal secretions during pregnancy, and infection with German measles during the early months of pregnancy. Because the facial features of a person with Down's disease resemble those of a Mongol (flattened skull and slanted eyes), the condition is sometimes called *mongolian idiocy* or *mongolism.* In addition, the hands are squat and broad, the limbs rubbery, the genitals small, the abdomen large, and the palate often deformed; the tongue is large and usually hangs from an open, drooling mouth. In spite of their inferior intelligence, these patients are often lively and imitative and therefore amenable to some training. Down's disease acounts for about one-fifth of institutionalized mentally retarded persons.

drama therapy. See *psychodrama.*

dramatism. Exaggeratedly pompous, theatrical speech and manner observed in some psychotics.

drapetomania. *dromomania.*

Draw-a-Person Test. Machover's projective test used to assay personality. The subject is required to draw a person of either sex, then to draw one of the other sex. The figures project the subject's feelings through his perception of the body image.

dream. According to Freud, a dream may be classified as an anxiety-dream, punishment-dream, or a wishful-dream. Every dream is an attempt at wish fulfillment (even when it represents a compulsion to relive an unpleasant experience). The dream in sleep, in contrast to the daydream, is marked by a strong feeling of reality, in some instances so real that the dreamer finds release from his predicament only by awakening. Although dream material often is recalled so sketchily as to seem like undirected meandering of thought, psychoanalysts believe that the dream is constructed through the medium of several unconscious mechanisms which produce a *manifest content* (finished dream which the dreamer can recall) derived from a *latent content* (repressed disturbing material and its emotional accompaniments). The resultant "story pattern" is molded into a form more or less acceptable to the dreamer's *ego*. The process of converting latent content into manifest content is called *dream work*. The unconscious mechanisms which make this possible are *condensation, displacement, distortion, secondary elaboration,* and *symbolism*.

dream analysis.   A psychoanalytic procedure employed to gain an understanding of the roots of a patient's mental and emotional problems. The analysis of the dream is accomplished over several sessions, in the course of which trends may be revealed which provide the therapist with keys to the patient's unconscious conflicts. From the therapeutic point of view, dream analysis gives the subject an opportunity for release from the tension and anxiety associated with the repressed material, to which he gains insight and of which he can rid himself through *catharsis*. The dream offers a fertile field for probing the depths of the personality because, once the barrier of censorship by the superego is broken down, concealed motivations, hatreds, frustrations, and guilt feelings may be discovered which might not be uncovered in any other way.

dream state.   A disorder of consciousness arising from inner mental stimulation rather than from such agents as toxins or microorganisms. The patient does not recognize his environment and may resort automatically to violence or act in a manner dia-. metrically opposite to his usual mode of behavior. The dream state is often seen in epilepsy and is not uncommon in some psychoneuroses. Cf. *automatism, blackout, delirium, fugue*.

dream work.   See under *dream*.

drive. In psychiatric parlance, synonymous with *motivation*. *Libido* implies sexually motivated drive.

dromomania. Compulsive wandering. Syn. *ecdemomania*.

drug addiction. See under *addiction*.

d.t.'s. *delirium tremens*.

dual personality. See *multiple personality*.

dual therapy. In institutional practice, treatment of a patient by two therapists. The usual procedure is that the psychiatrist in charge of a ward or service interviews the patient once a week while the assistant sees the patient two or more times a week for intensive therapy.

ductless glands. *endocrine glands*.

dura mater. The outermost membrane covering the brain and the spinal cord. See also under *meninges*.

dyadic therapy. Double and simultaneously administered modalities of treatment such as medical care for a patient's peptic ulcer and psychotherapy for his emotional condition.

dynamic therapy. *distributive analysis*.

dynamics, personality. The unconscious processes that contribute to the molding of the personality, in contradistinction to the conscious development of superficial, overt character attributes.

dysantigraphia. An *aphasia* characterized by loss of the ability to copy written or printed matter, caused by damage of the association pathway between the brain center that governs word recognition and the one that controls the forming of words in writing.

dysaphia. Impairment of the sense of touch.

dysarthria. Imperfect, often garbled speech.

dysbasia. Any kind of difficulty in walking. It may be due to organic or psychic causes.

dysbulia, dysboulia. Extreme weakness of volition.

dyschiria. Impairment of the ability to determine which side of one's body has been touched.

dysdiadochokinesia, -sis. Impairment of the ability to perform repeated alternating purposeful movements rapidly.

dysergasia. Meyer's term for inability to adjust to the demands of society, particularly common in psychoneuroses. See *ergasia.*

dysergia. Motor incoordination.

dysesthesia. Perversion of the sense of touch in which the subject complains of pain when he encounters a nonpainful stimulus; seen in organic conditions such as general paresis, in hysteria, and in regressed schizophrenics.

dysgeusia. Disordered sense of taste.

dysgraphia. Impaired writing ability, due to motor nerve pathology, tremor, ataxia, or "writer's cramp."

dyskinesia, -sis. Faulty performance of voluntary movements.

dyslexia. Impairment of the ability to read, due either to organic brain or eye disease or a neurosis. See also *strephosymbolia.*

dyslogia. Disturbance of one's ability to express thoughts in speech.

dysmetria. Faulty gauging of distance for bodily movements, sometimes due to cerebellar disease.

dysmimia. Impaired ability to express oneself with gestures or facial expression.

dysmnesia. Impaired memory. Syn. *hypomnesia.* Cf. *amnesia.*

dysmorphophobia. Morbid fear of being maimed or disfigured.

dysnomia. *amnestic aphasia.*

dysorexia. Unnatural or perverted appetite manifested by conditions such as allotriogeusia, bulimia, hyperorexia, pica, and polyphagia.

dysosmia. Defective or diminished olfactory sense.

dysostosis multiplex. *gargoylism.*

dyspepsia, nervous. Gastric distress, nausea, vomiting, and generalized nervousness, due to emotional disturbance.

dysphagia. Disturbance of swallowing. It may be due to organic conditions such as disease of the pharynx (e.g., a sore throat). It is seen in some psychoneuroses, particularly globus hystericus, and in Little's disease.

dysphemia. *stammering.*

dysphonia. Any impairment of voice.

dysphoria. A sense of ill-being, without organic basis. Cf. *euphoria.*

dysphrasia. Incoordination in speech caused by brain damage. See *syllabic utterance.*

dysplastic habitus. Kretschmer's constitutional type in which defects in personality are associated with congenital bodily malformations or glandular dysfunctions.

dyspraxia. Impairment of ability to perform coordinated movements, in the absence of pathology of motor nerves, or of motor tracts of the brain and spinal cord.

dyssocial reaction. A sociopathic personality disturbance in which the total pattern of an individual's behavior and attitudes demonstrates lack of a sense of responsibility to the community, even to members of his family. The dyssocial person displays no remorse for the injustices he perpetrates on others, insisting that he is the one who has been wronged.

dyssynergia. Disturbed muscular coordination caused by damage to the cerebellum.

dystasia, dystaxis. Difficulty in standing, seen in many conditions such as alcoholic intoxication, drug addiction, brain tumor, general paresis, hysteria, parkinsonism, and senility.

dysthymia. Melancholic hypochondriasis.

dystonia. Disturbance of tonus, either general or local.

ecdemomania. *dromomania.*

echographia. An aphasia in which a person is able to copy something that is already written or printed but cannot express his own ideas in writing. Cf. *dysantigraphia.*

echokinesia, -sis. Involuntary imitation of movements the subject is witnessing; the movements are jerky and irregular. Commonly encountered in catatonia. Syn. *echopraxia.* Cf. *echolalia.*

echolalia. Constant repetition of another person's words or phrases. Seen in both organogenic and psychogenic disorders. Syn. *echophrasia.* Cf. *cataphasia.*

echomatism, -mimia, -motism. *echokinesia.*

echomnesia. Obsessive meditation.

echophotony. Association of given colors with given sounds.

echophrasia. *echolalia.*

echopraxia. *echokinesia.*

ecmnesia. Amnesia with poor memory for recent events, but with relatively intact memory for events in the remote past.

ecology. See *environmental mental disease;* neoculturalism, under *Horney.*

ecomania. An emotional condition characterized by irritability or sadness over domestic relations in the face of a wholesome, harmonious family situation which the patient does not recognize. Syn. *oikomania.*

ecophobia. Unwarranted, exaggerated fear of the home or of the people associated with it. Syn. *oikophobia.*

écouteur. ("listener") One who derives excitation, usually sexual, from listening to pornographic accounts or obscene language. Cf. *frotteur, voyeurism.*

ecphorization. Bleuler's term for the mental process evoking the lasting trace in memory (engram) of a physical act performed by the subject.

ECT. Electroconvulsive therapy. See *electric shock therapy.*

ectomorph. Sheldon's body type characterized by a relatively delicate physique. It is associated with a personality type, cerebrotonia, that is marked by hypersensitivity, earnestness, and a predilection for seclusiveness. Syn. *hyperontomorphy.* Cf. *asthenic habitus.*

education. A form of directive psychotherapy in which the mentally or emotionally ill person is urged to acquire intellectual and emotional assets he never possessed. Cf. *re-education.*

EEG. *electroencephalogram.*

effemination. Abnormal personality development in the male, characterized by feminine feelings, behavior, and speech. Syn. *eonism, mulebriety.* Cf. *defemination, eviration, sexual inversion.*

effort syndrome. A type of *anxiety reaction* characterized principally by extreme fatigue accompanied by apprehension. Syn. *neurocirculatory asthenia, "soldier's heart."* Cf. *asthenia.*

ego. According to Freud, the basic component of the personality which is imbued with consciousness and is in contact with the environment. It is the ego that fosters the individual's concept of himself as a unique entity. See also under *personality.* Cf. *id, superego.*

ego cathexis. See under *cathexis.*

ego ideal. In psychoanalysis, the composite of personality characteristics of the individual's parents, older siblings and other relatives, and persons who influence him (teachers, clergymen, contemporary heroes, religious figures, and fictional characters) with whom he identifies himself. See also *identification.* Cf. *anaclitic object choice.*

ego libido. Libido concentrated on the self. Syn. *autoerotism, narcissism. subject libido.* Cf. *object libido.*

egomania. Excessive self-love. Cf. *autoerotism, narcissism.*

eidetic imagery. A mechanism which makes possible a mental afterimage; the vivid, accurate, and detailed reconstruction of a past experience. It is akin to what is popularly called a "photographic memory." Hallucinations are sometimes mistaken for examples of eidetic imagery; the differentiation lies in whether the individual recognizes that his experience is one of fantasy or of reality. Cf. *cryptomnesia, déjà vu, paramnesia.*

elaboration. See *secondary elaboration.*

Electra complex. In psychoanalysis, the counterpart, in the female, of the *Oedipus complex;* a pathologic attachment of a girl or woman to her father. In classical mythology Electra is said to have assisted her brother, Orestes, in avenging their father's death by slaying their mother (who had conspired with her lover to murder her husband).

electric injury. Disabling neuropsychiatric conditions frequently follow recovery from the immediate effects of injury from electric shock. Exposure to high voltage usually causes immediate loss of consciousness; exposure to lower voltage may result in delayed loss of consciousness. In the latter case, the patient may be confused and agitated after he recovers and suffer temporary loss of memory, transient muscular paralysis, or disorders in perception of touch, heat, and cold. Delayed manifestations such as headache, personality changes, and sexual impotence, have also been observed.

electric shock therapy (EST). A treatment procedure for mental disorder, in which a convulsive reaction is induced by passing an electric current through the cerebral cortex by means of electrodes placed on opposite sides of the patient's head. During the convulsion, the patient, who is unconscious, experiences no pain; afterwards he falls into coma. The chief benefits are relief of depression and reduction of excitement and agitation.

electroconvulsive therapy (ECT). *electric shock therapy.*

electroencephalogram (EEG). The recording produced by *electroencephalography.*

electroencephalography. A diagnostic procedure that produces a graphic record of the electrical activity within the brain. A pattern of *brain rhythm,* or *waves,* is obtained from electrodes that are placed over different areas of the skull. The graphic record of the brain waves is called the electroencephalogram (EEG). Electroencephalography is used specifically for diagnosis of *petit mal epilepsy,* for which the wave pattern is a 3-per-second rhythm, each wave having a "spike." The procedure is also used to diagnose *brain tumor.* Measurable differences observed between EEG's of normal and schizophrenic subjects are also beginning to provide criteria for specific diagnosis of schizophrenia with the electroencephalograph. Application of the digital computer to quantitative analysis of EEG recordings promises to broaden the diagnostic potential of the electroencephalogram beyond the fields of epilepsy and brain tumor, and add to its value in the prognosis of expected effects of psychotropic drugs. See also *alpha rhythm, beta rhythm, delta rhythm, gamma rhythm.*

electronarcosis. A form of treatment in which profound stupor is induced by the application of a mild electric current to the patient's temples; the current is insufficient to cause the convulsive reactions seen in electric shock therapy. The procedure is sometimes beneficial for rendering schizophrenics amenable to psychotherapy.

embolalia, embololalia. The interpolation of senseless words or phrases or syllables into speech. Cf. *embolophrasia.*

embolophrasia. A pattern of speech, compulsive in some depressive and insecure individuals, in which superfluous words and phrases such as "Indeed," "Y'know," "Really," etc., are constantly interspersed in otherwise normal utterances.

emetomania. A compulsive drive to vomit; the unconscious motivation is a desire to "eject" a painful conflict; seen in some psychosomatic conditions. See *organ language.*

emetophobia. A morbid fear of vomiting or having to vomit, sometimes seen in persons suffering hysterical digestive disorders.

emotiometabolic. Pertaining to, or generated by, the effect of emotion on metabolism or of metabolism on emotion. For instance, anger stimulates the adrenals through the sympathetic nervous system and thereby elevates blood pressure and accelerates heart action, the final result being an increase in the metabolic rate. Conversely, malfunction of the adrenals may start a chain of physiologic action which culminates in a display of irritability mounting in some cases to anger.

emotion. In the theory of William James (American psychologist, 1842-1910) the total response of an individual, including the subjective feelings and the physiologic changes, as well as the overt signs (such as tremor, perspiration, and a wide-eyed gaze). The word is also used in the narrower sense, to denote the subjective feelings alone. The characteristics of a given emotion are not fixed; opposite emotional reactions often occur in combination (see *ambivalence, -cy*).

Emotional response is made possible through the action of the autonomic nervous system, whose parasympathetic division (which maintains normal physiologic functioning) is blocked off so that the sympathetic division can marshal the bodily forces required to meet the emergency that stimulated the emotion. The hypothalamus is believed to be the controlling center of the emotions.

emotional charge. *investment.*

emotional delirium. Delirium in which the subject unquestioningly accepts false ideas and suggestions.

emotional instability. *lability.*

empiric. Based on demonstrated results, with little or no understanding of the processes that produced them. For example, in psychiatry it is known that electric shock therapy reduces anxiety and depression in some patients, but it is not known why this is so.

emprosthotonos. A muscular spasm which forcibly flexes the head and the body forward. Cf. *opisthotonos.*

encephalgia, encephalalgia.   *headache.*

encephalitis. A generic term applied to several brain disease processes that are inflammatory or degenerative, or both. Some mental symptoms are always present, ranging from irritability or insomnia to stupor or coma. It is a disseminated disease; i.e., more than the central nervous system is involved. Muscle movement is often disturbed, ranging from increased or decreased motion to paralysis. Frequently encephalitis is proved to be of long standing, many patients with chronic encephalitis revealing a history of severe "flu" which probably was acute encephalitis erroneously diagnosed. The common forms are: *paralysis agitans, epidemic* or *lethargic encephalitis, periencephalitis, polioencephalitis,* and *postinfectious encephalitis.*

encephalitis periaxialis diffusa.   *Schilder's disease.*

encephalogram. The developed X-ray film obtained by encephalography.

encephalography. X-ray visualization of the brain. Cf. *electroencephalography.*

encephalomalacia. ("softening" of the brain) A disorder of the nervous system arising from deficient blood supply to the brain—the "softening" of brain tissue is the final stage of the disease.

encephalomeningitis. Inflammation of the brain and its covering membranes (meninges). Syn. *meningoencephalitis.*

encephalomyelitis. Inflammation of the brain and the spinal cord.

encephalopathy. Any brain disease.

end pleasure. Psychoanalytic term for the emotional gratification that accompanies orgasm. Cf. *forepleasure.*

endocrine glands. The ductless glands, i.e., those not provided with ducts leading to surface exits from the body as are the lachrymal, salivary, and some other glands; the secretions of endocrine glands enter the blood stream. The functioning of these glands is closely interrelated with that of the autonomic nervous system. See *adrenal gland, gonads, pineal gland, pituitary gland, thyroid gland.*

endocrinology. 1. The science of the structure and function of the endocrine glands. 2. The medical specialty that deals with the diagnosis and treatment of diseases of the endocrine glands.

endocrinopathy. Any disorder or disease of an endocrine gland.

endogenous. Originating within the organism. Cf. *exogenous.*

endomorph. Sheldon's body type characterized by a rounded and soft physique. It is associated with a personality type, viscerotonia, which is marked by love of comfort, food, and relaxation, gregariousness, and dependency on others. Cf. *pyknic habitus.*

energizer, psychic. See *psychic energizer.*

energy, psychic. See *psychic energy.*

English, O. Spurgeon. American psychiatrist (1901-   ), a prime mover in the advancement of the psychosomatic approach to medical problems.

engram. In psychiatric terminology, the lasting trace left in the psyche by an emotional experience. See also *ecphorization.* Cf. *primordial image.*

enosimania. 1. Mania marked by extreme terror. 2. Obsession with the idea that one has committed an unforgiveable sin. Cf. *hadephobia, hamartophobia.*

entomophobia. An unreasoning dread of insects; the mere sound of buzzing may be sufficient to provoke fear in such a person, who usually displays symptoms of psychoneurosis.

entropy. In psychoanalysis, the inward turning of psychic energy. The tendency which all individuals have in some degree, to retain certain infantile components of their personalities and which may be regarded as an attempt to "conserve" one's psychic energy. Cf. *introversion, narcissism.*

enuresis. Involuntary urination. Though not unknown in adults, enuresis is of particular significance in child psychiatry. Encountered in children with *special symptom reactions*, it is regarded as an indirect manifestation of rebellion, in the same way that the child externalizes his hunger for attention through a tic or stammering (see *habit disturbance*), The enuretic youngster is usually unhappy and anxious, and his failure to master bladder control may be traced to fear, hostility, or jealousy. Enuresis may have an organic basis, as in the elderly, where it is due to loss of sphincter elasticity.

environment and mental illness. The demands of the environment must be assumed to play a role in the precipitation, though not necessarily in the underlying causation, of mental-emotional illness; some investigators, notably Horney, have held it to be a fundamental cause. There is, however, no proof that economic want, war, the clash of cultures, or lack of educational advantages are specific causes of mental illness. Mental disease is as prevalent among the wealthy as among the poor, as frequent during periods of prosperity as in a depression, and as common among peoples at peace as among those at war; nor is it characteristic of any given educational level, or of any given ethnic group or culture. It seems advisable to regard the environment as a testing ground in which the individual, mobilizing his capacity for adaptation, will either achieve stability and adjustment or fail in the effort and resort to fight (psychoneurosis) or flight (psychosis). Not infrequently the challenges of life are the very factors that make for a better integrated personality. See also *structured environment*. Cf. *heredity and mental illness*.

environmental therapy. *milieu therapy.*

eonism. *effemination.*

eosophobia. Morbid fear of the approach of a new day.

epidemic encephalitis. "Sleeping sickness." A form of encephalitis seen most often in spring and winter in epidemic proportions and marked chiefly by lethargy.

epilepsy. Once called "the falling sickness," a disorder of consciousness and motor control believed to be caused by sudden, excessive, disordered electrical disturbances in the gray matter of the brain. In its most severe form (*grand mal*), the patient collapses in a convulsion and loses consciousness. When, as in most cases, specific cause is not known or even suspected, epilepsy is said to be *idiopathic*. This form involves over a million persons in the United States. The disorder has many forms, of which the following are described under their individual headings:

affektepilepsie	Jacksonian epilepsy	pyknolepsy
akinetic epilepsy	myoclonic epilepsy	reading epilepsy
cursive epilepsy	nocturnal epilepsy	reflex epilepsy
grand mal	petit mal	sensory epilepsy
hysterical epilepsy	psychomotor epilepsy	status epilepticus

Although the outward manifestations of epilepsy indicate the organic nature of the disorder, a psychosis may accompany the condition, ordinarily reflecting the individual's preepileptic personality. Generally, however, even in the absence of mental disorder, the epileptic person is usually overwhelmingly egocentric, a personality feature that may take the form of a striking paranoid reaction. It has been widely thought that alcoholism aggravates epilepsy, but there is no conclusive evidence to support this belief.

epileptic aura. See *aura.*

epileptic cry. A peculiarly piercing, short utterance emitted by the patient at the beginning of an attack of grand mal epilepsy.

epileptic equivalent. Many conditions, some of them so minor as to escape notice, may be regarded as epileptic equivalents. They may recur over many years, with the patient being treated and hospitalized for various ailments until electroencephalography establishes the correct diagnosis of epilepsy. Some of the commonest epileptic equivalents are: attacks of abdominal pain, sleepwalking, impulsive aggresive acts, inattention, déjà vu, confusion, sporadic enuresis, and night or day terrors.

epileptic furor. See **furor.**

epileptiform, epileptoid. Resembling epilepsy.

epinephrine. The hormone secreted by the adrenal glands.

Called into action in an emergency situation by the sympathetic nervous system, it mobilizes the body for emotional response, especially by accelerating heart action.

epinosis. An illness superimposed on or following another. Cf. *secondary advantage.*

epistemophilia. Excessive preoccupation with the search for knowledge.

Equanil. Trade name for *meprobamate.*

eremitism. *eremophilia.*

eremophilia. Morbid desire for solitude. Syn. *eremetism.*

eremophobia. Unreasoning fear of being alone. Syn. *monophobia.* Cf. *claustrophobia.*

erethism. Abnormal increase in irritability or sensitivity, usually psychic in origin. It may be general or local.

ergasia. Meyer's term for the aggregate of an individual's physiologic functioning and his emotional reactions.

ergasiomania. A compulsion to be active, based on feelings of guilt over idleness.

ergophobia, ergasiophobia. A morbid fear of being active; based on the notion that any movement will have a harmful effect.

ergotamine tartrate. A chemical compound used in the treatment of migraine.

erogenous or **erotogenic zones.** Areas of the body where pressure or stroking arouses sexual desire.

Eros and Thanatos. Opposing drives postulated by *Freud,* Eros representing the libido, or "life instinct," Thanatos, the death instinct or death wish. In Greek mythology, Eros was the god of love, Thanatos the personification of death.

erotism, eroticism. Any expression of sexual desire. See also *alloerotism, anal erotism, autoerotism, oral erotism, psychosexual development.* Cf. *libido.*

erotization. 1. The unconscious association of certain areas of the body with sexuality. 2. The investment of the psyche with erotic attributes.

erotodromomania. The impulse to roam abroad, as an escape from a situation involving a sexual conflict. Cf. *dromomania.*

erotogenic. Provoking or emanating from sexual drive.

erotolalia. The compulsive use of vulgar erotic language, especially during sexual intercourse, to heighten excitement and achieve orgasm.

erotomania. Excessive erotic behavior or obsessive contemplation of it. Syn. *aphrodisomania, lagneia.* Cf. *nymphomania, satyriasis.*

erotopathy. Any sexual abnormality.

erotophobia. Morbid fear of, or aversion to, any aspect of sexual involvement.

escape mechanism. Any mental mechanism in which the individual avoids the pain of frustration, depriviation, or disappointment, by the unconscious shift of libido from painful or difficult situations to pleasant or easy ones. Cf. *defense mechanism.*

eschrolalia. *coprolalia.*

EST. *electric shock therapy.*

estheticokinetic. Pertaining to phenomena in which both psychic and sensorimotor aspects are combined.

estromania. Exaggerated sexual desire in a menstruating woman. Cf. *nymphomania.*

etiology. The facts concerning the origin and development of a patient's illness. Often used loosely to mean "cause," the term is actually more comprehensive, embracing predisposition, environmental influences, and other phenomena directly or indirectly involved in the development of the illness.

euphoria. Extreme and unwarranted elation and/or feeling of physical well-being, often accompanied by delusions. Some patients in a markedly deteriorated physical state have episodes during which they insist that they are in perfect health. Euphoria is commonly encountered in the manic phase of manic-depressive psychosis and in general paresis and multiple sclerosis. Syn. *hypercenesthesia.* Cf. *dysphoria.*

eupraxia. The normal capacity for performing coordinated movements.

euryplastic. A constitutional type, described by Bounak, corresponding to Kretschmer's *pyknic habitus* and Sheldon's *endomorph.*

eviration. Assumption of the feminine role by a male, expressed particularly by a preference for submission and passiveness in sexual relations. Cf. *effemination, sexual inversion.*

exhaustion delirium. Delirium provoked by extreme physical weakness or mental confusion.

exhibitionism. A form of sexual perversion in which erotic gratification is obtained from the exposure of parts of the body that have sexual significance. It is most commonly seen in men of advanced age, in whom it is a regressive symptom, a childish form of sexuality employed to compensate for sexual impotence. Cf. *voyeurism.*

existential psychiatry. An approach to psychiatric problems based on the principles of existentialism, whose keynote is a rejection of the past as a useful consideration. Stressing the importance of the "here and now," existentialists insist that diagnosis and treatment be undertaken within the framework of the prevailing conditions and the relation between the life the patient is attempting to live and the "stream of life" (environment) in which he finds himself. See also under *Horney.* Cf. *ontoanalysis.*

exogenous. Originating outside the organism. Cf. *endogenous.*

exophthalmos. Protrusion of the eyeballs, as occurs in goiter and other conditions.

expressive aphasia. *motor aphasia.*

externalization. *projection.*

extrapyramidal tracts. Motor pathways, other than those of the pyramidal tract, carrying impulses for movement from the brain to the spinal cord.

extraversion. Jung's term for healthy outward direction of libido. See *alloerotism, extravert, introvert.* Cf. *introversion.*

extravert. A person characterized by extraversion; the "outgoing" type. Cf. *introvert.*

fabrication. *confabulation.*

facies. Facial expression. See *ironed-out facies, masklike facies.*

fading of affect. A concept in psychoanalysis referring to the weakening of an *affect,* or emotion, associated with an unconscious wish. The change takes place at the level of the preconscious.

false anorexia. See under *anorexia nervosa.*

false pregnancy. *pseudocyesis.*

familial. Said of a disease or a special trait which appears frequently within a family. It is not synonymous with "hereditary," being used when a genetic basis is either not known or of secondary significance. See *heredity and mental illness.*

family therapy. A therapeutic program for a mentally ill person which includes interviews with members of the patient's family and, if necessary, treatment of a parent, relative, or spouse who has contributed to the patient's illness and who is also mentally disturbed. Cf. *milieu therapy.*

fantasy. 1. The mental process by which the individual creates images, usually unrealistic, which tend to provide satisfactions not obtainable in reality. 2. An image thus produced.

fate analysis. A variety of applied psychology originated by Leopold Szondi which allegedly bridges the gap between genetics and dynamic psychology. It is based on the premise that four mental illnesses are inheritable: *manic-depressive psychosis, epilepsy, homosexuality,* and *sadomasochism.* For this premise Szondi derives his concept of "genotypes," contributed by both parents, which determine what the individual does vocationally, the kind of persons he selects for love objects, and his personality in general. While the theory enjoys some popularity in Europe, Szondi's thesis is generally rejected by American psychiatrists and psychoanalysts.

father figure. See *parent figure.*

father image. See under *parent image.*

father surrogate. See *surrogate.*

fatigue, mental. It is doubtful that there is any such thing as "mental fatigue." What passes for this may be merely muscular weariness from the physiologic tensions generated by the emotional accompaniments of intellectual and emotional activity.

faute de mieux. ("for lack of something better") A description of the practice of homosexuality by heterosexually adjusted persons while they are in an environment that deprives them of the company of the opposite sex (as prisoners in a jail and military personnel in barracks).

fear. Many psychiatrists believe that fear is the fundamental motivation from which other motivations spring. For example, from the phylogenetic point of view, the procreative instinct may be prompted by unconscious fear of racial extermination. Fear is normal; without it the individual would lack the most effective protection he has, since fear serves to mobilize an organism to react to threatening situations. It may, however, be encountered in perverted or exaggerated forms. See also *anxiety, panic, phobia.*

Federn, Paul. Viennese psychoanalyst (1872–1958).

feeblemindedness. See *mental retardation.*

feeding habits. All aspects of the practices of feeding employed with a child which contribute to the early formation of his personality. Since feeding is the principal feature of the infant's daily life from the very first day of existence, rivaled in importance only by the experiences of the eliminatory process, the personality structure will be in part a reflection of the way he coped with these challenges and in part a result of the mother's management of these situations. See also *habit training, oral character, oral stage.*

feeling. Pleasurable or painful subjective experience in response to a stimulus. It may be localized (as in the application of heat to the skin) or generalized (as in listening to a musical performance or witnessing an automobile collision). Cf. *affect, emotion.*

fellatio. A sexual perversion in which the penis is mouthed. Syn. *irrumation.*

fellator, fellatrice. Respectively, a male and a female practitioner of *fellatio.*

feminism. The prevalence of strikingly female characteristics and impulses in a male. Cf. *effemination, eviration, sexual inversion.*

Ferenczi, Sandor. Hungarian psychoanalyst (1873-1933), an original disciple of Freud. See *amphimixis.*

festination. An involuntary tendency to increase speed when walking. It is seen particularly in parkinsonism. Also called "running after the center of gravity." Cf. *marche á petits pas.*

fetish. Any object employed symbolically to stimulate sexual excitation. It may be a part of the body (except the genitalia) or an article of clothing or some other object belonging to the desired person. See *antifetishism.*

fetishism. Habitual use of a *fetish.* Cf. *antifetishism.*

fiction, directive. See *directive fiction.*

"fight-or-flight" reaction. The manner in which an individual reacts to stressful situations. In the "fight" reaction he strives for adjustment; if he fails to solve the problem he may adopt a psychoneurosis as a compromise. In the "flight" reaction he may take refuge in a psychosis, which permits him to create a fancied situation in which he can control the problem or ignore its very existence.

Figure-Drawing Test. *Draw-a-Person Test.*

fit. *convulsion.*

fixation. In psychoanalysis, the continued attachment of libido to some earlier level of psychosexual development as the individual advances toward maturity. In the psychoses, especially the manic-depressive reaction and schizophrenia, regression to fixations at infantile levels is strikingly evident.

flagellation. A perversion wherein sexual excitation and satisfaction are sought through allowing oneself to be whipped (*masochistic* version) or through engaging in or witnessing the whipping of another person (*sadistic* version). See also *sadomasochism.*

flexibilitas cerea. Waxlike flexibility of extremities seen in catalepsy or catatonia. The patient makes no movement of his own volition and will maintain for an extended time any posture in which he is placed (for example, with upraised arm.) See also *catalepsy.*

flight of ideas. An abnormally rapid and copious recitation of associations, during which the patient frequently shifts the topic, does not return to his original point, and never reaches the goal of his narrative. The reaction is commonly encountered in manic-depressive psychosis. In a milder, nonpathologic form it is called "circumstantiality."

flight reaction. See *fight-or-flight reaction.*

focal epilepsy. *Jacksonian epilepsy.*

folie à deux, folie à trois, folie à beaucoup. Occurrence of identical manifestations of the same type of mental disorder (*folie*) in two, three, or more persons living in close association.

folie du doute. A syndrome observed in an anxiety reaction or an obsessive-compulsive reaction. It is marked by needless review and repetition of one's acts (e.g., "locking" a door several times), often to the point of being unable to proceed beyond the questioned act. It is also manifested by difficulty in making simple decisions (such as whether to turn a street corner or open an envelope.) Cf. *abulia.*

folie du pourquoi. An obsession in which the patient asks question after question, disregarding the answers and frequently ending in asking about totally unrelated, often abstruse matters.

folie de toucher. Compulsion to touch or handle objects or other persons.

foreconscious. *preconscious.*

forensic psychiatry. A subspecialty within psychiatry, concerned with the legal and judicial implications of mental illness and retardation.

foreplay. *contrectation.*

forepleasure. Pleasure derived from play that precedes sexual intercourse and may lead to orgasm. According to Freud, during the pregenital stage of personality development stimulation of erogenous zones constitutes the *end pleasure;* with the advent of the genital stage these zones are subordinated. He also described forepleasure as the *incitement premium.* See also *contrectation.*

formication. A paresthesia in which the individual feels that insects are crawling over or just beneath his skin. In cocainism it is known as "cocaine bug." Cf. *acanthesthesia.*

fortification figures or **spectra.** Bright colors or bursts of light flashing before the eyes without external stimulus; a common symptom in *migraine.* Cf. *teichopsia.*

free association. See *association, free.*

free-floating anxiety. Vague anxiety which, according to Freud, is always present in the personality and which is nonspecific until it becomes associated with some life problem. It is, in fact, the foundation for the fear reaction which the individual requires for self-protection. In an *anxiety reaction* (formerly called anxiety neurosis) it is out of proportion to the danger presented by reality. See also *fear, phobia.*

Freud, Sigmund. Viennese physiologist, neurologist, and psychoanalyst (1856-1939); founder of the psychoanalytic school. He pioneered probing into the normal development of the mind and personality. At first he was impressed with hypnotherapy. After studying with Charcot he sought a new concept of the treatment of neuroses. From this search came his dynamic approach to and interpretation of mental and emotional disorders and the psychoanalytic system of therapy. Basic Freudian concepts are too numerous to list here; outstanding among them are: the *preconscious* and *unconscious;* the *id, ego,* and *superego; dream analysis,* the *Oedipus, Electra,* and *castration complexes; psychosexual development;* and *transference.*

"Freudian slip." Any seemingly accidental error of speech, writing, or behavior (such as picking up the wrong object) regarded by Freud to be at least in some part an expression of an emotional conflict. Also called an *unconscious mistake.* See *lapsus linguae, lapsus memoriae.*

frigidity. In a woman, indifference toward sexual activity. Cf. *anaphrodisia, anorgasmy.*

Fromm, Erich. German psychoanalyst (1900-   ). Like Horney, he sees man in constant conflict with nature and with his surroundings, and believes that the individual's emotional problems must be approached in the light of his cultural environment. Along with the Chicago school, Fromm advocates short-term psychoanalysis.

frontal lobes. Segments of the forepart of the brain, where intellect, judgment, and spatial orientation are centered. Frontal lobe damage plays a role in many forms of aphasia. See also *cerebral cortex.*

frotteur. A person who obtains sexual gratification by rubbing against another person or by stroking an object that serves as a sexual symbol (see *fetish*). The act is known as *frottage.* Cf. *écouteur, voyeurism.*

frustration. In psychiatric parlance, failure to gain satisfaction of an impulse or to free the unconscious of tension arising from an inner conflict.

fugue. A flight from reality. Through the medium of temporary amnesia, the subject "runs away" psychologically from his customary environment. During this state he performs apparently purposeful acts, but seems to be in a dream state. When restored to conscious appreciation of reality he does not recall what he has done or where he has been during the fugue. Fugue is sometimes seen in a *psychomotor equivalent* of epilepsy. Syn. *twilight state*. Cf. *dream state*.

Full-Range Picture-Vocabulary Test. An easy-to-use, fairly reliable individual intelligence test based on verbal comprehension, providing norms for the chronologic age of 2 through the adult level. Its advantages are speed of administration (5 to 10 minutes) and the subject's not having to write or read. This makes it very useful in testing physically handicapped patients and those suffering aphasias.

functional. *psychogenic.*

furor. Uncontrolled, sometimes homicidal rage, as a choleric outburst that occurs during a grand mal seizure (epileptic furor).

gain, secondary. *Secondary advantage.*

gait. Certain gaits are specific indicators of disease of the central nervous system. See *ataxic gait, cerebellar gait, festination, helicopodia, marche à petits pas, scissors gait, spastic gait.*

galeanthropy. The delusion that one has been transformed into a cat.

galeophilia, -phobia. *ailurophilia, ailurophobia.*

gallows humor. Humorous deportment in the face of disaster or the threat of death, seen often in response to the hallucinations of delirium tremens.

gamma rhythm or waves. In electroencephalography, a rhythm of 40 to 60 cycles per second, recorded from the anterior regions of the brain; its clinical significance has not been determined. Cf. *alpha rhythm, beta rhythm, delta rhythm.*

gammacism. A defect of speech observed in young children who use "d" and "t" for "g" and "k"; commonly referred to as "baby talk"; encountered in hebephrenia.

gamonomania. Obsession with the idea of marriage, seen in a psychotic person given to making indiscriminate proposals of marriage, often under incongruous circumstances.

gamonophobia. Morbid fear of marriage. Cf. *coitophobia.*

ganglion (*pl.* **ganglia**). A collection of nerve cells situated outside the central nervous system.

Ganser's syndrome. A pattern of reaction named for the German psychiatrist, Sigbert J. M. Ganser (1853-1932). It denotes the behavior of an individual who gives false, usually ludicrous, replies to questions. Though frequently encountered in prisoners who are trying to feign mental illness, it may be encountered during an interview with a patient suffering a psychoneurosis, in which instance the content of the subject's replies and his manner may provide valuable keys to his unconscious conflict. Syn. *nonsense syndrome, syndrome of approximate answers.*

gargoylism. A congenital disorder strikingly marked by dwarfism and gross facial features and by mental retardation. Syn. *dysostosis multiplex, Hurler's syndrome, lipochondrodystrophy.*

gastrointestinal orientation. The overriding influence of the emotional patterns of infancy, which are concentrated on the processes of eating and elimination. It is often reflected in the behavior, attitudes, and personality of later life. See also *anal character, feeding habits, oral character.*

gastrointestinal reactions. Disorders of the digestive tract are often brought about by psychic disturbances which have affected the central nervous system and, via the autonomic nervous system, the digestive tract. Significant examples are *vagotonia* and *sympatheticotonia,* and a broad range of so-called "medical conditions," notably *peptic ulcer, mucous colitis,* and *ulcerative colitis.* All such reactions are regarded as psychosomatic disorders, management of which requires both treatment of the physical symptoms and psychotherapy. See also *conversion hysteria,* "*nervous indigestion,*" "*nervous stomach.*"

gelasmus. Spasmodic laughter, without apparent or appropriate reason, as encountered in hysteria and in hebephrenia (a type of schizophrenia).

gelophobia. Morbid fear of the sound of one's own laughter, seen in agitated depression when the patient believes it is sinful to laugh or that he is unworthy to enjoy happiness.

general paralysis of the insane. Obsolete term for *general paresis.*

general paresis. Widespread physical and mental deterioration due to syphilis that has attacked the central nervous system. A broad range of symptoms is seen. Delusions of grandeur are common, as well as both visual and auditory hallucinations. The patient may be irritable, sullen, and fractious, or unusually affable. As his condition worsens his speech grows more and more slurred and he omits syllables and words; his writing is similarly affected. Even when the ravages of syphilis are most virulent the patient may display *euphoria.* The emotional reaction depends in part on the prepsychotic personality. General paresis has become less common since the advent of antibiotic drugs, which have been effective in halting the inroads of the offending microorganism, *Treponema pallidum,* in the early stages. However, with the upsurge of incidence of venereal diseases at the beginning of the second half of this century, clinicians anticipate that neurosyphilitic disorders will again grow common. See also *juvenile paresis, malarial therapy.*

genital character. The final, adult personality, made up of the traits accumulated in prior stages of psychosexual development, as modified by social demands.

genital stage. The period of psychosexual development identified in two ways. Some psychiatrists place it in the period from the third to the seventh year between the narcissistic and homosexual stages. In this sense it denotes the child's emerging awareness of his or her genitals and the pleasure derived from their stimulation. Other psychiatrists equate the genital stage with the onset of puberty, i.e., following the *homosexual stage*. It is also referred to as the *phallic stage* regardless of sex, but Ernest Jones preferred the term *clitoral stage* for the female.

genius. Exceptionally high mental superiority demonstrated by creative achievement, usually in a specialized field of activity. Nonscientific literature has often hinted that genius is akin to psychosis, and while this thesis is without convincing support, neither has it been wholly disproved. The genius indeed presents an "abnormal" pattern of personality. He is, as a rule, withdrawn, egocentric, and either indifferent to, or impatient with, affairs beyond the perimeter of his special interests. His self-imposed "exile" from the contemporary social stream creates the impression that he is socially maladjusted.

genophobia. An unreasonable and morbid fear of sexual intercourse.

genotype. Any one of Szondi's personality or constitutional composites predetermined by inheritance. See under *fate analysis*.

geophagia, -agy. Eating clay or dirt. See also *pica*.

gephyrophobia. Morbid fear of crossing a bridge, trestle, or scaffolding, to the degree that the individual may refuse to make a trip involving such a structure.

geriatric psychiatry. A medical specialty concerned with the holistic challenge of old age—physically, socially, emotionally, mentally, and economically.

gerontophilia. Libidinal attraction to old persons. Hirschfeld regarded this as a manifestation of an infantile fixation on an elderly individual, such as a grandparent, or a father of advanced age. Syn. *grandfather complex*.

gerontophobia. Morbid fear or uneasiness when in the presence of elderly persons. It may be the result of an unresolved Oedipus or Electra complex or of mistreatment in early childhood at the hands of grandparents.

gerontotherapy, gerontotherapeutics. A treatment program which includes not only psychotherapy but the potential benefits of social, welfare, and religious agencies in the treatment of problems of the aged.

gestalt. (A German word meaning, approximately, "configuration.") A normal perceptual experience in which the whole is seen or understood as something more than merely the sum of its parts. The concept gave rise to the school of "gestalt psychology," the central precept of which holds that piece-by-piece association is not the sole basis of perceptual processes. Instead, it is assumed that as experience accumulates patterns are formed which act as integrated entities no longer requiring recall of all the component elements. The classic example is a drawing which can be perceived as either a vase or as two human faces; the way it is interpreted depends on a composite of the individual's interests and experiences. See also *Bender Visual Motor Gestalt Test*.

gigantism. See *cerebral gigantism*.

"gift of tongues." *glossolalia.*

girdle crisis, girdle symptom. A symptom of tabes dorsalis characterized by agonizing, viselike, pain encircling the abdomen that is seldom relieved by pain-killing agents. Syn. *zonesthesia*.

glacial age. According to Freud, the time just prior to puberty when the child is sexless in interests and drives.

global aphasia. Complete aphasia, the consequence of widespread destruction of the frontal and temporal regions of the left hemisphere of the cerebrum.

globus hystericus. A sensation of choking, or feeling of a "ball in the throat," observed in some hysterical reactions. Syn. *apopnixis. spheresthesia*.

glossolalia. Speaking in a jargon composed of unintelligible sounds, sometimes encountered in groups of ecstatic religionists. The earliest recorded example is the Pentecostal experience described in Acts 2:4, where the disciples "were all filled with the Holy Ghost, and began to speak with other tongues, as the Spirit gave them utterance." Thereafter, "speaking in tongues" (in the language of the angels, it was believed) was considered a spiritual gift. Often called "gift of tongues," or "speaking in (unknown) tongues." Cf. *asyndesis, cluttering, word salad.*

glossospasm. An episodic habit spasm, often lasting several minutes, in which the tongue is extended and retracted rapidly; an hysterical tic.

glove-and-stocking anesthesia. A hysterical paresthesia which prevails in areas roughly corresponding to those over which a glove or stocking would be worn. It is believed to be psychic in origin because nerve distribution does not parallel the outlines of the affected regions.

glue-sniffing. A non-addictive practice, particularly among adolescents, in which exhilaration is derived from sniffing glue containing toluene. Effects include excitement, nausea, vomiting, sleepiness, stupor, and, at the height of stimulation, a domineering attitude or uninhibited behavior.

goiter. Enlargement and swelling of the thyroid.

Goldstein, Kurt. American psychologist, born 1878.

Goldstein-Scheerer Test. A psychological inquiry into aptitudes and interests. Like the Hanfmann-Kasanin Test, it reveals weaknesses in concept formation and abstract thinking and is therefore also useful in differentiating between brain damage and schizophrenia.

gonads. The endocrine glands containing the reproductive elements: the testes in the male, the ovaries in the female.

gonadotropic, gonadotrophin. Influencing the nutrition and/or growth of the *gonads.*

gonadotropin, gonotrophin. See *chorionic gonadotropin.*

gonadotropism. An endocrine makeup in which the gonads exert a dominating influence over the other ductless glands.

Goodenough, Florence. American psychologist, born 1886.

Goodenough Drawing Test. A projective inquiry into personality devised by Florence Goodenough. The subject is asked to draw a human figure. Interpretations of the drawing are based on such considerations as whether the subject draws the whole figure or part of it, which components are given special attention and which ones are neglected, whether there is excessive elaboration, etc. The subject's responses provide clues to the degree of personality integration and to whether thinking is chiefly abstract or concrete. Cf. *Draw-a-Person Test.*

"goof butts." Cigarettes containing marihuana.

gout, juvenile. A metabolic disorder of children, precipitated by hyperuricemia (excess uric acid in the blood stream), manifested by severe mental retardation, extreme cerebral palsy, athetosis, and marked self-destructive tendencies, chiefly those of chewing away lips and finger tips. For want of a better term, juvenile gout is used, although there is no actual joint involvement. The brain damage is irreversible.

grand mal. The severe form of epilepsy, with convulsions and loss of consciousness. The sequence of events in a grand mal seizure is as follows: first, an aura and the epileptic cry; immediately afterward the patient falls to the ground and displays steel-like muscular rigidity (*tonic phase*) with suspended respiration and loss of consciousness; this is swiftly followed by the appearance of jerky movements that may be confined to one set of muscles (*clonic phase*), the movements usually spreading until the entire body is implicated. Involuntary tongue-biting and defecation and/or urination may occur. The convulsion lasts for a few minutes. Following a severe seizure, headache, nausea, transient memory defects, depression, or coma may be observed. Syn. *haut mal, major epilepsy.* Cf. *nocturnal epilepsy, petit mal, status epilepticus.*

grandeur, delusions of. See *delusions of grandeur.*

grandfather complex. *gerontophilia.*

graphology. The analysis of handwriting to assist in determining personality characteristics or diagnosing mental conditions. Thus, an exceptionally neat and uniform script, meticulously inscribed, may be indicative of an anal character.

graphomania, -orrhea. A compulsive reaction, especially common in the manic phase of manic-depressive psychosis , in which the individual writes ceaselessly, filling page after page, usually with incoherent, unrelated ideas.

Grasset, Joseph. French physician (1849-1918) who became interested in forensic psychiatry and introduced such concepts as legal responsibility, competence, and the criminal borderline type.

gray matter. The mass of nerve cells and nerve fibers, found in the brain and the spinal cord. Syn. *substantia grisa*. Cf. *white matter*.

group therapy. Psychotherapy in which a small group of psychiatric patients who have similar problems, and who are in reasonably good contact with reality, talk about their difficulties, with the therapist serving as moderator. As the patients discuss each other's problems, they gain insight into their own disturbed thinking and acting and discard some of their egocentric impulses. The procedure provides more treatment opportunities for a greater number of patients in a shorter time, and is therefore desirable from an economic standpoint. Group therapy is used not only at institutions and clinics but also in private practice. See also *multidimensional group therapy, psychodrama*.

guidance. In a special sense, the method of psychotherapy used by Adler. The therapist adopts a paternalistic role and guides the patient as he would his own child.

guilt, feelings of. Response to unconscious feelings of guilt pervades many aspects of the psychoneuroses and psychoses. In psychiatry the word seldom refers to conscious remorse over a reprehensible act, but rather to a deep-lying, undefined guilt which usually is not warranted and which is based as much on one's thoughts as on one's actions. The clearest indications of guilt feelings are seen in the obsessive-compulsive reaction, wherein ritualistic behavior serves as a "penance" for "transgressions." Depression and anxiety are often the conscious expressions of unconscious guilt feelings. Cf. *hamartophobia, punishment*.

guilt, moral sense of. Freud defined this as: "the expression of tension between the ego and superego." See also *inferiority and guilt*.

gymnomania. An uncontrollable impulse to view the naked human body. Cf. *écouteur, frotteur, voyeurism.*

gymnophobia. Morbid fear or uneasiness upon beholding or being close to a nude person, or of viewing part of the body that is customarily covered.

gynecomania. *satyriasis.*

gynophobia. Unreasoning or morbid fear of women.

gyrus (*pl.* **gyri**). *convolution.*

H

habit disturbance. A diagnostic entity within the general group of transient situational personality disorders. It embraces not only *habit spasm* but compulsive habits, such as thumb-sucking, nail-biting, and lip-smacking, and broader patterns of behavior (excessive masturbation, lying, stealing, truancy). Habit disturbances are most commonly seen in sociopathic personality disturbances of childhood and early adolescence.

habit spasm. A repeated, involuntary, stereotyped twitching, or tic (e.g., glossospasm), which may occur spontaneously or accompany a voluntary act. It generally involves a small muscle group, usually of the face, neck, or shoulders. Examples are spasmodic blinking and rapid sidewise jerking of the head. Habit spasms are believed to be generated by emotional conflict and to serve as a release for tension. The term is not used to describe muscular tics of organic origin.

habit training. The process of training an infant to adjust his eating, eliminating, and sleeping habits to the demands of the external world. More is involved than mere achievement of physiologic control and a regular schedule, for at the same time a foundation is being laid for the emotional responses and attitudes of the individual later in life. Many psychiatrists are convinced that the personality, malleable at this time, may be permanently determined in a general way by the infant's reaction to the measures employed in his training.

habituation. Acquisition of a desire for the effects of narcotic drugs (without physical dependency) following their repeated use for medical purposes. Cf. *addiction.*

habitus. Kretschmer's word for constitutional type. See *asthenic, athletic, dysplastic,* and *pyknic habitus.*

hadephobia. An exaggerated fear of hell. Cf. *theophobia.*

hallucinate. To experience and react to hallucinations.

hallucination. A subjective sensory experience which has no basis in objective reality. Because any of the senses may be involved, hallucinations are identified as auditory, gustatory, olfactory, tactile, or visual. Cf. *eidetic imagery, hypnagogic hallucinations, illusion, macropsia* and *micropsia, pseudohallucination.*

hallucinogen. Any substance (such as lysergic acid diethylamide or peyote) that induces hallucinations.

hallucinosis. The state of experiencing hallucinations.

hallucinosis, acute. See *alcoholic hallucinosis.*

hamartophobia. Exaggerated or unwarranted fear that one has committed an unpardonable sin or grievous error, accompanied by anxiety over the consequences; an expression of the feeling of guilt accompanied by the "need" for (anticipation of) punishment. See also *guilt, feelings of; punishment.* Cf. *enosimania, hadephobia.*

handedness. Handedness is controlled by the dominant cerebral hemisphere; for example, if the left hemisphere dominates, the person is right-handed. Much of the popular adverse attitude toward left-handedness is traceable to ancient times, when "left" (Lat., *sinister*) was synonymous with "evil." It has not been demonstrated that left-handedness is in any way or degree correlated with psychopathology. Psychological investigations reveal that the left-handed child is not physically handicapped or mentally inferior to the right-handed child. Nor is it at all certain that dire consequences are to be anticipated when a congenitally left-handed youngster is taught to use his right hand.

hand-washing complex or **compulsion.** A repetitive, in some cases almost constant, washing of the hands, seen in obsessive-compulsive reactions, as the expression of guilt feeling. Syn. *chirablutomania, Lady Macbeth complex.*

Hanfmann, Eugenia. American psychologist, born 1905.

Hanfmann-Kasanin Test. A psychological test similar to the Goldstein-Scheerer Test, designed to discover a subject's aptitudes and interests. The test exposes weaknesses in concept formation and abstract thinking and hence is useful in examining patients suspected of having suffered brain damage as well as those with schizophrenia.

haphalgesia. *aphalgesia.*

haphephobia. *aphephobia.*

haptephobia. *aphephobia.*

haptic. Pertaining to touch.

haptodysphoria. A perversion of the sense of touch in which contact with certain textures (such as peach-fuzz or velvet) imparts an unpleasant sensation. One interpretation is that the motivating unconscious factor is a traumatic experience associated with soft, fine hair.

harpaxophobia. An unreasoning fear of night prowlers and thieves.

Harrower-Erikson, Molly. Canadian psychologist (1906-   ), first to use the Rorschach Psychodiagnostic Method in examination of large groups (e.g., Royal Canadian Air Force). In 1939 she proved the test's reliability by detecting latent neurologic disease in otherwise healthy aircraft pilots.

hasheesh, -ish. See *Cannabis.*

haut mal. *grand mal.*

headache. Headache may be either organic or emotional in origin. Of particular interest to psychiatry are: the headache of migraine; tension headache, which may be associated with the individual's reactions to stressful situations; and headache caused by brain tumor. Syn. *cephalgia, cephalalgia.*

hebephrenia. A variety of schizophrenia marked by regression, silliness, mannerisms, introversion, hallucinations, and delusions.

hebetude (**Lit.** "youthfulness"). Childishness in speech and action, as in regression.

hedonophobia. An unreasoning dread of pleasure, motivated by unconscious feelings of guilt and unworthiness which result in masochistic feelings of need for punishment. Cf. *enosimania, hadephobia, hamartophobia.*

helicopodia. A dragging gait, in which the feet describe semi-circles. Observed in hemiplegia, it is also called *hemiplegic gait.*

heliophobia. An obsessive fear of the sun and sunlight, inter-preted by some psychoanalysts as a phylogenetic reflection of primitive worship and/or fear of the sun coupled with guilt feelings that are accompanied by unconscious need for punish-ment.

helminthophobia. Exaggerated horror of worms, or fear that one has become infested with them. Syn. *vermiphobia.* Cf. *acarophobia.*

hematophobia. *hemophobia.*

hemeralopia; hemeraphonia. Visual or vocal incapacity in bright daylight without anatomic or physiologic explanation. The hemeralopic (or hemeraphonic) person has difficulty seeing (or expressing himself) during the daytime but recovers these abilities when night falls. The reactions are encountered occasionally in hysteria.

hemianesthesia, hysterical. Loss of sensation on one side of the body or in one limb, observed in some cases of hysteria.

hemiataxia. Ataxia confined to one side of the body.

hemiballism(us). Violent jerking and twitching of one side of the body. Cf. *chorea, hemichorea.*

hemichorea. Occurrence of choreiform movements on one side of the body. Cf. *hemiballism(us).*

hemicrania. Pain on one side of the head, as in migraine.

hemiparalysis. *hemiplegia.*

hemiparaplegia. Paraplegia of one side of the body.

hemiplegia. A "half-stroke"; paralysis of one side of the body.

hemiplegic gait. *helicopodia.*

hemophobia. Extreme horror at the sight or mention of blood. Syn. *hematophobia.*

hemp. See *marihuana.*

hepatolenticular degeneration. A degenerative disease of the liver and of certain parts of the midbrain, in which such mental symptoms as irritability, childishness, and silliness are seen. Complete mental deterioration may ensue. Syn. *Wilson's disease.*

heredity and mental illness. With some exceptions there is no undeniable proof that mental illness or mental retardation can be inherited or that either is familial in nature. Constitutional predisposition does appear to play a role in some of these afflictions, just as one person may be unusually susceptible to certain physical ailments. Kallmann's investigations, especially his studies of identical twins, has yielded evidence that schizophrenia is not developed under the usual stresses of life unless a predisposition for this type of reaction has been inherited. While the emergence of a psychosis or a psychoneurosis in a given individual is determined by many factors, certain types of mental retardation are known to be inheritable; the outstanding example is Tay-Sachs' disease. It has also been shown that a predisposition to epilepsy is inheritable, since normal children of epileptic parents may produce epileptic brain rhythms as seen in electroencephalography.

heroinism. Addiction to the use of heroin, a narcotic drug derived from morphine and having sedative and analgesic properties.

heteroerotism. See *heterosexual level.*

heterolalia, heterophasia, heterophemia. A form of aphasia, characterized by the tendency to say one thing when something else is intended, often the reverse of what is meant. It may be restricted to certain elements, such as numbers, or pairs of antithetic words; the subject may say "World War One" when he means "World War Two," or he may say "funeral" when he intends to say "wedding." See also *Freudian slip.*

heterosexual. Pertaining to relations with the opposite sex.

heterosexual level. The final, mature level of psychosexual development. Although elements of narcissism and homosexuality may persist throughout life in varying degrees and in sublimated forms, the over-all picture of heterosexual adjustment is that of one who participates in socially accepted relations between the sexes, as reflected in courtship, marriage, and the raising of children (though these factors do not necessarily preclude homosexuality or bisexuality).

heterosexual panic. An individual's frantic pursuit of heterosexual activity in response to latent homosexual motivation. It is believed to be stimulated by an unconscious impulse to satisfy his superego and society that he does not harbor homosexual tendencies. Cf. *homosexual panic.*

heterosexuality. The state of having achieved sexual maturity. See *heterosexual level.* Cf. *altrigenderism.*

hieromania. Psychosis associated with religious fanaticism.

hierophobia. Fear based on religious beliefs and practices.

hippanthropy. In a psychosis, the patient's delusion that he has been transformed into a horse.

Hirschfeld, Magnus. German psychologist (1868-1935), known for his research into normal and abnormal sexual behavior.

histamine. A nitrogenous substance found in all animal and vegetable tissues. Among its properties are stimulation of gastric juices and dilatation of capillaries. Cf. *antihistamine.*

histrionism. *dramatism.*

hodophobia. A morbid fear of traveling. Hodophobia resembles *agoraphobia* in that the victim suffers anxiety when away from the security of home.

Hoffmann's sign. Flexion of the thumb when the index finger or the ring finger is snapped; a sign of disease of the central nervous system.

holergasia. Meyer's term for severe mental disorder (psychosis), which involves the whole person (e.g., schizophrenia), in contrast to *merergasia* (psychoneurosis), which is usually manifested only in a limited segment of the individual's life (e.g., obsessive-compulsive reaction).

holism, holistic approach. The approach to understanding an individual's personality that is based on the interplay of his inherited structure, his unique tendencies of thought and behavior, and the cultural pattern in which he lives, as well as such influences as disease and injury. Cf. *psychobiology.*

homichlophobia. Morbid fear of fog as a smothering, isolating force. Cf. *claustrophobia.*

homocystinuria. Presence of homocystine (a protein derivative) in the urine, probably due to faulty metabolism. It is a common finding in severely mentally retarded persons; convulsive seizures occur in about half the cases. A hereditary factor is suspected, though the condition is sometimes known to be caused by blood-clot formation. Syn. *cystathianuria.*

homoerotism, homoeroticism. See *homosexual, homosexuality.*

homogenitality. Pertaining to the active expression of homosexuality.

homosexual, homosexuality. Terms concerned with a broad range and degree of relations among persons of the same sex, and with the development of personality in this respect. Psychoanalysts hold that a homosexual level is one of the normal, transitional phases in the individual's evolution to maturity (heterosexuality). In the mind of the general public, however, the homosexual person is a man whose traits are predominately feminine or a woman with strong masculine characteristics (lesbian), and this notion is accompanied by the implication that such people engage regularly, perhaps exclusively, in erotic behavior with others of their own sex. These classic types are the extremes and form a minority when compared with persons who are not readily identifiable as "homosexuals" through their observable behavior, speech, or dress and who enjoy a superficial heterosexual adjustment, yet are actively homosexual. Contrary to popular belief, many individuals who engage in homoerotic practices are married, have children, shoulder community responsibilities, and follow vocations generally considered appropriate for their sex. Strictly speaking, however, such persons are correctly designated *ambisexual,* or *bisexual.*

According to Freud, the commonest causes of full-fledged homosexuality are: a child's excessive attachment to the parent of the opposite sex, with the result that later on, potential mates are rejected as unworthy and libido becomes directed toward persons of his or her own sex (an unsolved Oedipus or Electra complex); overvaluation of the phallus (castration complex, penis envy); fear of a harsh, unloving father or father figure; jealousy toward an older sibling; and homosexual seduction in childhood. A predisposition to homosexuality may be a constitutional factor. However, no one is completely masculine or feminine.

No statistical evidence is available to show whether the incidence of homosexuality has been increasing or decreasing over the past few decades or over the span of recorded history. Among persons suffering psychoses, homosexuality is most prevalent in paranoia and the paranoid type of schizophrenia; it is also common in alcoholism. Cf. *homogenitality.*

homosexual level.   In the psychoanalytic concept of personality development, the phase preceding puberty. Libido is directed toward persons of the same sex and homoerotic practices may occur, to be superseded, in normal development, by the emerging heterosexual level.

homosexual panic. A mental disturbance resulting in aggressive behavior, which may include assault by a person with strong homosexual tendencies of another of the same sex who has or is suspected of having made homosexual advances. In the latter instance, the desire is shifted by the mechanism of projection to the other person, and the physical attack enables the individual to "prove" to himself and society that he is not homosexual. Cf. *heterosexual panic.*

hormone. A substance produced by and within an endocrine gland and transported via the blood stream to another organ or tissue, where it inhibits or stimulates activity. The hormones of chief concern to psychiatry are those produced by the gonads, adrenals, pituitary gland, and thyroid gland. Cf. *antihormone.*

Horney, Karen. American psychoanalyst (1885-1952) who sought, through her concept of *neoculturalism,* to modify several fundamental Freudian concepts. She focused her attention on interpersonal relations as the main source of personality disorders and stressed the principle of *basic anxiety* as a prominent factor in all neuroses. She rejected Freud's theory of libido and his emphasis on the significance of infantile sexuality, and in general disregarded hereditary factors in mental illness in favor of cultural factors. See also *Fromm, Sullivan.*

Huntington's chorea. A progressive hereditary disease, the signs of which are irregular, uncontrollable, and eventually disabling movements; speech disturbances; and mental deterioration. Cf. *Sydenham's chorea.*

Hurler's syndrome. *gargoylism.*

hydrocephalus. A condition, usually congenital but which may be acquired through injury at any time, marked by an abnormal increase in the quantity of cerebrospinal fluid within the ventricles of the brain. The head may be grossly enlarged, the forehead disproportionately prominent. The condition is accompanied by mental retardation and, in some cases, convulsive seizures. The severely hydrocephalic infant seldom lives to the age of four.

hydrophobia. Fear of drinking fluids in a rabid person, due to spasms of swallowing apparatus. It is not a *phobia* in the psychiatric sense, but a symptom of rabies, for which the term "hydrophobia" is popularly but erroneously used. Cf. *aquaphobia.*

hydrotherapy. Treatment involving the external application of water by various methods. Once an important adjunct of psychotherapy, it consisted of continuous flowing tub baths, alternate hot and cold sprays, and other variations. The calming or stimulating effects of hydrotherapy cannot be denied, but its benefits are purely symptomatic and in no sense specific for any form of mental illness.

hyelophobia. Morbid fear of glass, in the belief that it exerts an evil influence.

hygrophobia. Morbid fear of dampness, in the belief that it contains noxious substances.

hypalgesia, -algia. Diminished sensitivity to pain in any area of the body. When seen as a symptom of hysteria, it is associated with the memory of a painful emotional experience. It can be induced by suggestion, particularly through hypnosis. Cf. *hyperalgesia.*

hypengyophobia. Unreasoning dread of responsibility, an outward expression of unconscious feelings of inferiority and insecurity.

hyperacousia, hyperacusia, -cusis. Heightened acuity of the sense of hearing, seen often in anxiety reactions and regarded as indicating a defensive mobilization of all the senses. The condition was frequently observed among soldiers during World War II.

hyperadrenal constitution. A constitutional type associated with excessive secretion of the medullary portion of the adrenal glands, usually seen in persons of the pyknic habitus. The personality is that of the manic-depressive person. In very young girls it is called *precocious matronism.*

hyperalgesia, -algia. A hyperesthesia marked by heightened sensitivity to pain. Cf. *hypalgesia.*

hyperaphia. Abnormally acute tactile sensitivity. Syn. *hyperpselaphesia.*

hyperboulia, hyperbulia. Excessive concentration of volition, sometimes seen in psychoneurosis (see obsessive-compulsive reaction); the subject stubbornly pursues an objective or clings to a particular type of behavior to a point beyond reason. Cf. *hypoboulia.*

hypercathexis. Disproportionate concentration of libido on a single object (person, thing, or idea). Cf. *hypolepsiomania.*

hypercenesthesia. *euphoria.*

hyperergasia. Meyer's term for overactivity as seen in the manic phase of *manic-depressive psychosis.* Cf. *hypoergasia.*

hyperesthesia. Heightened sensory responsiveness, particularly in regard to skin sensitivity. Cf. *hyperalgesia, hypesthesia.*

hypergeuesthesia. Exaggerated taste sensation.

hypergnosis. Expansion of simple concepts into complex philosophical systems, seen in psychosis, especially schizophrenia. The subject projects an everyday detail of life into an intricate mosaic of ethical and metaphysical concepts, which grows ever more inappropriate and disproportionate to the immediate situation.

hyperhedonia, hyperhedonism. Excessive pleasure upon gratification of a libidinal drive for satisfaction.

hyperinsulinemia. Excess of insulin in the blood. Cf. *hypoglycemia.*

hyperkinesia, -sis. A state in which purposeless movements are made; commonly seen in psychoses and in chorea and athetosis, and interpreted as an expression of unconscious conflict and tension. It may take the form of twitching or grimacing (as in a habit spasm) or vigorous generalized movement. Cf. *hypokinesia.*

hyperlysinemia. First reported by N. C. Woody, American pediatrician, in 1964, this condition is encountered in infants who are mentally retarded and who have convulsions, delayed physical development, and certain specific physical symptoms— all accompanied by an excess of lysin (a blood-destroying substance) in the blood plasma.

hyperlogia. Verbal overproduction as seen in the manic state.

hypermania. A reaction more pronounced than hypomania but not so violent as a full-blown manic attack.

hypermimia. Compulsive imitation of the movements and gestures of others, seen sometimes in the severe manic phase of manic-depressive reactions.

hypermnesia. Abnormally acute memory encountered both in normal persons and in certain psychoses, particularly paranoia and paranoid conditions. The patient makes use of many minute and accurate details of his past to weave an elaborate pattern of life history that satisfies his drive for self-aggrandizement.

hypermotility. Overactivity.

hyperontomorphy. *ectomorph.*

hyperorexia. *bulimia.*

hyperphrenia. The excitement seen in manic states.

hyperpragia. Elation, with excessive flow of ideas, as observed in the manic phase of manic-depressive psychosis.

hyperprosexia. Preoccupation, as in a mentally ill person who dwells upon his feelings and thoughts. Cf. *hypoprosexia.*

hyperpselaphesia. *hyperaphia.*

hyperthymia. Mental and physical hyperactivity similar to (but less intense than) that seen in the manic phase of manic-depressive psychosis. Cf. *cyclothymia, hypothymia.*

hyperthyroidism. The condition resulting from overactivity of the thyroid gland. In its severe form it is marked by anxiety, tremulousness, excitability, irritability, accelerated pulse rate and elevated blood pressure, goiter, and exophthalmos (protruding eyeballs). Syn. *Basedow's disease.* Cf. *hypothyroidism.*

hypertonia. Extreme tenseness or rigidity of a muscle or muscle group. Cf. hypotonia.

hypervegetative. Denoting pyknic habitus.

hypesthesia. Diminished sensitivity of the skin or the special senses due to either organic or functional causes. Cf. *hyper-esthesia*.

hyphedonia. A characteristic of depression in which acts that once brought pleasure to the individual no longer satisfy him.

hypnagogic hallucinations or **imagery.** Hallucinations which sometimes are experienced by persons who are extremely fatigued but unable to find the time or place to sleep. For example, a motorist driving late at night, while "half-asleep," suddenly "sees" the figure of a person run across the road in front of the automobile; when he applies the brakes he is jolted into wakefulness, to discover there is no one in sight.

hypnoanalysis. Psychoanalysis conducted while the patient is under hypnosis. If the subject sinks from the level of hypnotic trance into actual sleep, the procedure is properly termed *hypnonarcosis*.

hypnobasia. *somnambulism*.

hypnolepsy. *narcolepsy*.

hypnonarcosis. See under *hypnoanalysis*.

hypnophobia. An overwhelming fear of falling asleep motivated by the feeling that sleep symbolizes death; commonly seen in persons afflicted with psychosis due to cerebral arteriosclerosis.

hypnophrenosis. An inclusive term for all types of sleep disturbances.

hypnopompic. Relating to the persistence upon awaking from sleep, of an image seen in a dream.

hypnosis. The trance induced by hypnotism, in which voluntary actions and speech are virtually eliminated. While it can be used effectively as a psychotherapeutic measure to remove symptoms, it does not achieve a cure of the underlying psychosis or psychoneurosis. Its principal value in the treatment of mental illness is to render patients susceptible to the psychoanalyst's suggestions, so that repressed material in the patient's unconscious will come to light and can be used in subsequent therapeutic sessions. The psychiatrist can also make direct suggestions to the patient's unconscious for resolution of emotional problems into which the patient has gained insight. See also *Charcot* and *Janet*.

hypnotherapy. Psychotherapy employing hypnotism with or without the use of narcotic drugs. Cf. *hypnoanalysis, hypnonarcosis.*

hypnotic. *adj.* 1. Of or pertaining to hypnosis. 2. Inducing somnolence. *n.* 1. One who is hypnotized or readily hypnotizable. 2. Any means (drugs, hypnosis, suggestion, fatigue, etc.) that induces sleep.

hypnotism. The theory and practice of producing hypnosis. Cf. *mesmerism.*

hypoadrenal constitution. A type of physique associated with insufficient functioning of the adrenal glands, similar to Kretschmer's asthenic type. It is seen often among schizophrenics.

hypoboulia, hypobulia. Lowered will power, commonly observed in schizophrenic apathy. Cf. *demotivation, hyperboulia.*

hypocenesthesia. Diminution of the sense of normal well-being, a symptom of hypochondria. See *cenesthopathy.*

hypochondria(sis). A psychoneurotic disorder characterized by endless complaints about and preoccupation with real and imagined pains and organ malfunction. The complaints are employed either consciously or unconsciously by the patient to direct attention to himself and thereby gain satisfaction through recognition. See also *secondary advantage.* Cf. *cenesthopathy.*

hypoergasia. Meyer's term for diminution of activity owing to mental or emotional disorder. Cf. *hyperergasia.*

hypoesthesia. *hypesthesia.*

hypogeuesthesia, hypogeusia. Impaired sense of taste due to neurologic or psychiatric disorder.

hypoglycemia. Abnormal lowering of blood sugar, leading to excess of insulin. The patient sinks into coma which is usually accompanied by convulsions. Hypoglycemia is intentionally induced in insulin shock therapy.

hypogonadism. Diminished activity of the gonads, causing reduced sexual responsiveness.

hypokinesia, -sis. Decreased motor function or activity as seen in depressive reactions. Syn. *hypomotility.* Cf. *hyperkinesia.*

hypolepsiomania. Concentration of libido on one object (person, delusion, etc.), commonly seen in paranoia. Syn. *monomania.* Cf. *hypocathexis.*

hypologia. Reduction in productivity of speech, seen in many cases of brain damage, such as hemorrhage.

hypomania. Mania in moderate degree, sometimes seen in manic-depressive psychosis; the word is also used to describe a stage of excitability and overactivity without psychosis. Cf. *ergasiomania.*

hypomnesia. Impaired memory. Syn. *dysmnesia.* Cf. *amnesia.*

hypomotility. *hypokinesia.*

hypophrenia. *hypopsychosis.*

hyposphresia. *hyposmia.*

hypophyseal cachexia. *hypopituitarism.*

hypophysis cerebri. The pituitary gland.

hypopituitarism. Decreased activity of the pituitary gland, characterized by excessive deposit of fat in the body and failure of the subject to acquire adult physical features. It is often accompanied by shyness, fearfulness, and seclusiveness.

hypoprosexia. Inattention, as seen in *blocking* and *regression.* Cf. *hyperprosexia.*

hypopsychosis. Decrease in thinking as observed in profound depressive states and in regression. Syn. *hypophrenia.* Cf. *hyperphrenia.*

hypopselaphesia. Diminished tactile sense caused by damage to, malfunction of, or interference with sensory nerves carrying impulses to the brain. It is sometimes seen in hysteria and may be induced by hypnotic suggestion.

hyposmia. Weakened sense of smell; it may be produced by organic disorder such as skull fracture or traumatic tearing of the olfactory nerves, and functionally by psychoneurotic disturbances such as hysteria and hypochondria. Syn. *hyposphresia.*

hypotaxia. Emotional rapport between hypnotist and subject gained during the initial phase of hypnosis.

hypotaxis. Light sleep or hypnotic trance.

hypothalamus. That part of the brain which is regarded as the center for control of emotional expression. See also *thalamus.*

hypothymia. Lowered emotional response; emotional reaction inadequate to the situation. Seen in affective reactions such as involutional psychosis and the depressive phase of manic-depressive psychosis. Cf. *cyclothymia.*

hypothyroidism. Diminished functioning of the thyroid gland. In individuals who are affected congenitally or prior to puberty, the condition, if severe, is known as *cretinism;* if the disorder is acquired in adulthood it is called, except for mild cases, *myxedema.* The mental and emotional symptoms are described under these two headings. Cf. *hyperthyroidism.*

hypotonia. Decreased muscle tone as is seen in organic conditions such as advanced senility and cerebral arteriosclerosis.

hypsophobia. *bathophobia.*

hysteria. A form of psychoneurosis in which, according to Freud, a repressed emotional conflict finds overt expression through sensorimotor disturbances such as temporary blindness (e.g., hemeralopia), loss of sensation (e.g., hemianesthesia), in selected areas of the body, paralysis of limbs, or loss or impairment of speech function (e.g., hemeraphonia). See also *conversion hysteria, psychosomatic illness.*

hysterical anesthesia. See *glove-and-stocking anesthesia.*

hysterical epilepsy or hysteroepilepsy. A form of conversion hysteria in which epileptoid convulsions are manifested. It is significant that the patient seldom falls where he is likely to be injured, that he seldom has a seizure when alone, and that the attack does not conform to the classic pattern of epilepsy. Syn. *affektepilepsie*.

hysteromania. 1. nymphomania. 2. Mania seen in hysteria.

hysterophilia. A descriptive term for a psychosomatic disorder whose symptoms strongly resemble those of hysteria, such as asthma, anorexia nervosa, and torticollis.

hysterotraumatism. Hysteria caused by injury.

I

iatrogenic. Arising as a result of treatment by a physician. For example, a remark of a physician either addressed to or overheard by a patient which alarms the patient may lead to an *iatrogenic psychoneurosis*.

ice-needle brain surgery. See *cryopsychosurgery*.

ichthyophobia. Morbid fear of fish; their role as phallic symbols is thought to be a factor.

iconolagny. Compulsion to viewing nude statuary or pornographic pictures; a form of voyeurism. Cf. *gymnomania*.

iconomania. Morbid concentration of libido on images. Syn. *idolomania*.

▮ **ICT.** *insulin coma therapy.*

id. Freud's term for the primitive psychic force in the unconscious. He regarded the id as the repository for the instincts that are essential to propagation and self-preservation. See also *ego, personality, superego*.

idea(s). See *autochthonous ideas, idée fixe, imperative idea*.

ideas of influence. Ideas characteristic of a paranoid trend of thinking in which the patient feels that his actions, thoughts, speech, and attitudes are controlled by other persons or by external forces.

ideas of reference.   An aspect of a paranoid personality or trend of thought, expressed as the belief that the actions and spoken words of others are intended to apply to the subject, usually in a derogatory sense; the subject may even complain that certain articles of other people's clothing (e.g., a bright red necktie) were chosen with reference to him.

idealization.   As used by Freud, overvaluation of the love object. Cf. *identification.*

idée fixe.   An obsession that imbues the individual with a compulsion to carry out a specific act in order to prevent some vague catastrophe. See also *obsessive-compulsive reaction.*

identification.   A common defense mechanism through which the individual, in response to unconscious motivation, assumes the attitudes, behavior, and personal attributes of another person whom he has idealized (parent or relative, popular hero, teacher, clergyman, employer). It is employed normally at the conscious level, to bolster self-esteem; if, however, it is used to excess, it may delay or hamper development of an integrated ego. Syn. *appersonation, appersonification.* Cf. *incorporation, introjection, projection.*

identification, cosmic.   *magic omnipotence.*

ideophobia.   Fear or anxiety over a particular disturbing idea. One may, for example, be reluctant to recall the events surrounding the death of a loved one, in part because of the associated grief and in part owing to one's own fear of death.

ideoplasty.   "Molding" of a subject's thoughts in hypnosis. Syn. *suggestion.*

idiocy.   Obsolete term for severe mental retardation. See also *Tay-Sachs disease.*

idiohypnosis.   *autohypnosis.*

idiot.   See under *mental retardation.*

idiot-savant ("idiot sage"). An individual who is mentally retarded in general but who demonstrates remarkable talent in some restricted area such as memorization or rapid calculation.

idiogamy. Restriction of sexual capacity to intercourse with a mate having special characteristics (as red-haired women, short men, etc.). It is a form of fetishism.

idolomania. *iconomania.*

ikotah. *lata(h).*

illuminism. Any hallucination concerned with supernatural beings.

illusion. A false interpretation of a sensory stimulus, usually visual or auditory. The desert mirage of an oasis and the sound of the wind interpreted as the moaning of a human being are examples. Cf. *delusion, hallucination, pseudohallucination.*

illusion of negative doubles. *Capgras' syndrome.*

image. See *father image, mother image, primordial image.*

imagery. See *eidetic imagery, hypnagogic hallucinations* or *imagery.*

imago. In Jung's *analytical psychology*, a conception of another person that one acquires in infancy or childhood and carries through to adulthood in the unconscious. The conception is only partly founded in reality. See also *identification.*

imbecile. See under *mental retardation.*

imbecility. Obsolete term for moderate mental retardation.

imperative idea. An idea which, though distasteful or disturbing to the individual, persists in consciousness and cannot be rejected. It is often encountered in an obsessive-compulsive reaction.

impotence, -cy. Partial or total inability of a male to perform sexual intercourse. In the absence of organic pathology, it is called *psychic* or *cerebral* impotence and may apply to any stage of the sexual act, from inability to achieve or maintain erection to premature ejaculation, inability to accomplish orgasm, and other phenomena. Cf. *anaphrodisia, anorgasm, frigidity.*

IMPS. *Inpatient Multidimensional Psychiatric Scale.*

imu. *lata(h).*

inadequate personality. The inadequate personality is characterized chiefly by poor adaptability and judgment, failure to achieve the heterosexual level, ineptness in interpersonal relations, and reduced motivation.

incest barrier. A concept in psychoanalysis designating the composite of inhibitions built up while early sexual attachments to the parent of the opposite sex are being redirected.

incitement premium. *forepleasure.*

incoherence. Garbled speech is commonly seen as a symptom of schizophrenia and mania and in certain organic disorders such as carbon monoxide poisoning, general paresis, conditions caused by brain damage, and others.

incoordination. Inability to maintain harmonious action or movement in voluntary muscular activity; it may be organic or functional in origin. See also *coordination, disorders of.* Cf. *asynergia.*

incorporation. In psychoanalysis, the mental mechanism by which one makes some object or person a part of oneself. For example, according to Freud, the suckling infant assumes the mother's breast is part of himself, not merely because of the physical contact but because of the pleasure and feeling of strength he derives from it. This infant experience is the prototype of the mechanism known in later life as *identification.* Cf. *introjection.*

individual psychology. A psychiatric schema originated by Adler, who placed more emphasis on the ego than on sexuality and who viewed personality maladjustment as a result of conflict between the desire to dominate and a feeling of inferiority. From this concept grew Adler's term *inferiority complex.* See also *masculine protest.*

individuality and mental disorder. The tendency to generalize still plagues psychiatry. Since the causes of the majority of the conditions remain a mystery, diagnostic categories continue to be based principally on symptoms or syndromes (patterns of symptoms). However, symptoms of the same clinical entity are not the same for all individuals, nor are they always seen in the same degree. The efficacy of given therapeutic measures varies widely among individuals and the promise of improvement or recovery is irregular. These circumstances are due to the infinite range of mental and physiologic equipment with which people are endowed. Caution should therefore be adopted in assuming universal application of the characteristics given for one or another diagnostic group or for any treatment used.

indoklon. Known as *Bis ether,* a chemical used to induce convulsions for purposes of shock therapy, particularly in schizophrenia; it is administered by inhalation or intraveneously.

induced association. *association, controlled.*

infantile schizophrenia. See *autism.*

infantile sexuality. Prior to the emergence of Freud's psychoanalytic concepts, an infant was regarded as devoid of sexuality or of the ability to derive pleasure in the sexual sphere. However, it is clear that in his oral, anal, and phallic stages of psychosexual development he learns that stimulation of erogenous zones arouses pleasure (masturbation in the crib is commonly observed). Freud and his co-workers proved that sexual motivation functions actively long before puberty is attained, and that in addition to its being more primitive and diffuse, it differs from adult sexuality by its close association with ingestive and excretory functions and by its direction toward persons near the child, particularly the mother. It is this latter association that led to development of the psychoanalytic concepts of the incest barrier, the Oedipus complex, and other Freudian contributions. Syn. *pregenital sexuality.* See also *polymorphous perverse.*

infantile speech. Baby talk (lisping, lalling, or other faulty pronunciation) which persists beyond the stage where correct speech patterns would be expected to have been established. It is sometimes encouraged by overprotective parents and is sometimes employed deliberately by a child to gain love and favors. Syn. *gammacism*.

infantilism. 1. In medicine, persistence beyond puberty of the physiologic characteristics of infancy. Cf. *atelia.* 2. In psychiatry, an adult pattern of reaction dominated by repressed emotional experiences that occurred during infancy.

inferiority and guilt. Freud insisted that the sense of inferiority and sense of guilt are inseparable. He regarded the former as an expression of a feeling of inadequate virility (or fertility), the latter as a reflection of feeling over the violation of social dicta.

inferiority complex. The conflict, partly conscious, partly unconscious, which impels the individual to make strenuous efforts to overcome the distress that accompanies feelings of inferiority. The inferiority feeling may be real or imagined, and it may be specific or generalized. Adler believed that the inferiority complex is at the core of the psychoses and the psychoneuroses. See also under *individual psychology.*

inheritance of ideas. See *collective* or *racial unconscious.*

inhibition. An emotional force, capable of exerting its influence at conscious and unconscious levels, that prevents an action by an individual. Cf. *repression.*

inkblot test. *Rorschach Psychodiagnostic Method.*

Inpatient Multidimensional Psychiatric Scale (IMPS). A systematized series of questions asked of patients upon admission to a mental institution, the results enabling the examiner to place patients in one of ten syndrome-based psychotic types. Among the categories are: hostile-paranoid, excited-hostile, excited-grandiose, intropunitive, disorganized, and retarded. Thus, terms which are descriptive of attitude and/or behavior are used rather than clinical types (schizophrenia, manic-depressive, etc.) to determine, at the time of admission, where a patient should be placed in the institution and what immediate therapeutic steps are indicated.

instinct. An innate capacity which enables the individual to cope with some phase of environment at the primitive level. In spite of widespread disagreement on what should be regarded as instincts, most psychiatrists assume that acts enhancing self-preservation and propagation of the race are basic. In psycho-analytic theory, the only instincts are those of life and death (see *death wish*). The so-called "herd instinct" is believed to be a learned reaction. See also *Eros and Thanatos*. Cf. *anagogic, id, intelligence*.

insulin coma (**insulin shock**) **therapy.** A therapeutic method originated by Sakel in the mid-1930's. Increased doses of insulin are administered over a period of several days to weeks until a state of hypoglycemia is achieved. The resultant shock is followed by coma and sometimes is accompanied by convulsions; the coma is terminated by administration of glucose or orange juice. There is an improvement rate (about 70 percent), but recurrence of symptoms is common. The principal value of the procedure seems to be its effect of making mentally ill patients more responsive to psychotherapy. See also *stimulant therapy.*

integration. In psychiatric terminology, the harmonious cementing together of the various elements of the personality; in the more severe mental disorders, segments of the personality appear to "break off" (see schizophrenia) and the patient's absorption with these fragments hampers his total response to the environment. Cf. *reintegration.*

intellectual diversion. Intellectual diversion has long been employed as an adjunct to psychotherapy. Institutions for the mentally ill provide libraries and book clubs, arrange talks by volunteer authorities on literature, and encourage interested outsiders to donate games, books, and periodicals to the institutions.

intelligence. The capacity to adjust one's thinking to new and unexpected requirements that involve judgment, reasoning, or the appreciation of relationships in form, number, and conceptual content; the ability to benefit from experience. Although stress has been placed on the significance of innate intelligence, with the implication that it is a fixed quality, it has become increasingly evident that intelligence may develop irregularly; i.e., individuals who are slow learners at an early age may show spurts of increasing intelligence later on, even though environmental and other factors have not changed.

intelligence quotient (I.Q.). According to the Binet-Simon Scale, the intelligence quotient is interpreted as follows:

	I.Q.
genius	140 and over
very superior	120 - 139
superior	110 - 119
average	90 - 109
dull	80 - 89
borderline	70 - 79
mild retardation (moron)	50 - 69
moderate retardation (imbecile)	25 - 49
severe retardation (idiot)	0 - 24

intelligence tests. Intelligence tests are used in psychiatry to assist diagnosis (e.g., to differentiate mental retardation from simple schizophrenia), in the planning of therapeutic programs, and to determine the extent of a mentally retarded child's capacity for training.

intention tremor. See under *tremor.*

interpersonal relationships. Sullivan's term for the area of human experience which requires harmonious adjustment to others in one's milieu. The capacity for coping with interpersonal relationships begins to develop when the narcissistic stage is resolved, but individual success in making the adjustment varies widely among individuals.

intoxication, pathologic. A reaction to alcohol in which the subject, after imbibing even small quantities of an intoxicating beverage, gives vent to excessive emotional display (usually blind rage) along with violent, even homicidal, behavior upon the slightest provocation. Following recovery from intoxication, he does not recall any of his acts but is tearfully remorseful when informed of them.

intracranial neoplasm. A tumor upon or within the brain.

intracranial pressure. The pressure exerted by the cerebrospinal fluid on the contents of the skull cavity. Radical variations (usually increased pressure) may result from injury, tumor, hemorrhage, infection, or the effects of sympathomimetic drugs; relief is obtained by drawing cerebrospinal fluid from the spine or from the cranial cavity.

introjection. The mental mechanism by which an individual incorporates into his ego structure the qualities of others in his milieu as he has interpreted them. In many cases (and especially in paranoia) the subject unconsciously uses this device to turn back upon himself antagonism and aggression formerly directed toward another person, or persons. Cf. *identification, incorporation, projection.*

introspection. Absorption with one's own thoughts; imperviousness to the external world. Cf. *hyperprosexia.*

introversion. Jung's term for inwardly directed libido reflected in the tendency to shun interpersonal relations and to be absorbed by egocentric thoughts. One whose personality is dominated by the tendency to introversion is called an *introvert.* Cf. *asynodia, entropy, extraversion.*

inversion, sexual. See *sexual inversion.*

inversion of affect. Freud's term for the unconscious mechanism by which an emotion is transformed into its opposite (as love into hate, joy into sorrow), usually in defense of the ego. Syn. *counteraffect, reversal of affect, displacement of affect.*

invert. A person given to sexual inversion.

investment. In psychoanalysis, the endowment of an object or an idea with emotion. Syn. *cathexis, emotional charge.* Cf. *counterinvestment.*

involution. ("a turning inward"). The stage of life (roughly, the middle years) in which growth diminishes or comes to a halt and is replaced by regressive and degenerative processes. See also *climacteric.*

involution melancholia. Earlier term for the melancholic type of involutional psychosis.

involutional psychosis. A group of reactions peculiar to middle age. The symptoms are, in general, those of the depressed phase of manic-depressive psychosis. There are two types, the melancholic and the paranoid. The *melancholic* type is characterized by agitation, anxiety, depression, and feelings of guilt, futility, and inadequacy, along with gastrointestinal and other somatic complaints which may take the form of delusions. The patient may talk of, or even attempt, suicide. In the *paranoid* type, delusions of persecution accompany the aforementioned symptoms. Although involutional psychoses are usually thought of as occurring in women at, during, or immediately following the menopause, they are not uncommon in the male.

ironed-out facies. An expression in which facial folds are flattened out due to loss of muscular tone from disease, as in catatonia. When the subject's mental illness abates, the expression becomes normal. Cf. *masklike facies.*

irritability. In psychiatry, marked excitability and extreme peevishness in response to environmental situations with which the subject cannot or will not cope, even in the face of friendly approaches and offers of assistance. It is particularly common in organic disorders such as cerebral arteriosclerosis and hyperthyroidism, and in emotional states such as hypochondria.

irrumation.   *fellatio.*

ischnophonia.   *stammering.*

isolation.   According to Freud, the separation of an object (idea, experience, or memory) from the emotions associated with it, resulting in external impassivity toward the object. It is a compromise mechanism that makes it possible for a psychoneurotic to neutralize his anxiety.

J

Jacksonian epilepsy. A form of epilepsy described by John Hughlings Jackson, an English neurologist (1834-1911), characterized by irregularly occurring spasmodic contractions of muscle groups or by intermittent paresthesias of various skin areas; due to damage or disease of the cerebral cortex. Syn. *cortical epilepsy, focal epilepsy.*

jactation, jactitation. Extreme restlessness.

James-Lange theory of emotions. The concept advanced by William James, American psychologist and philosopher (1842-1910), which maintains that an emotion is the sum of all feelings and reactions that occur in response to an emergency. That is to say, the frightened stare, the increased pulse rate, the tremor in the extremities are not the consequences of emotion, but the emotion itself. Stated another way, without bodily changes there is no emotion.

Janet, Pierre. French psychiatrist (1859-1947), best known for his investigations into hysteria. He drew attention to the ritualistic nature of behavior in the psychoneuroses and the importance of unconscious motivation in hysteria.

Jocasta complex. The psychoanalytic concept of a mother's pathologic attachment to her son. Cf. *Oedipus complex.*

Jones, Ernest. British psychoanalyst (1879-1958), an early associate of Freud, who introduced psychoanalysis to Great Britain; best known for his three-volume biography of Freud and for his influence as founder of the London School of psychoanalysis.

jumper's disease. *lata(h).*

Jung, Carl Gustav. Swiss psychiatrist (1875-1961). A pioneer in psychoanalysis. At first he supported Freud, but later broke with him. Jung minimized the role of sexuality in the dynamics of personality and developed the school of *analytical psychology.*

juvenile paresis. Syphilis of the central nervous system in a child. It is usually congenital but can be acquired by the infant when nursing at the breast. Manifestations seldom appear before the age of ten, sometimes not until adolescence. The outstanding symptom is progressive physical and mental deterioration. There may be disturbances of gait and vision. Symptoms are not so well defined as in the adult form (general paresis) and may be masked by convulsions and mental retardation, as well as by depression or excitement, delusions, misbehavior, and faulty memory.

juvenile tabes. A form of syphilis of the central nervous system that closely imitates that in the adult (tabes dorsalis). It is acquired in the same manner as *juvenile paresis.*

Kahn Test of Symbol Arrangement (KTSA). A three-dimensional projective test devised by Theodore C. Kahn, American psychologist. The subject is presented with plastic shapes of common objects in different sizes and colors. His method of identification gives a clue to his psychosexual development. For example, he may identify a well-known object, such as a locomotive engine, as a "choo-choo train" (indicating childishness or regression) or as a "diesel locomotive engine" (indicating mature personality development and acquisition of knowledge).

kainophobia, kainotophobia. *neophobia.*

kakergasia. Meyer's term for faulty organization of the personality.

kakorrhaphiophobia. Obsession with fear of failure.

Kalinowsky, Lothar B. German-American psychiatrist (1899-
    ), who introduced electric shock therapy into the United States in 1939 after association in Italy with Bini and Cerlutti, the originators of this method of treatment.

Kallmann, Franz J. German-American psychiatrist and geneticist (1897-1965), best known for his investigation of the factor of heredity in schizophrenia, through his study of identical twins.

Kasanin, Jacob S. American psychiatrist (1897–1946).

kata-. See *cata-.*

kayak fright. *piblockto.*

kathisophobia. *acathisia.*

kenophobia. *agoraphobia.*

Kent Test. A test consisting of ten oral questions which provide a quick estimate of general intelligence.

keraunophobia. A morbid fear of thunder and lightning storms; common in psychoneurosis and regarded as an expression of an unconscious fear of superior and powerful forces. Cf. *tonitrophobia.*

kinesalgia. Pain caused by movement; it may be organogenic or psychogenic, as in conversion hysteria.

kinesia paradoxa. A phenomenon of locomotion seen in persons suffering advanced parkinsonism who, although otherwise slow in movement, suddenly resort to violent walking and/or running for a few seconds. Syn. *Souque's sign.*

kinesophobia. Morbid fear of making any kind of movement for fear of self-injury, even when no danger exists.

king-slave fantasy. A sadomasochistic trend of thought in which a man imagines himself alternately in the role of king and slave in relation to someone he loves. Cf. *pageism.*

kleptolagnia. Sexual excitement experienced in stealing. Cf. *kleptomania.*

kleptomania. Compulsive stealing or desire to steal, without desire for the objects stolen or for economic gain. Cf. *kleptolagnia.*

kleptophobia. An obsessive fear that one may steal something, observed in some psychoneurotic patients.

knee jerk. *patellar reflex.*

kolnotropy. Meyer's term for heterosexual adjustment. Syn. *extraversion.*

kopophobia. A morbid fear of fatigue and of imagined consequences thereof.

Korsakoff (-ov, -ow) psychosis or syndrome. A form of alcoholic psychosis described by Sergei S. Korsakoff, Russian neurologist (1854-1900). It is characterized by disorientation, terrifying auditory hallucinations, retention defect (the patient cannot remember anything told to him) and confabulation (he will give some kind of answer, often absurd, in an effort to cover up the memory defect). He is highly suggestible and usually jolly and childish after the phase of hallucinations has passed. Cf. *amnestic syndrome.*

Kraepelin, Emil. German psychiatrist (1856-1926), whose most significant contribution to psychiatry was a classification of mental disorders that was the basis for descriptive diagnosis until the 1920's.

Krafft-Ebing, Richard von. German neurologist (1840-1902), known for his classic descriptions of sexual psychopathology.

Kretschmer, Ernst. German psychiatrist (1888-1964), known for his classification of body types which he associated with personality types and mental disorders. See *habitus.*

KTSA. *Kahn Test of Symbol Arrangement.*

lability. The tendency to rapid, spontaneous variations in emotional reactions. It is observed in such organic conditions as cerebral arteriosclerosis and in affective disorders such as manic-depressive psychosis and schizophrenia. Syn. *emotional instability.*

Lady Macbeth complex. *hand-washing complex.*

LAE. *lysergic acid monoethylamide.*

lagneia. *erotomania.*

lagneuomania. An obsessive-compulsive state characterized by absorption with, and the impulse to engage in, lustful actions, or to indulge in lewd talk.

lagnosis. *satyriasis.*

laliophobia. Morbid fear of talking, brought about by anxiety over stammering or stuttering.

lallation, lalling. Unintelligible utterance such as an infant's prattling, the mumbled speech of an alcoholic, and a schizophrenic patient's "word salad."

lalopathy. *logopathy.*

lalorrhea. *tachylalia.*

lambitus. *cunnilingus.*

lapsus calami, lapsus linguae. A slip of the pen and tongue, respectively, regarded in psychoanalysis as an indication of an unconscious conflict.

lapsus memoriae. A failure of recall, whether organic or functional in origin.

laryngeal crisis. Acute and painful spasm of the voice box, seen in tabes dorsalis.

lata(h), latta(h). A compulsive reaction endemic to the southwest Pacific region, characterized by spasmodic jumping. Syn. *ikotah, jumper's disease, tokkoni.* Cf. *piblockto.*

latency period, latent stage. In psychoanalysis, the stage of psychosexual development between early childhood (about five years of age) and puberty. Normally, sexual expression in this period is transferred, through sublimation, to the reaction patterns typical of the period (e.g., prudery is substituted for sexual interest).

latent content. See under *dream.*

laughter, compulsive. Hearty laughter unprovoked by any

appropriate stimulus, commonly manifested in schizophrenia, particularly the hebephrenic type.

Laurence-Moon-Biedl syndrome. *adiposogenital dystrophy.*

lead encephalopathy. Brain damage due to *plumbism.*

lay analyst. A practitioner of psychoanalysis who does not possess a medical degree.

lay therapist. Anyone who conducts psychotherapy who is not a psychiatrist; most often a psychologist, psychiatric social worker, or clergyman.

left-handedness. See *handedness.*

learning defect. A child's inability to profit by basic school instruction in a fundamental subject such as reading, writing, or arithmetic, sometimes in all three. The cause may be a *habit disorder,* organic brain disease, psychoneurosis, or psychosis. An example of learning defect is *strephosymbolia.*

lesbian. A homosexual female; the term usually refers to the aggressor in an erotic relationship between two women. Syn. *tribade.* See also *homosexuality.*

lesbianism. Persistent practice of sexual relations as a lesbian.

letheomania. *narcomania.*

levophobia. Morbid fear of objects or persons situated or moving on one's left, probably an outgrowth of the ancient concept of left being "wrong" or "evil." See *handedness.*

liar, pathologic. See *pathologic lying.*

libido. (*adj.* **libidinal, libidinous.**)   Freud's term for the dynamic force in the personality, to which he also referred as "psychosexual energy." See also *ego libido, object libido.* Cf. *drive.*

life goal. Adler's term for the unconscious drive for superiority which compensates for the major inferiority. See also *compensation; directive fiction; guilt, feelings of; inferiority complex; individual psychology.*

life lie. Adler's term for a psychoneurotic's belief that he has failed, or will fail, because of the injustice of others or owing to circumstances beyond his control.

life plan. Adler's term for a type of behavior that enables one to prevent his "superiority" from suffering embarrassment at the hands of reality. See also *compensation*. Cf. *plus gesture*.

liminal. Barely perceived by the senses. Cf. *subliminal*.

lipochondrodystrophy. *gargoylism*.

litigious paranoid. A person suffering a psychosis (usually *paranoia*) who is habitually engaged in lawsuits which he pursues with fervor, treating even minor issues as major causes célèbres.

Little's disease. A generic term for a group of disorders named for William John Little, English physician (1810-94). They are characterized chiefly by bilateral spastic paralysis and mental retardation in some cases. The signs include scissors gait, masklike facies, involuntary laughing and crying, chorea and athetoid movements, and sometimes *dysarthria* and *dysphagia*. Syn. *spastic diplegia*.

lobectomy. In psychosurgery, removal of a part of a lobe of the brain, (usually the prefrontal lobe) to reduce or eliminate extreme agitated depression. The procedure is used as a last resort; since the advent of tranquilizers it has fallen into relative disuse. Cf. *lobotomy*.

lobotomy. In psychosurgery, cutting into a lobe of the brain (usually the prefrontal) to sever certain fibers or groups of fibers, for the same purpose as that of *lobectomy*.

locomotor ataxia. *tabes dorsalis*.

logagnosia. *alexia*.

logagraphia. *agraphia*.

logamnesia. *alexia*.

logasthenia. Inability to understand spoken language. Cf. *sensory aphasia*.

logoclonia.   stuttering. Syn. *logospasm.*

logokophosis.   *word deafness.*

logomania.   *tachylalia.*

logophasia.   *dysarthria.*

logopathy.   Any disturbance of speech function, whether organic (as in general paresis) or psychogenic (as stammering). Syn. *lalopathy.*

logoplegia.   *motor aphasia.*

logorrhea.   *tachylalia.*

logospasm.   *logoclonia.*

London School, The.   A term applied to Ernest Jones and fellow British psychoanalysts who supported Melanie Klein and her daughter in their vigorous differences with Anna Freud on child psychiatry.

love object.   In psychoanalysis, a person, animal, or thing toward which libido is directed. Inanimate love objects are normally observed in pursuits such as stamp and coin collecting, the arts, sports, etc.

LSD.   *lysergic acid diethylamide.*

lucid interval.   A period of relative mental clarity between periods of irrationality, seen especially in organic conditions such as cerebral arteriosclerosis and delirium.

lumbar puncture.   *spinal tap.*

Luminal.   Trade name for *phenobarbital.*

lunacy, lunatic.   Obsolete terms for psychosis and for a psychotic individual, respectively.

lygophilia.   A morbid desire to be in darkened surroundings; a form of eremophilia. Cf. *nyctophilia.*

lying.   See *confabulation, pathologic lying.*

lypothymia, lypophrenia.   *melancholia.*

lysergic acid diethylamide (LSD). A nonnarcotic but powerful hallucinogen (derived from ergot, a rye fungus). Under the influence of this drug an individual experiences a "psychosis in miniature." Some psychiatrists have claimed that it breaks the shackles of repression, enabling a patient to bring past traumatic experiences into consciousness. Others state that certain emotional experiences are so painful for the patient to recall that they may impel him to commit suicide, and that these repressed memories are better left buried in the unconscious. In practically every state it is illegal to manufacture or sell LSD because it is a dangerous drug; it can cause irreversible psychosis and, injudiciously used, may prove to be fatal. Most jurisdictions are permitting enough of the drug to be manufactured for legitimate research purposes, such as experiments in learning ability (the use of minute doses of LSD allegedly improves learning capacity in young children).

lysergic acid monoethylamide (LAE). An ergot derivative which can induce a state closely resembling the stupor of catatonia.

M. A. *mental age.*

macrocephalia, -ly. Extreme enlargement of the head often observed in certain mentally retarded persons. Cf. *hydrocephalus, microcephalia.*

macroesthesia. *macropsia.*

macrogenitosomia. See under *cerebral gigantism.*

macrologia. Meaningless stuttering.

macromania. The delusion that one's body has assumed or is assuming enormous proportions. Cf. *micromania.*

macropsia. A visual disturbance in which objects in the immediate environment seem to be larger than they really are. It is a common experience of persons under the influence of marihuana and is sometimes seen in hysteria. The subject feels that he is a Lilliputian in a world of giants, and may fear that he will be crushed by people or objects in the vicinity. Syn. *macroesthesia.* Cf. *micropsia.*

magic omnipotence. The belief that one has supreme power over his environment, normal in infancy and early childhood but also encountered in schizophrenia. Syn. *autarchy.* Storch's term for magic omnipotence was "cosmic identification."

magnetism, animal. See *mesmerism.*

maieusiophobia. An unreasoning dread or fear of pregnancy and childbirth.

major epilepsy. *grand mal epilepsy.*

Make-a-Picture-Story Test (MAPS Test). A variation of psychodrama in which a miniature stage is provided and the subject selects the actors from 67 cutout figures of male and female adults and children, people of indeterminate sex, and animals; in addition there are more than 20 backgrounds the patient can choose. After he has set up the stage, the subject is asked to tell the story of what he is attempting to present and to answer questions put to him concerning the setup. Certain signs have been found to differentiate schizophrenics from normal subjects as, for example, the more frequent selection of characters of indeterminate sex.

maladjustment. An individual's inability or unwillingness to adapt himself to the conditions under which he lives. The conditions range from the person's family milieu, a new situation (such as leaving civilian for military life), or one of the successive critical periods of life (such as adolescence, adulthood, marriage, and middle age). The individual is truly maladjusted if, though the conditions may be changed for the better, he still cannot adjust. The commonest symptoms are irritability, anxiety, and depression. These may become aggravated and progress to a psychoneurosis or even a psychosis. See also *adjustment, transient situational personality disorders.*

malarial therapy, malariotherapy. A procedure for the treatment of general paresis, originated by Julius Wagner von Jauregg, German physician and Nobel laureate (1857-1940). The unusually high fever induced in the patient (by the intravenous introduction of malaria organisms) destroys the causative germ, *Treponema pallidum.* This treatment procedure enjoyed widespread use until the advent of antibiotics.

malingering. Attempts to simulate emotional and mental disorders are not uncommon among accused persons, criminals, and men who wish to avoid selective military service. Most such frauds are easily detected because the perpetrators lack complete knowledge of the pattern of symptoms of the mental disorder they are imitating. For the few who are skillful enough to be convincing, the Rorschach Psychodiagnostic Method, or some other personality inquiry or neurologic test, is employed. Personal history data obtained from other persons also helps to check on the individual's statements and behavior.

malleation. A compulsive movement of the hands resembling the gesture of hammering, especially while talking, sometimes seen in psychoneurosis.

mania. A state of disturbed thought, emotion, and action, characterized by continued, uncontrollable activity in the form of excessive and often rapid speech (logorrhea), exaltation of mood (euphoria), and violent, destructive behavior. Cf. *hypomania, pseudomania.*

mania à potu. *intoxication, pathologic.*

manic. *adj.* Pertaining to mania. *n.* One afflicted with mania; in this form it has replaced the obsolete word "maniac," meaning a violent psychotic person.

manic-depressive psychosis or **reaction.** An *affective reaction* in which the outstanding symptoms are outbursts of emotional displays and overactivity accompanied by elation, or extended periods of apathy, underactivity, and depression. Usually one or the other of these reactions predominates in a given patient. In the *circular type* there are mood swings between the extremes of these manifestations. The *mixed type* includes elements of both manic and depressive types (e.g., overtalkativeness, hyperactivity, and depression) without either type dominating the clinical picture. Many psychiatrists feel that manic-depressive psychosis is merely an early affective type of schizophrenia. Syn. *thymergasia*. See also *depression, mania*.

manifest content. See under *dream*.

mannerism. A grimace, or other action that is peculiar to an individual, such as blinking (*nictitation*), gritting the teeth (*bruxism*), biting the fingernails, or tapping of a foot. Such actions are common in the behavior of persons suffering psychoses and psychoneuroses. Their significance must be interpreted in the light of the total reaction of the individual patient. Cf. *tic*.

MAO. *monoamine oxidase inhibitors*.

maple syrup urine disease. A metabolic disorder seen in some mentally retarded infants whose urine has a characteristic odor.

MAPS Test. *Make-a-Picture-Story Test*.

marche à petits pas. A gait marked by mincing steps, seen in parkinsonism. Cf. *festination*.

Marie Three-Paper Test. A test of recall, devised by Pierre Marie, French physician (1853-1940), in which the patient is handed three slips of paper and instructed to dispose of them in three different ways. Ordinarily a patient with a severe memory defect will fail to carry out one or all of the instructions. See also *retention defect*.

marihuana, -juana. A hallucinogen, formally regarded as a narcotic, produced from the leaves of *Cannabis indica* or *Cannabis sativa*, most commonly taken in the form of cigarettes. It produces euphoria, a false impression of efficiency in physical performance, and disturbance of time and space appreciation. Micropsia and macropsia are common experiences. The drug is not habit-forming in the strict sense of the word, but it is especially pernicious because it prepares the way for the use of addictive drugs. Marihuana is readily accessible; it has been found growing in fields, vacant lots, windowsill flower-pots, and even in tin cans on fire escapes.

masculine protest. Adler's term for the reaction pattern of both men and women who are motivated by a desire to escape from the feminine submissive role. In women the protest occurs at an early age, with the emergence of aggressive, dominant behavior and attitudes (the "tomboy" and later the tyrannical mother or wife). In the male it takes the form of an exaggerated display of masculine traits in response to real or imagined doubt by others of his masculinity; it may derive from the subject's own uncertainty of his role.

masklike facies. A "flattened" facial expression, seen in parkinsonism. It is not reversible, as is the ironed-out facies in catatonia.

masochism. Sexual gratification derived from submitting to the infliction of pain or indignities. In a less specific sense, it means taking pleasure in one's own deprivation, discomfort, etc. (the role of martyr). The term is derived from Leopold von Sacher Masoch, Austrian novelist (1836-1895), whose characters derived sexual pleasure from being treated cruelly. Syn. *algophilia.* See also *flagellation, sadomasochism.* Cf. *sadism.*

masturbation. Solitary sexual activity usually by manipulation of the genital organ. Though credence is no longer placed in statements of its damaging physical and mental effects, there can be little doubt that serious emotional problems may be generated by feelings of guilt over the act. See also *contemplative, pseudomasturbation.*

matronism, precocious. See *precocious matronism.*

maturity. In psychiatry, the state of full psychosexual development, i.e., the attainment of the *heterosexual level.* It usually occurs in late adolescence but this is extremely variable among individuals. Indeed, in most persons some signs of immaturity are lifelong traits.

meconeuropathia, -thy. A nervous or mental affliction due to morphinism or opiumism.

medulla oblongata. The hindmost part of the brain, connecting the pons with the spinal cord. It is also known as the *bulb* (evidences of damage to the medulla are called *bulbar syndromes*).

Meduna, Ladislas Joseph. Hungarian-American psychiatrist (1896-   ), known chiefly for his carbon dioxide therapy and for the introduction of metrazol shock therapy into psychiatry in the mid-1930's.

megalocephalia, -ly. *macrocephalia.*

megalomania. The delusion that one occupies a position of supreme power and esteem. The subject usually adopts the role of some legendary, historic, or currently eminent person. Syn. *delirium grandiosum.*

melancholia. Profound depression accompanied by restlessness and sharply limited verbal activity. Regarded as a symptom rather than a diagnostic entity, it denotes a type of *involutional psychosis.*

melomania. Pathologic obsession with musical sounds, sometimes those of a particular theme or mood, or with musical effects in general. Syn. *musicomania.*

Memory-for-Designs (MFD) test. A simple drawing test of perceptual-motor coordination devised by F. K. Graham and Barbara S. Kendal, American psychologists. This psychological inquiry is said to be an extremely sensitive detector of brain injury of many types. It depends on immediate memory and is suitable for use in the age range of about 8 to 60 years. The procedure usually takes less than ten minutes. Its proponents recommend it for quick, effective differentiation of functionally based behavior disorder from that ordinarily associated with brain injury.

meninges (*sing.* **meninx**). The membranes that cover the brain and the spinal cord. From outside to inside they are: the *dura* *mater,* the *arachnoid,* and the *pia mater.* The pia mater and the innermost layer of the arachnoid are so closely associated that they are sometimes referred to as one layer, the *pia-arachnoid.*

meningism, meningismus. A display of symptoms resembling those of *meningitis* without actual infection of the meninges.

meningitis. Inflammation of the *meninges,* due to invasion by meningococcus, pneumococcus, or other pus-forming micro-organisms or viruses. Symptoms, which vary with the severity and the area affected, include severe headache, delirium, drowsiness, localized or generalized convulsions, rigidity or twitching, projectile vomiting at times, and hemiplegia. Syn. *cerebrospinal fever.*

meningoencephalitis. *encephalomeningitis.*

mental acuity. See *age and mental acuity.*

mental age (M.A.). A measurement of the extent of a subject's mental attainment, determined by the accomplishment of certain mental tasks in standardized intelligence tests. It is used as the numerator, with the chronological age as denominator (the result being multiplied by 100), to arrive at the intelligence quotient.

mental apparatus. Freud stated that the three provinces of the mental apparatus were the id, ego, and superego. See also *consciousness, characteristics of.*

mental deafness. *mind deafness.*

mental defect or **deficiency.** *mental retardation.*

mental defective. A mentally retarded person.

mental disease, disorder, disturbance. See *disease, disorder, disturbance, mental illness.*

mental disease and diet. Until very recently, there was little evidence that dietary disorders played a direct role in the causation of mental disorders other than in the case of rare illnesses such as pellagra and the chronic varieties of alcoholism. It is now recognized that faulty diet and metabolic disorders exert a considerable adverse influence on learning ability and the development of mental intelligence. See *maple syrup urine disease, phenylpyruvic acid deficiency.*

mental fatigue. See *fatigue, mental.*

mental hygiene. The total program for the prevention, treatment, and sociolegal management of mental illness and mental retardation from the public health point of view. Cf. *orthopsychiatry.*

mental illness. Any persistent disabling disturbance of mental and/or emotional equilibrium, usually manifested through persistent maladjustment and more or less irrational, even bizarre behavior and speech, whether psychic or organic in origin. The term is relative in force, there being a wide range of severity, from mere "nervousness" (see *nervous,* def. 2) and the mild transient situational personality disorder, through the psychoneuroses, to the thoroughly debilitating psychoses. See *classification of mental disorders.*

mental retardation. The currently accepted term for "mental deficiency." Although the newer term is admittedly a euphemism, it was adopted because "deficiency" implied a permanent, totally unmodifiable state. Many mentally retarded persons have been and still are needlessly stigmatized by this older concept.

A mentally retarded person is one whose intelligence quotient, as determined by the Stanford-Binet Scale, is below 70. The three major clinical designations are: (1) *Severe* (formerly "idiot"), including subject whose I.Q. is less than 25—such individuals cannot take even nominal care of their personal needs and are unable to protect themselves against ordinary physical dangers; (2) *Moderate* (formerly "imbecile"), for I.Q. of 26 to 49—these persons can protect themselves against ordinary dangers but are incapable of managing themselves or their affairs; (3) *Mild* (formerly "moron"), for I.Q. of 50 to 69—such a person may require care, supervision, and custody to protect himself and others, and though he may be able to learn simple skills from highly specialized teaching, he cannot profit from ordinary school instruction. A fourth level, *borderline,* for I.Q. of 70 to 79, is also recognized. In a broader sense, the term "mentally retarded" is sometimes applied to an individual whose learning capacity has been slowed, even if only temporarily, and might therefore include an uncommunicative psychoneurotic, a withdrawn psychotic, or an autistic child—whose problems are not based on innate defect but on failure to employ their mental talents. Syn. *oligophrenia.* See also *Binet-Simon Scale, intelligence, intelligence quotient, intelligence tests, Kent test, Wechsler-Bellevue Scales.*

mental retardation and malnutrition. Studies in Latin America and Africa have indicated that protein-calorie malnutrition can cause mental retardation. Testing of large numbers of subjects has shown that improperly nourished children in these areas have impaired learning capacity and psychomotor changes, and evidence of brain damage. The inference is drawn that whole populations, owing to the historic imbalance of their diets, may be thus prevented from achieving their full mental and social potential.

Mental Status Schedule (MSS). A diagnostic inquiry introduced into psychiatric practice in 1963. It comprises an inventory of 248 matched questions related to small units of pathologic behavior. The interviewer is not restricted to the prescribed question, but may ask additional questions and pursue salient clinical features as he deems them to be germane and necessary. The inquiry is holistically oriented, and recognizes factors such as age, socioeconomic and ethnic status, and religion.

menticide. *brainwashing.*

meprobamate. Generic term for a chemical substance whose tranquilizing effect derives from its capacity to slow the transmission of nervous impulses. Trade names: Equanil, Miltown.

merergasia. Meyer's term for partial disorganization of the personality. The psychoneuroses are examples of merergastic reactions. See *psychobiology.* Cf. *kakergasia.*

merinthophobia. An overwhelming dread that one is going to be tied up.

meroparesthesia. Paresthesia in the extremities; an organic form occurs in neuritis due to chronic alcoholism; a psychogenic form is *glove-and-stocking anesthesia.*

merosmia.   Partial loss of the sense of smell; it may be organic in origin (e.g., nasal polyps, sinusitis), or due to hysteria.

merycism.   *rumination.*

Mesanthoin.   *methoin.*

mescaline.   The fermented juice of cactus, used as a hallucinogen. Syn. *peyote.* Cf. *adrenochrome.*

mesmerism.   Hypnotism as a therapeutic technique of the early 1800's; championed by Franz Anton Mesmer, an Austrian (1733-1815). Mesmer believed hypnotism to be based on a force he called "animal magnetism." His procedure involved elaborate paraphernalia, theatrically presented. See *hypnosis.*

mesomorph.   Sheldon's body type characterized by a muscular physique. He associated it with a personality type, somatotonia, which is marked by aggressive temperament and comparative independence. Cf. *athletic habitus, somatotypes.*

metabolism.   The process by which the body assimilates some ingested materials for its growth and repair and selects others for elimination as waste. Metabolic disorders in which mental retardation is a feature include: adiposogenital dystrophy, cretinism, cat cry syndrome, hemicysinuria, hyperlysinemia, Laurence-Moon-Biedl syndrome, maple syrup urine disease (oasthouse urine disease), phenylketonuria, pyridoxine dependency, the adrenal genital syndrome, and Tay-Sachs' disease. Metabolic disorders in which there are features of mental and emotional illness include: histidinemia, hyperthyroidism, hypoglycemia, myxedema, and pellagra. See also *emotiometabolic; weight at birth.*

metallesthesia.   An unusual tactile capacity, allegedly possessed by certain neurotic and hypnotized persons, that enables them to differentiate metals solely by the sense of touch.

metallophobia.   An unreasoning fear of metals.

metamorphosis, sexual.   *transvestism.*

methadone hydrochloride. A derivative of opium whose action is similar to that of opium but much less toxic. It is used as a substitute for heroin in treating the withdrawal syndrome. Once a maintenance dosage is established for the addict his craving for heroin subsidies, though it does not disappear completely.

Methedrine. A trade name for amphetamine.

methionine. An amino acid found naturally in the body. It is essential for growth, and its faulty metabolism causes mental retardation, particularly when the metabolic deficiency is familial. See also *maple syrup urine disease.*

methoin. An anticonvulsant chemical substance especially effective in the treatment of the grand mal type of epilepsy. Trade name: Mesantoin.

meticulosity, -lousness. In psychiatry, pathologic absorption with detail, orderliness, tidiness, and punctuality—all, in their extreme forms, regarded as personality reflections of excessive discipline in the toilet-training period. The over-all pattern, described as the *anal erotic personality,* is seen in the "fuss-budget," the hoarder, the "on-the-nose" keeper of appointments. Such traits are commonly observed in the obsessive-compulsive reaction. Whether or not meticulosity is pathologic depends on the degree to which it interferes with the demands of everyday reality.

metrazol shock therapy. A chemotherapeutic technique introduced by Meduna in the 1930's. Metrazol is a camphorlike agent which immediately induces violent convulsions. Since the advent of electric shock therapy, metrazol has practically ceased to be used in psychiatry.

metromania. A compulsive urge to compose verse or to talk in verse, sometimes encountered in manic-depressive psychosis.

Meyer, Adolf. Swiss-American psychiatrist and neurologist (1866-1950), originator of the discipline of psychobiology. He applied broad biologic concepts to the understanding of mental illness and insisted upon a complete review of every factor concerned with the patient's difficulties, whether physical, environmental, intellectual, or emotional. See also *distributive analysis, holism, psychobiology.*

MFD Test. *Memory-for-Designs Test.*

microcephalia. Abnormally small size of the head, a congenital defect, accompanied by mental retardation. Cf. *macrocephalia.*

microbophobia. *bacillophobia.*

micropsia. A visual disturbance in which objects and persons are perceived as much smaller than they actually are. It is a common experience of persons under the influence of marihuana, who may even fear to walk across the room lest they step on someone. It is not uncommon in hysteria and epilepsy. Syn. *microesthesia.* Cf. *macropsia.*

migraine. Popularly called "sick headache," migraine is a paroxysmal, recurrent headache often accompanied by visual disturbances such as *fortification figures,* nausea, and vomiting. Attacks last for hours to days. The pain is most often confined to one side of the head (hemicrania). Although the cause is unknown, there are strong indications of psychogenic factors. Migraine is commoner in women, often being associated with menstruation.

milieu therapy. An attempt to improve the condition of a mentally ill or retarded person by improving his environment (especially the home). It frequently uncovers the fact that personality disturbance in a spouse, parent, or sibling has been a major factor in precipitating the patient's mental disorder. Syn. *environmental therapy.* Cf. *family therapy.*

Miltown. A trade name for meprobamate.

mind. A loosely employed term having many meanings, of which the most widely used are: (1) the individual's capacity for mental activity, as evidenced by his available stock of memories and adaptive responses; (2) the sum of the individual's experiences of thinking, knowing, feeling, and reacting, whether in the conscious or the unconscious; (3) the mechanisms through which the individual receives, records, and reacts to external and internal influences. Earlier concepts made a strict distinction between "body" and "mind"; the inseparability of the two is now universally accepted. Some investigators suggest that all mental and emotional experiences can ultimately be explained on the basis of activity in the central nervous system, and that in time such terms as "mind" and "consciousness" will be superfluous—this is the extreme form of the theory known as *behaviorism*. Syn. *psyche*.

mind deafness. An aphasia in which the auditory apparatus is intact but the sounds heard are meaningless to the subject. Syn. *mental deafness, psychic deafness*. Cf. *word deafness*.

Minnesota Multiphasic Personality Inventory (MMPI). A personality inquiry based on 550 standardized true-false questions printed on cards. The subject is left alone with instructions to sort the cards into boxes according to his answers ("yes," "no," "don't know"). The profiles of answers by "normal" subjects differ markedly from those of psychiatric patients. Classification of responses are: depression, hypochondriasis, hypomania, hysteria, masculinity-femininity, paranoia, anxiety, phobias, and obsessive-compulsive reactions, personality and character disorders, and schizophrenia. See also *computer diagnosis, Self-Analysis Scale*.

minor epilepsy. *petit mal.*

mirror speech. Habitual utterance of words in transposed order, a perverse trend sometimes seen in the manic phase of manic-depressive psychosis.

mirror writing. A visual-motor disturbance in which the subject writes words, lines, even whole passages backwards, so that they can be read normally in a mirror. Syn. *retrography*.

misocainia. *neophobia.*

misogyny. Exaggerated hatred of women, by a person of either sex. It may reflect, though for different reasons, a strong homosexual component in the personality.

misologia. A profound aversion to speaking or conversing; seen in some anxiety reactions, depression, and catatonia.

misopedia. Unconsciously generated hatred of or distaste for children, believed by psychoanalysts to be due to unconscious guilt over lascivious urges toward them, as a residue from an unresolved Oedipus complex.

mistake, unconscious. See *Freudian slip.*

mite. *quiet delirium.*

mixed. In certain diagnostic categories (e.g., schizophrenia and manic-depressive psychosis), a subgroup labeled "mixed" is reserved for patients in whom one or another subtype of reaction does not predominate.

mixoscopia. *voyeurism.*

MMPI. *Minnesota Multiphasic Personality Inventory.*

mnemonic. Of or pertaining to the memory. A prop for the memory is called a mnemonic device, an example of which is fixing in memory the spaces on a musical staff by the word F-A-C-E.

mnemonics. The art or technique of reinforcing the memory.

mogilalia. Hesitancy or irregularity in speaking, sometimes the result of blocking.

mogiphonia. Difficulty in forming correct sounds in speech.

molysmophobia. *mysophobia.*

mongolism. *Down's disease* or *syndrome.*

monoamine oxidase (MAO) inhibitors. A group of chemical compounds which are potent inhibitors of monoamine oxidase, an enzyme that is believed to destroy hormonal substances such as serotonin. These drugs are used to treat depressive states, sleep disturbances, fatigue, anxiety, and psychomotor retardation.

monochorea. Chorea affecting only one limb or one part of the body.

monomania. *hypolepsiomania.*

monoparesthesia. Paresthesia of a single limb or of a circum- scribed area of the body. Organic monoparesthesia is seen, for example, in severe inflammation of a sensory nerve; it may be observed in hysteria, and it can be induced under hypnosis.

monophasia. Aphasia characterized by the ability to utter only one word or phrase.

monophobia. *eremophobia.*

monoplegia. Paralysis of a single limb.

mood swings. Alternate manifestations of feelings of elation and of depression. Although they are common in normal personalities, the swings in manic-depressives are much more abrupt, each succeeding phase is more intense, and the contrast between phases is much more noticeable. See also *cyclothymia.*

Moreno, Jacob L. Rumanian-Austrian-American physician (1892-   ), who devised the technique of psychodrama for the diagnosis and treatment of emotional and mental disorders.

moria. An irresistible urge to jest, often seen in the manic phase of a manic-depressive reaction.

moron. Obsolete term for a person who is mildly mentally retarded.

morphinism. Addiction to morphine, the chief and most active alkaloid of opium. The symptoms of morphinism are the same as those of *opiumism.*

mortido. Federn's term for the death wish; the opposite of libido.

mosaic test. A psychologic projective test, more popular in Great Britain than in the United States, intended to reveal personality traits. The subject makes a design according to size, shape, and color of cut-out pieces selected by him from a large assortment. The choice of black, for example, as in the Rorschach Psychodiagnostic Method, signifies depression.

mother figure. See *parent figure.*

mother image. See under *parent image.*

motion sickness. A comprehensive term for the several forms (air sickness, carsickness, seasickness, and train sickness) of a condition characterized by nausea and vomiting, accompanied by anxiety, induced by motion. There is strong evidence that emotional elements, along with disturbance of the vestibular apparatus in the inner ear, play an important role, as seen in the fact that the symptoms can be produced vicariously by a motion picture taken from a rolling ship or from the back end of a rapidly moving train.

motor.   *adj.* Causing or involved in stimulating movement of a muscle or muscle group. Cf. *sensory*.

motor agraphia.   *anorthographia.*

motor aphasia.   Complete or partial loss of the ability to express ideas in words, due to a lesion of the left prefrontal lobe of the brain. Syn. *expressive aphasia, logoplegia.* Cf. *sensory aphasia.*

motor centers.   See under *cerebral cortex.*

motor dominance.   *cerebral dominance.*

motor tract.   *pyramidal tract.*

MSS.   *Mental Status Schedule.*

mucous colitis.   A psychosomatic condition, in which the unconscious conflict, whose overt expression would be socially unacceptable, is drained off through bodily (somatic) illness in the form of spasm of the bowels and with pain in that area, passage of blood-tinged mucous matter, and alternating diarrhea and constipation. Removal of the precipitating circumstances often relieves the condition, but if this is not possible, psychotherapy is required. Syn. *irritable colon syndrome.*

mulebriety.   *effemination.*

multidimensional group therapy.   Group therapy involving three units: the patients, their relatives, and the patients together with their relatives ("mixed group"). The patient assumes different roles when treated in the "patient group" and in the "mixed group." At the meetings of relatives the family members have the opportunity to ventilate their feelings about the patients in a mutually supportive and understanding atmosphere. Their self-esteem is raised and this enables them to deal more constructively with their sick family member. It seems that defensive family attitudes are broken down when the relatives of a patient meet with the relatives of other patients. Paradoxically, when the patients are released from the institution they seem to establish a closer-than-ever relationship with their families.

multiple neuritis. Widespread inflammation of symmetrically distributed nerves, sometimes accompanied by nerve degeneration. It is encountered in certain infections, chronic alcoholism, and vitamin deficiencies.

multiple personality. Coexistence in an individual of two or more clearly differentiated personalities whose characteristics appear episodically, one personality succeeding the other. Classic examples are extremely rare. The schizophrenic, who is commonly thought of as having multiple personalities ("split personality"), is usually so disorganized that he is not capable of mobilizing even one well-integrated personality pattern, let alone several. Cf. *dissociative reaction.*

multiple sclerosis: A chronic, progressive, degenerative disease of the central nervous system, in which scattered areas of hardened nerve tissue replace previously healthy tissue. One of the early signs is nystagmus (involuntary oscillation of the eyeballs) and loss of abdominal reflexes. The patient usually first complains that his handwriting is becoming illegible or that he has difficulty in urinating or in controlling urination. Later the disease presents such mental symptoms as *scanning speech* and *euphoria.* A psychotic state resembling schizophrenia may follow. The cause is unknown and there is as yet no cure. Syn. *disseminated sclerosis.*

multiple sensations. See *synesthesia.*

music therapy. All institutions for the mentally ill and the mentally retarded use music as a means of recreational therapy. Patients with musical abilities are encouraged to be performers as well as auditors. In general, psychotic persons respond to music with the appropriate mood displayed by normal persons, although schizophrenics and manic-depressives misinterpret the mood of a given musical composition more often than do either normal individuals or those suffering from simple depression. The response to music demonstrated by autistic children is characterized by a profound preoccupation, a rote memory for melodies, and in some instances, singing as a means of communication when other forms of social contact are avoided or rejected. Oddly, patients who show improvement during music therapy often show a decline in their interest in this medium of expression.

musicogenic epilepsy. See under *sensory epilepsy.*

musicomania. *melomania.*

mussitation. Compulsive movement of the organs of speech, particularly the lips and the tongue, resulting in muttering or no sound at all; a manifestation of psychotic regression. Cf. *mutism.*

mutilation. See *self-mutilation.*

mutism. A form of negativism in which there is total absence of speech, usually because the person refuses to talk. It occurs in response to inner dictates, usually confusion and conflict, and is commonly observed in catatonic patients and in those suffering from hysteria, stupor, or depression. Cf. *mussitation, negativism.*

myeloencephalitis. *encephalomyelitis.*

myelomeningitis. Inflammation of the spinal cord and its meninges.

myelopathy. Any disease of the spinal cord.

myelophthisis. *tabes dorsalis.*

myeloplegia. Paralysis of the spine.

myesthesia. Muscle sensibility.

myoclonia, -clonus, -kymia. Chronic muscular spasm.

myoclonic epilepsy. A form of petit mal epilepsy characterized by isolated jerks of flexor muscles without loss of consciousness.

myopsychosis, myopsychopathy. The existence of any neuro-muscular disease in association with mental symptoms, such as parkinsonism, Sydenham's chorea, etc.

mysophilia. *coprophilia.*

mysophobia. Exaggerated fear of becoming dirty or contaminated. Syn. *molysmophobia.* Cf. *bacillophobia, coprophobia, handwashing complex.*

mythomania. *pathologic lying.*

myxedema. The adult form of hypothyroidism; it is characterized by a dry, waxy type of swelling of the skin, puffy lips, thickened nose, and unusual indifference, apathy, and disinclination to engage in activity. Cf. *cretinism.*

narcism, narcissism. Self-love; the term is derived form the Greek legend of Narcissus, who, upon seeing his reflection in a pool, fell in love with his own image. In the psychosexual development of the individual, the narcissistic stage occurs between the autoerotic and the homoerotic stages, covering roughly the span of life from the second to the fourth year, when active interest in other children has yet to evolve. Narcissistic elements often persist in the personality well into adulthood, and some remnants of it are never discarded. Examples are frequent visits to barber shops and beauty parlors, preoccupation with clothes.

narcissistic neurosis. Freud's original all-inclusive term for a psychoneurosis (such as obsessive-compulsive reaction, hypochondriasis) which is characterized by extreme autoerotism. Cf. *transference neurosis.*

narcoanalysis. Psychoanalysis of a patient in a trance state induced by a narcotizing drug, such as sodium amytal or pentothal sodium. Cf. *hypnoanalysis, narcosynthesis.*

narcohypnia. A sensation of numbness, usually in a limb or digit, sometimes experienced upon rousing from a deep sleep or hypnotic trance.

narcolepsy. A sudden impulse to sleep regardless of where the person is or what he is doing, and not caused by physical fatigue or sleep deprivation. Unlike syncope (fainting), this sleeping state is natural. It lasts from seconds to a few minutes. If the slumberer is wakened, he promptly falls asleep again and upon awakening spontaneously, he feels refreshed. This affliction usually affects obese young men, who often are also sexually impotent. The drug amphetamine sulfate controls the condition effectively. Syn. *paroxysmal sleep.*

narcomania. An uncontrollable morbid desire for a narcotic drug. Syn. *letheomania, narcosomania.*

narcosis. Deep unconsciousness induced by narcotic drugs.

narcosynthesis. A therapeutic procedure, similar to *narcoanalysis,* in which the patient, under the influence of a narcotic relives his emotional reactions to past traumatic experiences and is induced to re-evaluate and understand them.

narcotic. *adj.* Producing or pertaining to sleep or stupor. *n.* A drug having analgesic and soporific effects.

narcotism. Chronic use of narcotic drugs, or chronic addiction or habituation to narcotic drugs such as cocaine, heroin, morphine, and opium. See also *addiction, habituation.*

necromania. Erotic stimulation by viewing or being in the presence of a corpse. Cf. *necrophilia.*

necromimesis. In a psychotic person, the delusion that he is dead; frequently he adopts a moribund position or attitude.

necrophilia, -ly. The desire for sexual contact with a dead body, up to and including coitus. Cf. *necromania.*

necrophobia. Abnormal fear of a corpse.

necrosadism. Sadistic pleasure in mutilating or "torturing" a corpse.

Neftel's disease. *atremia.*

negativism. In psychiatry, a trend of behavior and attitude characterized by refusal to cooperate even with reasonable requests and the tendency to do the opposite of what others desire. It is most often seen in catatonic schizophrenia. It may be active or passive. In *passive negativism* (as in catatonia) the patient is often seen curled up in the fetal posture, immobile, mute, and exhibiting a fixed, impassive facial expression but occasionally indulging in the grimace of schnauzkrampf. In *active negativism* the patient, in resisting suggestion, is belligerent, impulsive, and may be homicidal or suicidal. Cf. *denial. mutism.*

neoculturalism. See under **Horney.**

neologism. A verbal manifestation commonly heard in manic-depressive psychosis and schizophrenia in which the patient uses coined words meaningless to others but probably meaningful to him, or attaches to ordinary words meanings that are inappropriate. Syn. *paragrammatism.* Cf. *contamination, glossolalia.*

neophilia, -lism. Abnormal attraction to or fondness for anything that is novel. Syn. *philoneism.* Cf. *neophobia.*

neophobia. Morbid fear of new or unaccustomed things, persons, or circumstance. Syn. *cainotophobia, misocainia.*

nervous. 1. Pertaining to a nerve or the nervous system; in this sense it is often used to distinguish a disorder with a background of organic pathology from one that is functional, or a somatogenic from a psychogenic disorder. Syn. *neurologic.* 2. In common parlance, anxious, restless, irritable.

"nervous breakdown." A popular euphemism for any disabling mental disorder. It is an outright misnomer, since the nervous systems of most psychotics or psychoneurotics are intact, though misdirected.

"nervous indigestion." A popular term for any psychogenic gastrointestinal reaction, such as irritable colon, peptic ulcer, ulcerative colitis.

"nervous stomach." A popular term for a gastrointestinal reaction to fear over failure or embarrassment, as stage fright or mike fright.

nervous system. See *autonomic, central, parasympathetic,* and *sympathetic nervous system.*

neural. Belonging or pertaining to a nerve or nerves.

neurasthenia. ("nerve weakness") A term once attached to a condition that was marked by chronic fatigue, sensations of pressure on the scalp, tension in the neck, pain along the spine, and an inability to concentrate. Clinical experience has shown that these are manifestations of a deep-seated *anxiety reaction.* The diagnostic category of "neurasthenia" no longer appears in the official APA classification of mental disorders.

neurocirculatory asthenia. *effort syndrome.*

neurologist. A physician who is certified in the specialty of neurology by the American Board of Psychiatry and Neurology.

neurology. The body of knowledge concerned with the structure, function, and pathology of the nervous system, as well as the diagnosis and treatment of its disorders.

neuropathology. 1. The science concerned with neuropathy. 2. Any disease or disordered state of the nervous system or of one of its divisions.

neuropathy. Structural or functional disorder in the nervous system or any of its parts.

neuropsychiatrist. A loose term for a physican who is certified as a specialist in both neurology and psychiatry. The preferred term is "neurologist and psychiatrist."

neuropsychiatry. Neurology and psychiatry regarded as one combined discipline.

neurosis, neurotic. *psychoneurosis, psychoneurotic.*

neurosyphilis. Any of several forms of syphilis of the central nervous system. See *general paresis, juvenile paresis, juvenile tabes, tabes dorsalis.*

neurotic anxiety. Freud's term for apprehension and tension arising from unconscious fear. Cf. *objective anxiety.*

neurotic depression. A psychoneurotic reaction in which the dominant manifestation is depression, regarded as pathologic because of its unwarranted duration and intensity.

neurotic epilepsy. *psychomotor epilepsy.*

neurotic fear. See under *conditioned fear.*

neurotic stupidity. A type of psychoneurotic behavior marked by rigid and repetitive behavior which creates the false impression that the patient is mentally retarded.

nictitation. Involuntary spasmodic blinking.

night terror. *pavor nocturnus.*

nightmare. A frightening dream, far more common in children than in adults. The pattern of the dream (see *manifest content* under *dream*) involves a dire threat or a revolting spectacle, and an attempt to escape from it. The dreamer does not quite extricate himself from his predicament, but neither are the fatal consequences realized, and he awakens still experiencing the fear reaction, with accelerated pulse and respiration, and often bathed in perspiration. The dreamer can usually recount this kind of dream. Cf. *pavor nocturnus.*

nihilism. A delusion that no one and nothing exists; it may be observed in profound psychotic depressive states. Cf. *dissociation.*

nirvana principle. According to Freud, the expression of the "death instinct," the desire for nonexistence. In contrast, the pleasure principle represents the claims of the libido and the reality principle. The nirvana principle finds temporary expression in ecstatic states, intoxication, and narcotism. Cf. *mortido.*

nitrous oxide gas addiction. In some communities where statutes and police enforcement are effective in controlling the availability of addictive drugs, some individuals resort to nitrous oxide for "kicks." The user of nitrous oxide commonly states that he is imbued with a feeling of happiness, giddiness, convulsive laughter (as reflected by lying on the floor and laughing until tears appear), and a marked increase in sexual drive, both hetero-sexual and homosexual.

noctambulism. *somnambulism.*

noctiphobia, nyctophobia. Fear of night or darkness. Syn. *achluophobia.*

nocturnal epilepsy. Grand mal epilepsy that occurs during sleep; the patient is usually unaware of the seizure until he wakens at his customary hour and discovers blood on his pillow, indicating that he had bitten his tongue during an attack.

nomadism. *dromomania.*

nominal aphasia. *amnestic aphasia.*

non-Freudian psychoanalysis. The theories and practices de-veloped by students and followers of Freud who differed from him in certain areas of interpretation of personality dynamics. See *Adler, Fromm, Horney, Jung, Rank, Sullivan.*

nonsense syndrome. *Ganser's syndrome.*

noöklopia. *castrophrenia.*

noöpsyche. The intellectual process of the mind. Cf. *thymo-psyche.*

norepinephrine. One of the hormones secreted by the adrenal glands. Closely related to epinephrine, it has a stimulating effect on the sympathetic nervous system. Syn. *arterenol.*

nosomania. A psychotic person's delusional conviction that despite his physical good health he is suffering from a dread, if not fatal, disease.

nosophobia. Morbid fear of illness, in a person who is in good or relatively good health.

nostomania. Intense homesickness.

nostophobia. An overwhelming dread of returning home, prompted by unconscious guilt feelings.

nyctophilia. An obsessive preference for nighttime or darkness. Cf. *lygophilia.*

nyctophobia. *noctiphobia.*

nyctaphonia. Loss of vocal power at night or in darkness, seen in persons suffering from hysteria who have complete power of speech during the day or in a lighted environment.

nympholepsy. Erotic ecstacy.

nymphomania. Insatiable desire in a female for coitus. Syn. *andromania, clitoromania, hysteromania.* Cf. *satyriasis.*

O

oast-house urine disease. The British term for *maple syrup urine disease.*

obesity. See *overweight, psychic factors in.*

object cathexis. See under *cathexis.*

object choice. The person or thing that is the recipient of libido. See also *love object.*

object libido. Libido that is directed to another person. Many analysts enlarge the concept of object libido to include an object within the person himself (e.g., preoccupation with a "pet idea").

objective anxiety. Freud's term for fear precipitated by a real threat to the individual's security. Cf. *neurotic anxiety.*

obnubilation. Mental haziness immediately preceding loss of consciousness.

obsession. A persistent preoccupation with a thought or constellation of thoughts, observed commonly as an element of the obsessive-compulsive reaction. Cf. *compulsion.*

obsessive-compulsive reaction. A psychoneurosis marked by ritualism and by preoccupation with a single idea or desire. Usually there is some concern on the part of the patient over the fact that he is wasting so much energy and time on such unrewarding activity and thinking, but he nevertheless finds his ritualistic impulses unshakeable. Syn. *anancastia.*

occipital. Pertaining to or located in the back of the head (the occiput).

occupational neurosis. Any psychoneurosis the disturbing factors of which are derived from the circumstances of one's occupation. The scientific validity of the term is questionable, since the occupation provides only the soil in which the psychoneurosis flourishes and not the seed for its creation.

occupational therapy (O.T.). Nonmedical psychotherapy which provides the patient with the environment and facilities for purposeful, constructive activity, usually some type of handicraft. Under psychiatric supervision, occupational therapy is used to modify the behavior of the excitable, destructive patient and, conversely, to awaken social interests in the depressed, withdrawn patient. The underlying psychodynamics involve a redirection of aggression and libido.

ochlophobia. Morbid fear of crowds. Syn. *demophobia.* Cf. *anthropophobia, xenophobia.*

odontoprisis. *bruxism.*

Oedipus complex. In psychoanalysis, an abnormally strong and prolonged attachment of a son to his mother, with incestuous overtones. The term was suggested by Sophocles' drama, *Oedipus Rex,* in which Oedipus, who had been brought up by foster parents, unwittingly kills his father and marries his mother. The Oedipus complex denotes the early parent-child relationship, which generates, on the one hand, sexually charged love for the mother and on the other hand, antagonism toward the father as a rival for her affections. Exactly how the Oedipus complex is resolved is not really known. With the advent of puberty, parent attachments are fitted into the wholesome pattern of increasingly mature pursuits and object attachments, and the Oedipus complex is finally repressed (see *repression*).

In the psychotic patient, however, the Oedipus complex remains unresolved. The patient simply rejects the idea that he has parents; his mother is his "mate" and his father "does not exist." This conception is very frequently the core of schizophrenic ideation, hallucinations, and delusions. Cf. *Electra complex, Jocasta complex.*

oikomania.   *ecomania.*

oikophobia.   *ecophobia.*

oinomania.   1. *Delirium tremens.*   2. *Alcoholism.*

OIT.   *Organic Integrity Test.*

olfactory agnosia.   See under *agnosia.*

olfactory center.   See under *cerebral cortex.*

oligophrenia.   *mental retardation.*

oligoria.   Melancholic apathy.

ombrophobia.   Morbid fear of rainstorms.

omnipotence.   See *magic omnipotence.*

oneiric delirium.   Delirium occurring in sleep and persisting after the subject has awakened.

oneirism.   A form of automatism seen in an individual who appears to be in a dreamlike state while awake. Cf. *fugue.*

oneirology.   Scientific study of dreams.

oneironosus.   Morbid dreaming.

oniomania.   Uncontrollable compulsion to make purchases or otherwise incur expenses without regard for need or ability to pay. It is often encountered in the manic phase of manic-depressive psychosis and in general paresis.

onomatomania.   The compulsion to repeatedly utter certain words or sounds; a manic tendency.

onomatophobia.   Morbid fear of hearing a certain word or phrase.

ontoanalysis.   A branch of psychiatry that combines psychoanalysis with existentialism.

ontogenetic. Pertaining to the development of an individual's physical or mental traits, as distinguished from those of the species. Cf. *phylogenetic*.

onychophagia. Nail-biting; a habit disturbance frequently seen in tense and insecure children.

onychotillomania. Compulsive plucking at a nail. The patient often persists until the form of the nail is permanently changed. It is a type of self-mutilation, interpreted psychoanalytically as a symbolic action whose purpose is to erase an unconscious feeling of guilt.

ophidiophilia. Abnormal attraction to or fondness for snakes (or objects resembling them) as phallic symbols. It provides a socially acceptable expression of interest in the penis.

ophidiophobia. Morbid fear or horror at the sight of snakes, based on the fact that these animals are phallic symbols.

opiate. 1. Any derivative of opium.   2. Popularly, any narcotic substance or any activity which induces serenity or dulls the senses. Cf. *narcotic*.

opiomania. *opiumism.*

opisthotonos. A spasm of the muscles of the back, producing a backward arched posture with the patient resting on the back of his head and his heels. It can be a manifestation of hysteria (as in hysteroepilepsy) or organically produced (as in meningitis). Cf. *emprosthotonos*.

opiumism. Addiction to the use of opium, which is derived from the dried juice of unripe pod of the poppy *Papaver somniferum*. Opium contains many alkaloids, the most prominent of which is morphine. Opium is narcotic, analgesic, and somnifacient. Injection of the drug in the chronic user is marked first by euphoria, then a disinclination to move about and preoccupation with rich fantasies, and finally capitulation to sleep. Upon emerging from slumber, the addict experiences a sense of heaviness and lethargy. In chronic opiumism (morphinism) the addict eventually presents a picture of emotional and intellectual deterioration; he is enfeebled, emaciated, and anemic with sallow complexion, constricted pupils, and foul breath. Tremors may be observed, and his sensitivity is lowered. He is sexually impotent, complains of bizarre skin sensations (paresthesias), and may develop a paranoid trend.

opsomania. An obsessive craving for delicacies or special foods. It is psychiatrically interpreted as a substitution of oral for sexual satisfaction.

oral character. Descriptive of the adult personality in which features of the oral stage have persisted to an unusual degree. If the sucking period was pleasurable, the adult personality usually reflects optimism and self-confidence, perhaps overconfidence. In addition there is an attitude of carefree generosity. Frustration during the oral stage may be manifested in the adult personality as pessimism, a generalized sense of futility, and anxiety. The biting period of the oral stage is later mirrored as sadism, particularly if the infant has not been curbed in his biting at the breast or bottle. Cf. *anal character, genital character.*

oral erotism, oral eroticism. Sexual drive centered upon repressed conflicts that were generated by infantile feeding experiences. Cf. *anal erotism.*

oral-facial-digital syndrome. A form of mental retardation marked by cleft tongue and palate, "pug" nose, narrow upper lip, and fingers that may be extremely short, webbed, or supernumerary.

oral sadism. Expression of aggressive impulses through eating habits.

oral stage. The initial stage of psychosexual development, corresponding to the first twelve to eighteen months of life. The primary characteristic is preoccupation with the feeding experience, emotional gratification being derived chiefly through the mouth. This emotional accompaniment of the feeding experience is incorporated into the personality and, to a greater or lesser degree, colors the attitudes and behavior of later life. The oral stage is divided into the sucking period and the biting period. See also *feeding habits.* Cf. *anal stage, genital stage.*

organ language. The expression of an unconscious emotional conflict through a somatic symptom. For example, the psychoneurotic person with gastrointestinal complaints may be saying, symbolically, that he "cannot stomach" or "cannot swallow" a distressing situation; a feeling of compression in the chest and other symptoms of asthma may accompany feelings of frustration. See also *psychosomatic*.

Organic Integrity Test (OIT). A diagnostic inquiry designed to differentiate between brain disease and schizophrenia (and other emotional disorders). The test is based upon the fact that total form perception is a function of the central nervous system, and defective functioning of that system will be manifested by a loss of form perception.

organic psychoses. Mental diseases caused by physical changes in an organ or group of organs, as opposed to functional, or psychogenic, causation. An organic brain disorder produces mental symptoms due to damage to brain tissue; the usual signs are memory defects, impaired judgment, and either emotional, mental, or conduct disorder.

organotherapy. The treatment of disease with natural (i.e., nonsynthetic) substances such as insulin and thyroxin. Because these agents are used to overcome deficiencies or reduced function, the method is also called *replacement therapy*.

orientation. Awareness of one's surroundings (persons, places, time).

orthochorea. Choreic movements executed while standing.

orthopsychiatry. The branch of psychiatry that specializes in the prevention of mental illness and the correction of incipient mental disorders. Cf. *mental hygiene*.

osmodysphoria. Abhorrence of certain odors which are not regarded as obnoxious by most people. Cf. *osmophobia*.

osmolagnia. Pathologic sexual stimulation by an odor.

osmophobia. Morbid fear of some odors prompted by the belief that they are harmful. Cf. *osmodysphoria*.

osphresiolagnia. A patient's delusion that his body exudes a disagreeable odor. Often such a patient sexualizes the delusion, which, if directed against himself, is masochistic and if against others, sadistic. An osphresiolagniac is also called a *renifleur*.

O.T. *occupational therapy.*

overcompensation. Compensation indulged in to such a degree that it interferes with the subject's adjustment to his environment. For instance, a man who feels inferior culturally and compensates by taking adult education courses and accumulating books is indulging in normal compensation, but if he becomes obsessed with the acquisition of "culture," to the point of shunning companionship and neglecting his job and his personal appearance, he is overcompensating. See also *compensation*.

overweight, psychic factors in. While overweight can arise from fundamental organic causes such as disturbances of the pituitary, psychogenic factors are far more prominent. In the absence of organic pathology, the one and only factor responsible for overweight is overeating. Diet programs usually fail because of the subject's resistance to the curtailment of food intake due to underlying psychologic motivation.

oxycephalia, -ly. Cone-shaped malformation of the skull, most often congenital. Though it is frequently seen in mentally retarded infants, the anomaly does not always affect mentality. Syn. *pinhead*.

oxylalia. *tachylalia.*

P

pageism. A masochistic fantasy in which a male imagines himself as the humble servant (page) of a woman, who dominates him. Cf. *king-slave fantasy*.

pain. In psychiatry, the disagreeable emotional reaction associated with frustration of drives.

palilalia. Obsessive-compulsive repetition of spoken syllables, words, or phrases. Syn. *palinphrasia.*

palingraphia. Persistent repetition, in writing, of certain syllables or words.

palinkinesia, -sis. Obsessive-compulsive repetition of movements.

palinphrasia. *palilalia.*

pallanesthesia. *apallesthesia.*

palsy. See *cerebral palsy, parkinsonism.*

pananesthesia. Widespread loss of the capacity to perceive sensation, sometimes restricted to the loss of the senses of touch and temperature.

panic. Sudden groundless or exaggerated fear. Although it is typically a group reaction, panic has specific significance for the individual in psychiatry, as in *heterosexual panic* and *homosexual panic.*

panophobia. ("fear of everything") Morbid fear of an unidentified danger or impending disaster. Syn. *pantophobia.*

pamplegia. Paralysis of all the limbs and the trunk.

pantophobia. *panophobia.*

parabulia. Bleuler's term for a disturbance of volition in which one motive suddenly and inexplicably replaces another; seen in schizophrenia.

paradox, psychoneurotic. Masochistic persistence in behavior inimical to one's own best interest, despite recognition of the damaging effects. It suggests that the patient is deliberately trying to punish or destroy himself.

paradoxia sexualis. Sexual manifestations inappropriate to one's age. Examples are: precocious sexuality in prepubescent youngsters (which may be due to glandular hyperfunction, as in macrogenitosmia); and exhibitionism in senile persons, especially men. See also *adrenogenital syndrome.*

paraepilepsy.   A type of epilepsy in which there is only an aura, and no convulsion. Cf. *psychomotor epilepsy.*

parageusia.   Perverted sense of taste. Cf. *pseudogeusia.*

paragrammatism.   *neologism.*

paragraphia.   An aphasia in which the individual writes one word or letter instead of another or transposes letters or words. Cf. *paraphasia.*

parahypnosis.   Any abnormality of sleep (e.g., somnambulism, narcosis).

parakinesia, -sis.   Bizarre motions due to disturbed motor functioning; examples include the tremors in parkinsonism and the athetoid movements in cerebral palsy.

paralalia.   Any disturbance of speech whether organic (as in some aphasias) or psychogenic (as in stammering).

paralexia.   Disordered reading ability, marked by transpositions of letters, syllables, or words, Syn. *dyslexia.*

paralepsy, paraleptic episode.   *psycholeptic episode.*

paralgesia.   A painful paresthesia.

paralipophobia.   Unwarranted and obsessive fear of neglecting one's duty.

paralogia.   Illogical or disorganized speech due to disordered reasoning brought about by transient or prolonged emotional stress or by a psychosis. It is called *thematic paralogia* when the subject harps on one topic. Cf. *verbigeration.*

paralysis.   Loss of movement with or without loss of sensation, usually with reference to a part of the body amenable to voluntary control (digits, limbs, trunk). See also *general paresis, Little's disease, tabes dorsalis.*

paralysis agitans.   *parkinsonism.*

paramimia. A variety of apraxia marked by faulty or inappropriate gesturing. It may be organic in origin (as in Huntington's chorea) or functional (as in hebephrenic schizophrenia). See *apraxia*.

paramnesia, -sis. A memory defect in which the subject confuses fantasy and reality. Cf. *cryptomnesia, déjà vu, eidetic imagery*.

paramusia. An aphasia in which a once intact musical sense is impaired, with inability to recognize that one has produced improper, usually cacophonous, tones.

paranoia. A psychosis characterized by suspiciousness and egocentricity woven into a pattern of a highly organized, often complex system of persecutory delusions. There is usually evidence of fixation of libido at the homosexual level. A person who suffers from paranoia is called a *paranoiac*.

paranoid personality. A personality that is characterized by unwarranted suspiciousness, the feeling that others are talking about one, a tendency to resort to *double-entendre*, and "eye-for-an-eye" attitude, and a constant "chip-on-the-shoulder" toward the world.

paranoid state or **trend.** A delusional complex involving suspicion and distrust. A normal person is said to exhibit a paranoid trend when he engages in combative action or speech that is based on illogical, prejudiced, or specious thinking.

paranoid type. A diagnostic subcategory, marked by unorganized persecutory ideas, and/or delusions of reference and influence, commonly encountered in schizophrenia and in involutional and senile psychoses. In a looser sense, a personality type colored by feelings of persecution.

paraphasia. A mild form of any aphasia.

paraphia. Impairment of the sense of touch.

paraphilia. Sexual perversion.

paraphobia. A mild phobia, understood and more or less controlled by the individual.

paraphonia. Any abnormality of the voice.

paraphrasia. *paraphasia.*

paraplegia. Paralysis of the legs, often involving the lower trunk.

parapraxia, -praxis. 1. Freud's term for minor behavioral accidents, such as slips of speech and writing, misplacing of objects, etc. (See *Freudian slip.*) 2. In neurology, the inability to perform purposive movements correctly.

parasexuality. Proclivity for sexual perversion.

parasitophobia. Morbid fear of parasitic organisms. Cf. *bacillophobia, mysophobia.*

parasympathetic nervous system. The division of the autonomic nervous system which controls the basic involuntary functioning of the body's organs and systems. Cf. *sympathetic nervous system.*

parasympatheticotonia. *vagotonia.*

parasympathomimetic. Descriptive of drugs or other agents that stimulate activity of the parasympathetic nervous system.

parateresiomania. Compulsive peeping. Cf. *voyeurism.*

parathymia. Inappropriate emotion, a disturbance of *affect.* For example, a person may respond to a bit of good fortune with gloom, or to bad news with a joyous outburst. It is common in schizophrenia.

parent figure. A substitute or symbolic parent (as a teacher). See also under *parent image.*

parent image. According to Jung, the unconscious concept of a primordial parent, the source of life. To the newborn infant the mother is not a *female* parent; she is *the* parent. Only after a brief period (days to a few weeks) the baby learns by observation that there are two parents. As the infant grows to adulthood, he forms a *father image* and a *mother image.* This is the individual's concept, developed both consciously and unconsciously, of the roles of the father and the mother, with respect to authority, love, and special characteristics of personality. From this concept the individual molds his relations with teachers, employers, clergymen, and objects of hero worship, who serve as *parent figures.*

parergasia, parergastic reaction. Meyer's term for all forms of schizoid behavior, including withdrawal from reality, incongruous behavior, delusions of reference and influence, and hallucinations.

paresis. Partial paralysis. The word is also widely used to refer to general paresis.

paresthesia. Any false or distorted sensation, usually of touch or of the body surface (as burning, itching, or prickling) not organically explained. Cf. *acanthesthesia, formication, pseudoesthesia.*

parkinsonism, Parkinson's disease. A progressive disease of the central nervous system, named for James Parkinson, English physician (1755-1829), who first definitively described the condition. It is marked by masklike facies, incoordination of movement, rigidity, and tremors. In the later stages, the patient walks with rapid, small steps. Syn. *paralysis agitans, shaking palsy.* See *dopamine.*

paronira. Morbid dreaming.

parorexia. *pica.*

parosmia. Any disturbance of the sense of smell. See *osmodysphoria, osmolagnia, osmophobia, osphresiolagnia, pseudosmia.*.

paroxysmal, paroxysmic. Occurring or appearing unpredictably, abruptly, violently, and at irregular intervals.

paroxysmal sleep. *narcolepsy.*

parthenophobia. An unreasonable fear of virgins (girls). Cf. *genophobia, gynophobia.*

passive resistance. See *passive negativism* under **negativism.**

passive-aggressive personality. Personality disorder marked by attempts to adjust through stress on either passive or aggressive behavior, or both alternately. The *passive-dependent* type is helpless, indecisive, a "clinging vine," requiring strong emotional support in all situations. The *passive-aggressive* type is stubborn and obstructionistic, the classic example of "passive resistance." The *aggressive* type is given to irritability, tantrums, destructiveness, grudges, and hatreds.

passive-dependent type.   See under *passive-aggressive.*

passive negativism.   See under *negativism.*

passivism.   Meek submission to or cooperation with another's unnatural sexual acts.

passivity.   Adjustment in which the individual abandons the struggle against adverse circumstances, accepting his humiliation or frustration as insoluble.

past-pointing test.   Bárány's test, in which a subject is required to point at a fixed object (usually the nose) with eyes alternately open and closed. Repeated error with the eyes closed suggests a damaged cerebellum. Syn. *finger-nose test.*

pastoral psychiatry.   Counseling by a clergyman who has had intensive training in the principles and practices of psychiatry.

PaTE   *Psychodynamic and Therapeutic Evaluation.*

patellar reflex.   The so-called "knee jerk." With the leg hanging, a smart tap on the tendon just beneath the patella (kneecap) normally produces contraction of the anterior muscle of the thigh, resulting in a forward kick of the foreleg. Absence of the reflex suggests central nervous system pathology or a break in the continuity of the reflex arc for that area.

pathergasia, pathergastic reaction.   Meyer's term for personality maladjustment due to organic causes.

pathognomonic.   Indicative of a given disease and thus serving to differentiate it from others; thus, three-per-second spike waves in the electroencephalogram of an epileptic is "pathognomonic" of petit mal.

pathologic intoxication.   See *intoxication, pathologic.*

pathologic lying.   A compulsive trait encountered in some mental disorders in which the patient indulges in a mixture of partial truths and outright falsifications although he will not benefit from them. Pathologic lying is commonly observed in the Korsakoff syndrome and in sociopathic personality disorders. It is popularly but erroneously used to describe people who lie frequently for advantage. Syn. *mythomania, pseudologia fantastica.* Cf. *confabulation.*

pathomimesis. Psychoneurotic imitation of the symptoms of a disease; or such imitation in malingering. *adj.* pathomimetic.

Pavlov, Ivan. Russian physiologist (1849-1936) known for his pioneering studies of the conditioned reflex. His discoveries strongly influenced J. B. Watson in his school of behaviorism.

pavor diurnus. Ill-defined fear experienced by a child during a day-time nap.

pavor nocturnus. A frightening dream which differs from the nightmare in that no aspect of the dream is recalled upon awakening.

PBI. *Serum protein-bound-iodine test.*

pederasty. Anal intercourse, usually between an older man and a boy or youth. Syn. *retrocopulation.* Cf. *sodomy.*

pederosis. Forel's term for sexual passion for children; it does not necessarily imply sexual intercourse. Syn. *pedophilia.* Cf. *pederasty.*

pediculophobia. Morbid fear of lice, nits, etc. Syn. *parasitophobia.* Cf. *acarophobia.*

pedologia. Baby talk.

pedophilia. *pederosis.*

pedophobia. Morbid anxiety in the presence of children; a reaction formation against pederosis.

pellagra. A deficiency disease caused by lack of nicotinic acid, a component of the vitamin B complex. The physical consequences (chiefly gastrointestinal disorder and skin eruption) are often accompanied by delirium and mental deterioration.

penis envy. According to Freud, an early aspect of psycho-sexual development in the female, in which the young girl, having discovered the male genital organ, believes it to be a token of masculine superiority and feminine inferiority. Since she has no penis, her unconscious is imbued with frightening fantasies of organ deprivation which finds expression in the *castration complex.* This, in turn, provokes envy of the person with the penis (i.e., the father), but he also symbolizes superiority and she is drawn to him (see *Electra complex*). Freud arrived at this concept through studies of many psycho-neurotic women in whom psychoanalysis revealed unconscious feelings of inferiority and deprivation traceable to early envy of the penis.

pentothal sodium. A trade name for a barbiturate used in narco-analysis or narcosynthesis. Also known as *sodium pentothal* and *truth serum.* Cf. *sodium amytal.*

peotillomania. Compulsive, constant manipulation of the penis. Syn. *pseudomasturbation.*

peptic ulcer. Erosion of the mucous membrane of the digestive tract, due to overproduction of gastric juices, especially hydro-chloric acid. It is believed that unconscious conflicts play an important role in causing peptic ulcer, as suggested by such expressions as "eating one's guts out," "griping," etc. When surgery is resorted to (if medical treatment has failed to produce healing of the lesion), it is customary to sever those branches of the sympathetic nervous system that innervate the digestive tract; this is done to counteract *vagotonia.* See also *gastrointestinal reactions, organ language.*

perichareia. A sudden, excited outburst of joy, in the absence of any manifest stimulus, seen in manic reactions and in general paresis. Cf. *euphoria.*

periconscious. According to Daniel Schneider, American psychoanalyst, that part of the mind lying between the conscious and the unconscious which maintains the image of the heart. It is similar to but not the same as Freud's foreconscious.

periphrastic aphasia. An aphasic condition, of psychogenic background, in which superfluous words are used, suggesting that the subject is uncertain as to whether he has expressed an idea adequately.

perseveration. Pathologic persistent repetition of words or gestures, common in schizophrenia and severe cerebral arteriosclerosis. For example, new questions may be asked of the patient, but he continues to respond to earlier ones.

persona. Jung's term to denote the cloak of personality assumed by an individual, in contrast to his real personality (anima). The persona was the mask worn by an actor in ancient Greek drama to identify the mood of the character he was portraying.

personal unconscious. According to Jung, those thoughts, along with their emotional tone and motivations, which are acquired during one's lifetime and which are repressed. Cf. *collective unconscious.*

personality. The sum of the behavioral and attitudinal characteristics by which one is recognized as an individual. The pattern of the personality is a mosaic of both manifest and latent factors, of conscious experiences and unconscious mechanisms, of inherent and acquired traits. From the psychiatric viewpoint, personality is strongly influenced by the infantile environment, through rearing practices (feeding, toilet habits, and severe, mild, or lax discipline). The core of the personality is the *ego ideal,* a composite of the traits of admired persons in the subject's milieu. On a more superficial level, group patterns of personality (those influenced by race, nationality, religion, and socioeconomic background) must be recognized as having their bearing. Personality is also altered in some degree as the individual is exposed to more experiences in his environment.

Among the many contributions to our knowledge of personality development are: Freud's theory of the influence of psychosexual development; Jung's concepts of the collective unconscious and of extraversion and introversion; Adler's emphasis on the struggle to overcome original feelings of inferiority; Rank's theory of the life-long striving to heal the "birth trauma"; and Horney's stress on *neoculturalism.*

Kretschmer, Sheldon, and others have proposed categories that match body with personality types (see *habitus, somatotypes*).

personality disorders. One of the diagnostic categories under "disorders due to psychogenic origin or without clearly defined tangible cause or structural change" in the 1952 APA classification of psychiatric disorders. As defined, there are four sub-groups of personality disorders: *personality pattern disturbances, personality trait disturbances, sociopathic personality disturbances,* and *special symptom reactions.* See *classification of mental disorders.*

persuasion. The method of psychotherapy of Paul-Charles Dubois, French psychiatrist (1848-1918) in which resistant or withdrawn mentally ill patients are constantly urged to engage in various activities, to analyze their problems, and to adopt new views.

petit mal. A mild form of epilepsy characterized by attacks of momentary unconsciousness, without convulsions. Following the attack the sufferer may experience slight confusion; several attacks may occur during a day. The three forms of petit mal are: *akinetic epilepsy, myoclonic epilepsy,* and *pyknolepsy.* Syn. *minor epilepsy.* Cf. *grand mal.*

peyote. *mescaline.*

phallic stage. *genital stage.*

phallic symbol. In psychoanalytic doctrine, any form resembling the penis (snake, tower, obelisk, pencil, post). Examination of the dreams and thought processes of individuals—normal, psychoneurotic, or psychotic—frequently reveals the employment of such symbols in an effort to disguise a sexual desire.

phallus. The male genital organ.

phaneromania. A compulsion in which the person constantly fingers a pimple, a lock of hair, a hangnail, or some other component of the skin.

phantasmatomoria. Ridiculous fancies or delusions occurring in psychotic regression.

phantasmophobia. Fear of ghosts. Syn. *phasmophobia.*

phantasmoscopia. Visual hallucinations depicting ghosts or spirits.

phantasy. *fantasy.*

phantom tumor. In a hysterical person, temporary swelling of the abdominal wall. The swelling results from disturbance of the body's processes in response to emotional upset. Syn. *pseudotumor.*

pharmacomania. A tendency to indulge in an endless search for new medicines, often characterized by addiction to health fads, uninformed preference for certain medicines, and a readiness to believe extravagant claims for the efficacy of the preparations. Cf. *hypochondria(sis).*

pharmacophobia. A morbid fear of medicines.

pharmacopsychosis. A psychosis associated with addiction to alcohol or drugs.

pharmacotherapy. The use of drugs for treatment of mental illness. Syn. *chemotherapy.*

phasmophobia. *phantasmophobia.*

phenacetylcarbamide. An anticonvulsant that is especially effective in the treatment of petit mal. Its benefits are sometimes offset by complications the symptoms of which are gastrointestinal upset, malaise, and fever. Seclusiveness and apathy may follow protracted use of the drug. Trade name: Phenurone.

phengophobia. Fear of daylight, so that the subject feels at ease only in the protective cloak of darkness. Syn. *photodysphoria.* Cf. *photomania, scotophilia.*

phenobarbital. Phenoldiethylbarbituric acid; a chemical variety of barbital. Trade name: Luminal.

Phenurone. Trade name for phenacetylcarbamide.

phenylketonuria. See under *phenylpyruvic oligophrenia.*

phenylpyruvic oligophrenia. Severe mental retardation resulting from an inheritable disorder of metabolism characterized by faulty processing of proteins. The disorder, called *phenylketon-uria* (PKU), is manifested by the appearance of an excess of phenylketone in the urine; a routine diaper test performed immediately after birth determines the existence of PKU and makes it possible to institute early dietary treatment that averts the physiologic and mental consequences. It is seldom necessary to continue the diet after the child's third or fourth year.

pheochromocytoma. A tumor of the adrenal medulla. It affects the sympathetic nervous system and is manifested by signs and symptoms of sympatheticotonia. Cf. *precocious matronism.*

philoneism. *neophilia.*

phobia, phobic reaction. A compelling, persistent, unwarranted fear associated with a given class of objects, animals, persons, phenomena, or situations. Fear is, of course, a normal reaction; without it no animal or human being could long survive. The term "phobia" is appropriately used only when the thing feared is not dangerous per se (e.g., a mirror); when the fear is out of proportion to the danger (e.g., being at a great height but fully protected from falling); when the fear is inconsistent with the rest of the subject's personality pattern (e.g., a brave soldier being terrified by a harmless spider); and when the tension and anxiety or the subject's actions in response to the phobia interfere with his customary daily activities. Cf. *conditioned fear.*

phobophobia. A morbid fear of being afraid, as in anticipation of failure or of embarrassment (e.g., stage fright).

phonophobia. Fear of certain sounds.

photodysphoria. *phengophobia.*

photogenic epilepsy. See under *sensory epilepsy.*

photomania. An obsessive craving for light. Cf. *noctiphobia.*

phrenasthenia. *mental retardation.*

phronemophobia. Morbid fear of thinking; the subject is apprehensive of entertaining a thought which may disgrace or "destroy" him.

phronesis.   Sound mental health.

phthiriophobia.   An unreasoning fear of body lice, usually accompanied by the complaint of being infested with them.

physical therapy (P.T.).   Therapeutic application of light, heat, cold, water, electricity, exercise, and mechanical agents, used principally in the interest of restoring and maintaining the general health of patients.

physiotherapy.   See *physical therapy.*

pia-arachnoid.   The pia mater and the arachnoid regarded as a single membrane.

pia mater.   ("tender mother") The innermost of the three membranes (meninges) that encase the brain and the spinal cord.

piblockto, piblokto.   A hysterical outburst seen among Eskimos, chiefly affecting females. The subject dashes about the igloo, destroying furnishings; or she runs outside, rips off all her clothing, throws chunks of ice at pursuers, and plunges into icy water. The attack is followed by a deep sleep, and the victim awakens completely recovered. Syn. *arctic madness.* Cf. *lata(h).*

pica.   A perversion of the appetite marked by the ingestion of materials that are not fit for food: wood, paper, clay, dirt, feces. In psychotic adults it is construed by psychoanalysts to be the result of an unconscious impulse to revive the oral stage of psychosexual development. In children it is seen by psychoanalysts as rejection of the parent, usually the mother (i.e., by eating anything other than what she offers for sustenance). Syn. *allotriophagia, parorexia.*

Pick's disease.   Cerebral atrophy, first described by Arnold Pick, Czechoslovakian neurologist and psychiatrist (1851-1924).

Picture-Frustration Test.   Rosenzweig's projective psychological inquiry into a subject's behavior patterns and attitudes and the deviations therefrom. Cartoons representing everyday frustrations, accompanied by unfinished dialogues in caption, are presented to the subject and he is asked to complete the dialogues.

pineal gland, pineal body. A small cone-shaped gland attached to the roof of the third ventricle of the brain. Its function has not been determined. However, tumors of the pineal gland are known to be associated with macrogenitosomia.

Pinel, Philippe. French psychiatrist and hospital administrator 1745-1826), noted for his reforms (e.g., introduction of "intellectual diversion") in the treatment and management of the mentally ill, and for having ordered removal of fetters from patients in French "insane asylums."

Piotrowski's signs. Ten possible pathologic responses during a Rorschach Psychodiagnostic Inquiry. If at least six such responses are displayed, the subject is suspected of suffering from a neurologic disease.

pithiatism. Suggestion as a means to alleviate or eliminate symptoms of hysteria.

pituitary gland. A small rounded endocrine gland lying within the sphenoid bone (at the roof of the nasal cavity) and attached to the brain by a stalk. It is regarded as the master gland of the endocrine system owing to its role as regulator of hormonal production in general. Syn. *hypophysis cerebri.*

pituitary basophilsm. *Cushing's disease* or *syndrome.*

pituitary cachexia. *hypopituitarism.*

PKU. Phenylketonuria. See under *phenylpyruvic oligophrenia.*

placebo. ("I shall please") Any nonpharmacologic substance (as sugar in a capsule) given for its suggestive effect to a patient, who assumes that it is a medicine.

plateau speech. The monotonous, "flat" speech of many epileptics.

play therapy. In child psychiatry, a means of diagnosis and of planning for treatment. The child is provided with toys and encouraged to amuse himself, with no one else present; later he is allowed to join in play with others his age. His reactions are studied by a psychologist or psychiatrist through a one-way window.

pleasure principle. Freud's concept denoting the demands of the id and their modification by the reality principle or resolution by gratification. Cf. *nirvana principle.*

pleonexia. Unrestrained greed, a trait of the *anal character.* Syn. *plutomania.*

plumbism. Lead poisoning; of psychiatric interest in that a reaction resembling the Korsakoff syndrome frequently ensues when the onset is slow. The psychic manifestations of acute lead poisoning include delirium, insomnia, confusion, tremors, emotional outbursts, hallucinations and delusions, and a paranoid reaction. Syn. *saturnism.* Cf. *lead encephalopathy.*

plus gesture. Adler's term for the attempt to compensate for a feeling of inferiority through superior accomplishment. Cf. *compensation, life goal, life plan, overcompensation.*

plutomania. *pleonexia.*

poisoning, psychoses due to. Strictly speaking, psychoses which are directly traceable to poisonings. Narcotism and the alcoholic psychoses are not included in this category because addiction to alcohol or drugs is presumed to be the result rather than the cause of personality defects. Syn. *toxic psychoses.* See *barbiturism, carbon monoxide poisoning, plumbism.*

poliomeylitis. Inflammation of the gray matter of the spinal cord, caused by a virus. It is usually brief in its acute course, which is marked by respiratory and gastrointestinal symptoms which may be followed by spastic paralysis.

polydipsia. Extreme thirst not based on deprivation of liquids.

polyesthesia. A symptom of neurologic disorders in which a single touch is felt at two or more places simultaneously.

polymorphous perverse. A Freudian term describing the young child's capacity for various forms of sexual activity. When manifested by adults such activities are regarded as perversions. See also *infantile sexuality*.

polyorexia, polyphagia. *bulimia.*

polyphobic. Pertaining to the coexistence in an individual of more than one phobia.

porencephalitis. Encephalitis in which cavities are formed in the gray matter of the brain. The defect may result in severe mental retardation.

poriomania. *dromomania.*

porphyria. A disorder of metabolism marked by production of abnormal types of pigment compounds known as porphyrins. Such psychic changes as irritability, emotional tension, and schizoid tendencies are sometimes seen.

posiomania. *dipsomania.*

posthypnotic suggestion. A procedure in psychotherapy in which the subject, in a hypnotic trance, carries out a therapist's suggestion after emerging from the trance. As a rule the subject will not obey a command to perform an act that threatens his security or that of others, or one that is radically in opposition to his moral principles.

posttraumatic neurosis. *traumatic neurosis.*

posttraumatic psychosis. *traumatic psychosis.*

posttraumatic syndrome. Any mental disorder following physical injury, usually to the skull. The symptoms depend upon the pretraumatic personality. The clinical picture may be that of a psychosis or a psychoneurosis, or that of an abruptly changed personality. (irritability in a usually calm person, capriciousness in one formerly serious-minded). See also *traumatic neurosis, traumatic psychosis.*

potamophobia. Morbid fear of rivers. Cf. *antlophobia, aquaphobia.*

pragmatagnosia, -sis. *agnosia.*

pragmatamnesia.   Loss of the ability to remember the appearance of an object. See *amnesia.*

precocious matronism.   Pende's term for the condition in which, as a result of excessive production of adrenal gland hormones, a very young girl displays sexual maturity. See also *adrenogenital syndrome, hyperadrenal constitution, paradoxia sexualis, pheochromocytoma.*

preconscious, the.   According to Freud, that level of mental functioning in which partially repressed memories can be summoned into consciousness when an associated idea or environmental stimulus brings them into awareness. Syn. *foreconscious, subconscious.* Cf. *conscious, unconscious.*

prefrontal.   Situated in or referring to the anterior part of the frontal lobe of the brain.

prefrontal lobectomy.   See under *lobectomy.*

prefrontal lobotomy.   See under *lobotomy.*

pregenital sexuality.   *infantile sexuality.*

pregenital stage.   In psychoanalytic theory, the time in childhood immediately preceding the advent of puberty. Sadism and masochism are given full and equal expression.

pregnancy, mental disturbances during and after.   A wide variety of more or less pathological mental and emotional symptoms may be seen during and after pregnancy, the commonest being an affective reaction which may be manic, depressive, or mixed. Pregnancy, however, is the trigger for the reaction rather than its specific cause. The course is usually brief and the condition responds well to therapy.

premature ejaculation.   Experience of orgasm by the male prior to or immediately upon penetrating the vagina. It is common in persons who, because of their incomplete psychosexual development, unconsciously regard coitus as a form of masturbatory self-satisfaction; and in those who, owing to unconscious feelings of inferiority or guilt accompanied by the need to "punish" themselves, lack confidence in their ability to function sexually.

prepsychotic. Prior to the appearance of symptoms of a psychosis.

presbyophrenia. Disorientation along with memory loss and confabulation, seen often in senile psychoses. Ordinarily, judgment is not impaired. Syn. *Wernicke's syndrome.*

presenile psychosis. *Alzheimer's disease.*

pretransference. In Freudian psychoanalytic therapy, the emotional response by the analysand when he begins to regard the analyst as a parent figure or as part of himself.

priapism. Abnormally sustained erection of the penis, observed in organic conditions such as leukemia and in mental disorders such as regressed phases of schizophrenia.

primordial image. According to Jung, a deposit in memory of a phylogenetic relic that is heavily charged with mythologic reference and that reappears frequently in the individual's mental experiences, particularly in dreams. See also *collective unconscious.*

proctophilia. *pederasty.*

proctophobia. 1. A morbid fear of anything referrable to the anus. 2. Exaggerated anxiety over rectal disease in the absence of symptoms suggesting it.

prodromal. 1. Pertaining to the earliest indications of a disease. 2. Premonitory of a disease.

projection. A defense mechanism in which the subject unconsciously attributes his own unacceptable ideas or impulses to another. For example, a man who has failed to gain promotion ascribes to his employer or supervisor those of his own characteristics which have thwarted his advancement. Cf. *identification, incorporation, introjection.*

projective test. A diagnostic inquiry in which the subject is confronted with stimuli that induce him to project his personality into his responses. Such tests offer rapid access to facets of the personality that might otherwise be uncovered only through hypnosis or prolonged psychoanalysis or psychotherapy. Examples are the MAPS and Szondi tests and the Rorschach Psychodiagnostic Method.

propulsion.   A tendency to fall forward, as seen in parkinsonism.

prosceniophobia.   Stage fright.

prosopagnosia, -sis.   Inability to retain a mental image of a face well known to the subject. See *agnosia.*

protein-bound-iodine test (PBI).   *Serum protein-bound-iodine test.*

pruritus, psychogenic.   Intense, persistent itching, when it is caused by anxiety.

pseudagraphia.   1. Pseudographia.   2. Partial agraphia in which the subject is able to copy from a model but cannot produce original written material.

pseudamnesia.   1. Sham amnesia   2. Transient amnesia seen in organic brain disorders such as apoplectic stroke.

pseudesthesia.   *pseudoesthesia.*

pseudoangina.   Anxiety in which symptoms of coronary heart disease are expressed though no pathology is present.

pseudoanorexia.   See *false anorexia* under **anorexia nervosa.**

pseudoathetosis.   Movements similar to those in *athetosis.* They can be induced by having the patient close his eyes and extend his hands. The background is a neurologic disorder.

pseudochorea.   Hysterical twitching that resembles chorea.

pseudocyesis.   False pregnancy; symptoms of pregnancy are manifested, but they are in response to psychogenic factors that upset bodily processes. The principal factor is believed to be an impulse for wish-fulfillment.

pseudoepilepsy.   1. Sham grand mal epilepsy.   2. A condition resembling epilepsy; not uncommonly, children with high fevers suffer convulsive attacks which do not recur once the elevated temperature has abated.

pseudoesthesia. 1. A sensation, lacking an external stimulus. 2. A sensation whose intensity is out of proportion to the degree of stimulation.

pseudogeuesthesia. A condition in which taste sensations are accompanied by the sensation of color. Syn. *color taste*.

pseudogeusia. A hallucination of taste. Cf. *parageusia*.

pseudographia. A condition in which the subject attempts to write but produces only meaningless scrawls or distortions of letters and words. Cf. *agraphia, paragraphia, pseudagraphia*.

pseudohallucination. A hallucination recognized as such by the subject. Cf. *illusion*.

pseudologia fantastica. *pathologic lying.*

pseudomania. 1. Sham psychosis. Cf. *malingering*. 2. Self-accusation of criminality by a depressed person, commonly seen in involutional psychosis and due to overwhelming feelings of guilt.

pseudomasturbation. *peotillomania.*

pseudomeningitis. Inflammation of the innermost layer of the meninges producing symptoms resembling meningitis.

pseudomnesia. Fallacious memory of events that have never occurred; common in cerebral arteriosclerosis, senility (with or without psychosis), and Korsakoff's syndrome. Cf. *déjà vu*.

pseudonarcotism. A stuporous state, hysterical or psychotic, which strongly resembles the unconsciousness due to continued misuse of narcotic drugs or to overdosage.

pseudoneurotic schizophrenia. Schizophrenia, most often in an early stage, that is characterized by symptoms of neurosis (e.g., anxiety, nervousness, tension).

pseudoparalysis. 1. Impairment of voluntary muscle power owing to pain and without paralysis, resulting in incoordination and diminished motion. 2. Hysterical paralysis. Syn. *pseudo-plegia*.

pseudoplegia. *pseudoparalysis.*

pseudopregnancy. *pseudocyesis.*

pseudosmia. Any hallucination of smell. Cf. *parosmia.*

pseudotabes. A condition resembling tabes dorsalis but without Argyll Robertson pupils, and without laboratory evidence of syphilis. It usually yields quickly to symptomatic treatment.

pseudotumor. *phantom tumor.*

psychagogia, -gy. Psychotherapy that emphasizes interpersonal relationships.

psychalgia. Extreme mental distress, observed sometimes in psychoneurosis and psychosis. Patients may actually complain of "pain" in the mind.

psychataxia. Profound mental disorganization with agitation and inability to focus attention, as seen in manic-depressive psychosis, general paresis, and several other psychiatric conditions.

psyche. The mind.

psychedelic. ("mind-opening") *n.* Any agent or force that brings unconscious material to conscious levels. An example of a psychedelic is LSD.

psychentonia. Nervous exhaustion (tension) from excessive application of mental powers.

psychiatry. That branch of medicine concerned with the diagnosis and treatment of mental illness and mental retardation. See *child psychiatry, existential psychiatry, forensic psychiatry, orthopsychiatry.*

psychic. In psychiatry, pertaining to the psyche, or mind; mental.

psychic deafness. *mind deafness.*

psychic energizer. Any substance, particularly a pharmaceutical preparation, which stimulates a person psychically, especially one who is apathetic or depressed. The amphetamines are most commonly used.

psychic energy. According to Freud, that part of the mind's force expended in any mental activity. Cf. *libido*.

psychic impotence, -cy. See under *impotence, -cy.*

psychic trauma. See *trauma.*

psychoactivator. *psychic energizer.*

psychoanalysis. 1. A form of psychotherapy originated by Freud, often referred to simply as "analysis." The patient, in a reclining position with the analyst out of his line of vision, is instructed to talk of anything that comes into his mind (free association). His words are recorded and his emotional tone is noted by the analyst. Seldom is the patient interrupted. This process of producing repressed material from the unconscious enables the analyst to be alert for "indicators"—slips of speech, significant gestures, or emotional manifestations, which may provide him with clues to the motivation underlying the patient's hidden difficulty. At the outset the analyst explains the procedure, and the patient is told not to expect advice or assistance with his practical personal problems during analysis. Treatment is regarded as completed only when the analysand (the patient) has accepted and understood the analyst's final interpretation. Success is measured by the degree of insight the patient has gained into the unconscious motivation for his behavior, thoughts, and emotional responses, and by his ability to apply this new knowledge to the solution of his life problems. Freud postulated that the analysand must be intelligent, have a genuine desire to get well, and be neither very young nor very old, and have sufficient funds to avoid financial worry during the analysis. See also *abreaction, countertransference, direct psychoanalysis, dream analysis, free association, non-Freudian psychoanalysis, repression, transference, unconscious.*

2. The body of principles for the interpretation of personality dynamics evolved by Freud while he was formulating his therapeutic approach to personality difficulties. Many persons believe that psychoanalysis is exclusively a specialized form of psycho-

therapy. On this, Freud said in one of his lectures: "I did not want to commend it (psychoanalysis) to your interest as a method of treatment but on account of the truths it contains, on account of the information it gives us about what concerns human beings most of all—their own nature—and on account of the connections it discloses between the most different of their activities. As a method of treatment, it is one among many, though, to be sure, *primus inter pares*. If it was without therapeutic value it would not have been discovered, as it was, in connection with sick people and would not have gone on developing for more than thirty years."

psychoanalgesia. Relief of pain by any means other than physical therapy or pharmaceuticals, such as psychotherapy, suggestion, soft music, etc.

psychoanalyst. A psychotherapist specially trained in psychoanalytic technique. A primary requisite for training is that the analyst himself undergo psychoanalysis. Cf. *lay analyst*.

psychobiology. A school of thought in psychiatry founded by Adolf Meyer, who insisted that mental illness can be properly understood only in the light of the total life experience of the patient: his inherited constitution, his environment, and events that have been meaningful to him. Syn. *biopsychology*. Cf. *holism*.

psychocatharsis. *catharsis*.

psychochromesthesia. A variety of synesthesia in which a nonvisual stimulus gives rise to a sensation of color.

psychodiagnostics. Procedures used to diagnose a mental illness without recourse to physical examination. The term is applied specifically to the *Rorschach Psychodiagnostic Method*.

psychodrama. Moreno's form of group therapy. In a theatrical setting, patients assume roles which provide them with the opportunity to act out their conflicts and perhaps to reveal repressed material which is disturbing them. Psychodrama is designed to help the patient gain insight and to render him more amenable to psychotherapy.

Psychodynamic and Therapeutic Evaluation (PaTE). A schema of psychological inquiry that combines the Wechsler-Bellevue Scales of Intelligence and the Kahn Test of Symbol Arrangement. Its purpose is to evaluate the intellectual and emotional capacities of a subject, determine the degree of his maturity, and delineate the specific emotional problems he is experiencing. The procedure is said to afford a "quick penetration into the basic core of the personality structure," which makes possible a swift decision on specific psychotherapy and thus earlier commencement of treatment.

psychodynamics. Mental forces, without regard for organic structure and physiologic activity.

psychogenic. Arising from the psyche rather than from organic causes. Syn. *functional.*

psycholagny. Sexual excitation derived from mental imagery.

psycholepsy. Intense but transient depression. Syn. *paralepsy.* See *psycholeptic episode.*

psycholeptic episode. A vividly remembered past event in the patient's life which a mentally-emotionally ill person is convinced is the cause of his disorder. Syn. *paraleptic episode.*

psychologist. Anyone with accredited training in psychology, regardless of the special field in which he is engaged. Of particular application to psychiatry are the *psychometrist,* who is skilled in the administration of tests of intelligence and personality inquiries, and the *clinical psychologist,* who is specially trained in the nonmedical diagnosis of mental disorders and in such therapy as can be accomplished by purely psychological methods.

psychology. The science of the mind and its processes and of the overt behavior and subjective experiences that are the products of these processes. Syn. *psychonomics.* See also *analytic(al) psychology.*

psychometrics, psychometry. That branch of psychology concerned with the creation, administration, and interpretation of tests of intelligence, test results, and other mental processes and of personality dynamics.

psychomotor. *adj.* Pertaining to voluntary muscular activity.

psychomotor epilepsy, psychomotor equivalent. A form of petit mal epilepsy marked by momentary impairment of consciousness, stereotyped movements and, at times, outbursts of fear or homicidal rage. It may resemble epileptic furor but is differentiated from it by a negative finding in the electroencephalogram. Syn. *neurotic epilepsy.* See *epileptic equivalent.*

psychoneurosis. A mental disorder which reflects an unconscious attempt to achieve, through compromise, at least superficial adjustment to an unconscious conflict. In some of its forms and degrees it is incapacitating, but unlike a psychosis it does not destroy the integrity of the personality or break the individual's contact with the environment. Whereas a psychosis is regarded as a flight from reality, a psychoneurosis is regarded as an attempt to come to terms with it. See *cardiac neurosis, "fight or flight" reaction, pseudoneurotic schizophrenia, traumatic neurosis.*

psychoneurotic paradox. See *paradox, psychoneurotic.*

psychoneurotic reaction. *psychoneurosis.*

psychonomics, -omy. *psychology.*

psychopath. *sociopath.*

psychopathic personality. See *sociopathic personality disturbance.*

psychopathology. 1. The science concerned with the study of mental disorder. 2. The abnormal mental functioning in a given case of mental disorder.

psychopathy. Any mental disease or disorder.

psychophysiology. The science of the organic structures and functions involved in mental activity.

psychorrhea. An incoherent stream of thought characterized by bizarre ideas, usually absurd philosophical theories.

psychosexual development. In Freudian psychoanalysis, the emergence of the personality through several stages to that of the "normal" heterosexual adult. The successive stages are: *autoerotic* (subdivided into oral and anal, the oral further being subdivided into the sucking and biting periods), *narcissistic, genital, homosexual,* and finally the *heterosexual.*

psychosexual energy. *libido.* Cf. *psychic energy.*

psychosexual stage. The stage of psychosexual development attained.

psychosis. A major mental disorder principally characterized by deviant, often bizarre thinking and behavior, by withdrawal from the normal stream of life, and frequently by a complete denial of reality. Some of the symptoms commonly observed in psychosis, and not encountered in psychoneurosis, are hallucinations and delusions, disorientation, regression, and verbalization of aberrant ideas. The distinctions between psychosis and psychoneurosis are further outlined in the following table:

DIFFERENTIAL DIAGNOSTIC CRITERIA

FACTORS UNDER CONSIDERATION	PSYCHONEUROSIS	PSYCHOSIS
1. Dynamics (according to Freud)	Ego *vs.* the id. "Fight" reaction.	Ego *vs.* the outer world. "Flight" reaction.
2. Personality	Generally intact; only partially changed.	Totally disorganized; changed in whole.
3. Reality	Patient usually feels reality means the same for him as for the rest of the community.	Patient usually rejects reality.
4. Mechanism of Projection	Conscious sense of guilt.	Unconscious sense of guilt.

DIFFERENTIAL DIAGNOSTIC CRITERIA (*con't*)

FACTORS UNDER CONSIDERATION	PSYCHONEUROSIS	PSYCHOSIS
5. Language	Unchanged.	May be disturbed, incoherent, given to "neologisms" (new words).
6. The Unconscious	Is expressed indirectly.	Is given direct verbal expression.
7. Infantile Regression	Not present.	Reflected in behavior as, for example, unashamed soiling.
8. Affect and Thought	Harmony undisturbed.	Frequently not in harmony.
9. Flow of Libido	Outward to the world of reality (transference).	Inward to the self (narcissistic).
10. Object Attachment	Erotic: makes for strong object attachment.	Autoerotic: makes for weak object attachment.

psychosomatic. Involving both the mind (psyche) and the body (soma). A broad range of illnesses may have a psychosomatic factor with underlying conflicts being reflected in symptoms which may have originated organically or in the psyche. Strong psychic elements have been observed in bronchial asthma, hyper- and hypothyroidism, migraine, mucous colitis, and peptic ulcer, to name but a few. The organic symptoms tend to mask an unconscious disturbance. Syn. *psychophysical, somatopsychic.*

psychostimulant. *psychic energizer.*

psychosurgery. Brain surgery undertaken to correct mental disorder, as distinct from brain surgery undertaken for the removal of brain tumor or the alleviation of other known brain pathology. See *cryopsychosurgery, lobectomy, lobotomy, topectomy.*

psychotherapeutic adjuvant. Any measure employed to support psychotherapy which can be carried out by trained personnel other than physicians, e.g., occupational and recreational therapy, physical therapy, and psychiatric social work.

psychotherapy. Treatment of mental illness or of a psychosomatic condition by purely psychologic means, such as hypnosis, psychoanalysis, simple counseling, or suggestion.

psychotic. (*adj.*) Suffering from a psychosis. (*n.*) A person so afflicted.

psychotropic. Influencing the mind; said of drugs used to combat mental disorder, whether they be tranquilizers or energizers.

psychroesthesia. A sensation of coldness in a part of the body that is actually warm.

psychrophobia. An unreasoning fear of the cold and its possible harmful effects.

P.T. *physical therapy.*

puberty. See *genital stage.*

puerilism. Childish behavior and speech in adulthood, seen in its most exaggerated form in regression (as in hebephrenia). Cf. *infantilism.*

puerperal psychosis. See *pregnancy, mental disturbances associated with.*

"punch drunk." A slang term for the disturbed mental state of a pugilist who has suffered brain damage following repeated blows to the skull. The symptoms include clouded consciousness, dulling of the intellectual facilities, garbled speech, unsteady gait, faulty memory, inability to concentrate, tremors, nodding of the head, and slowness of movement.

punishment. In psychiatric parlance, a mental mechanism by which the subject indulges in self-directed aggression as a means of neutralizing unconscious guilt feelings. In the *psychoses* punishment sometimes takes the form of self-mutilation and attempted suicide; in the *psychoneuroses* it may be reflected in compulsive behavior, as in the handwashing complex. The concept of punishment applies to both normal and abnormal unconscious mental activity. The cultural background of the individual plays a vital role.

punishment dream. See under *dream.*

pyknic habitus. A constitutional type with stocky build and short limbs, said by Kretschmer to be correlated with the extraverted, social type of personality. When this type of individual is mentally disturbed, he tends to show manifestations of a psychoneurosis or psychosis whose dominant features are emotional extremes and mood swings. Syn. *endomorphy.*

pyknolepsy. A form of petit mal epilepsy characterized by momentary periods of unconsciousness and immobility or by a few muscle jerks. Cf. *narcolepsy.*

pyknophrasia. Thickness of speech.

pyramidal tracts. The motor pathways from the brain to the spinal cord. Syn. *motor tracts.*

pyridoxine dependency, pyridoxine deficiency. Metabolic disorder due to lack of pyridoxine (vitamin B6) in the newborn infant. Characteristics include violent epileptiform convulsions, hyperirritability, rolling eyes, grimacing, brief periods of breath-holding, and a cry of distress. If untreated or if therapy is instituted too late, permanent brain damage and mental retardation may result.

pyrolagnia. Sexual stimulation and gratification at the sight of a fire. Cf. *pyromania.*

pyromania. A morbid compulsion to start and witness fires as a means of obtaining erotic satisfaction.

pyrophobia. Unreasonable, exaggerated fear of fire, as in the refusal to walk past a cooking range (in the belief that the burners will spontaneously burst into flame) or to strike a match or even to view a picture of a conflagration.

Q

quadriplegia.   Paralysis of all four limbs. Syn. *tetraplegia*.

quiet delirium.   Delirium marked by low-pitched, incoherent utterances. Syn. *delirium mite*.

Quincke's disease.   *angioneurotic edema.*

R

racial unconscious.   *collective unconscious.*

radiation surgery.   Destruction, by X-rays, laser beam, or ultrasonic radiation of certain parts of the brain (e.g., part of the temporal lobe in epilepsy) to combat intractable epilepsy that cannot be controlled by medication. It is also employed as a technique in lobotomy and topectomy for psychotic patients who are not benefited by tranquilizers or shock therapy; in these cases the surgery is regarded as a check rather than as a cure.

radioactive iodine, radioiodine (I^{131}).   Radioactive iodine is used for the diagnosis and treatment of malfunctioning of the thyroid gland (e.g., hyperthyroidism). See also *serum protein-bound-iodine test*.

Rank, Otto.   Viennese psychoanalyst (1884-1939) and a student of Freud, best known for his theory of *birth trauma*.

rational psychotherapy.   A therapy based on the theory that emotional disturbances usually result from the influence of irrational thoughts, beliefs, or attitudes. Practitioners of rational psychotherapy believe that people can be taught to change their negative and disturbed feelings by correcting the false beliefs and inaccurate interpretations that underlie and accompany them. Also known as *rational-emotive psychotherapy*.

rational-emotive psychotherapy.   *rational psychotherapy.*

rationalization.   The defense mechanism by which the individual, faced with frustrations or with criticism of his actions, finds justification for them by disguising from himself (as he hopes to disguise from others) his true motivations. It is often accomplished, to the subject's satisfaction, by a protracted chain of excuses that are actually believed by the subject. Rationalization is effected in the unconscious though the "excuses" are consciously expressed.

Rauwolfia serpentina.   An herb indigenous to India now cultivated in South America, from which several tranquilizers (e.g., rerserpine) have been derived.

reactive depression.   *neurotic depression.*

reaction-formation.   According to Freudian psychoanalysis, the acquisition or development of socially acceptable behavior or attitudes diametrically opposed to the individual's repressed unconscious impulses.

reaction-type.   Any of Meyer's behavior patterns, or *-ergasias.* See *dysergasia, holergasia, merergasia, parergasia, thymergasia.*

reading disabilities.   Psychiatrically speaking, difficulties in learning to read resulting from emotional maladjustment. These difficulties, in turn, aggravate the emotional problems, and the effects are especially pernicious since reading is the gateway to most learning. Disabilities in other subjects are bound to follow (if the child cannot read satisfactorily he cannot be expected to know what is required for a problem assigned from his arithmetic book). Causes include resistance to the maturation process (the child prefers to remain dependent on the parent); resistance to authority (the teacher, as parent surrogate, is the target for hostility toward an overprotective or tyrannical parent); and a traumatic early classroom experience.

reading epilepsy.   This form of sensory epilepsy, first described as a clinical entity in 1956 is divided into primary and secondary types. In *primary* reading epilepsy there is no brain damage. It is marked by generalized convulsions which occur only while the subject is reading; the attack begins with an aura and is characterized by involuntary jerking or clicking of the jaw. If reading is continued, a typical grand mal seizure develops. In *secondary* reading epilepsy, reading is but one of several possible sensory stimuli that may set off convulsive attacks and usually there is neither jerking nor clicking of the jaw; it may be due to brain damage.

reality principle. Freud's concept denoting the restrictive effect of the demands of society upon the demands of the id as they are expressed in the pleasure principle. In the normal progression to maturity, the demands of society are incorporated within the individual's personality.

reality-testing. The effort of the ego to achieve a balance between external restrictions and the striving for recognition as an individual. Reality is tested in such "safe" ways as fantasy and projection. It may be a normal method of adjustment but is exaggerated in psychoneurosis (where it tends to become ritualistic and to consume an inordinate amount of the subject's time) and in the regression of a psychosis (where it may become a "way of life").

receptive aphasia. *sensory aphasia.*

recovery. Psychiatrically speaking, complete disappearance of mental and emotional symptoms. As is the case with the word "cure" in all fields of medicine, the force of the term is relative. A psychiatric patient is regarded as recovered when he is capable of assuming most or all of his previous responsibilities outside the institutional environment (or without further private psychiatric consultation), though he may require occasional psychotherapeutic or other medical support on an outpatient basis. The distinction between "recovery" and "improvement" is a highly individual matter.

recreational therapy. A form of adjuvant therapy consisting of diversion, usually in the form of group activity. It provides the patient with an outlet for aggression and hostility, thereby permitting healthy expenditure of libido, and opens avenues of self-expression (musical programs, games, pageants, "little theatre," picnics, etc.). From the standpoint of mental hygiene, recreation is considered to have value to the degree that it actually provides relaxation and is not applied routinely without definite purpose.

rectal aerophagia. See under *aerophagia.*

redintegration. *reintegration.*

re-education. A nonmedical type of *directive psychotherapy* advocated by Stekel. Its object is to teach the mentally ill individual to regain emotional and intellectual assets he once possessed but lost because of a psychotic disorder, or, perhaps, to acquire assets he never possessed. Fortified with these assets, the patient is able to readjust to the world of reality. Cf. *education.*

re-evolution. Jackson's term for a triad of events in recovery from grand mal seizure: (1) word deafness (patient hears only sounds, not words), followed by (2) perception of speech (hears words but without comprehension) with echolalia superimposed (does not reply, merely repeats words of examiner), and finally (3) a return to full perception and comprehension. See also *Jacksonian epilepsy.*

reflex. See *conditioned reflex.*

reflex epilepsy. Epilepsy in which a grand mal seizure is triggered by sensory stimuli such as a sudden flash of light or an unexpected sound (audioepilepsy), or a sudden blow to or jarring of the body.

regression. Reversal of psychosexual development; a primary feature of schizophrenia. In some cases it is so extreme that the patient adopts not only the general behavior of infancy but even the fetal position. He retraces his steps back to the protective shell of security of babyhood and there, beyond the reach of society's demands, constructs his own thoroughly satisfying world of fantasy where he can rule supreme. See also *magic omnipotence.*

Reik, Theodor. German psychoanalyst (1888-   ), a disciple of Freud. He regards narcissism as a later developmental experience, rather than an instinctive state appearing in the latter stage of infancy. Reik attributes psychoneurosis to a loss of self-confidence which arouses anxiety and inhibitions.

reintegration. If the personality has disintegrated (as in a severe psychosis) but recovery ensues so that the fragmented components of the personality become a single whole again, it is said to have undergone reintegration. Syn. *redintegration.*

release therapy. *play therapy.*

reinfleur. One who is given to *osphresiolagnia.*

replacement therapy. *oranotherapy.*

repression. An unconscious mental mechanism wherein unacceptable desires, memories, and thoughts are excluded from consciousness. It provides the means by which the true origin of an emotional conflict is concealed from the individual.

reserpine. A tranquilizer derived from *Rauwolfia serpentina.*

resistance. In psychoanalysis, the effort on the part of the patient to prevent the entry into consciousness and to withhold revelation to the analyst of painful memories that have been repressed. According to Freud, resistance is a force of the super-ego, operating partly on the conscious level, which strengthens a repression previously established. See also *blocking, censorship.* Cf. *passive negativism* under **negativism.**

rest tremor. See under *tremor.*

restitution. In psychiatry, the performance of conscious acts of kindness, generosity, charity, etc., in an effort to assuage unconscious guilt feelings.

retardation. See *mental retardation.*

retention defect. A severe defect of memory due to either mental or physical causes. It is revealed by the patient's inability to retain facts for as brief a time as four minutes. See also *Marie Three-Paper Test.*

retrocopulation. *pederasty.*

retrograde amnesia. See under *amnesia.*

retrography. *mirror writing.*

retrogression. Reversion to an earlier, less mature mode of behavior or thinking. The term does not apply to unconscious mechanisms, as does *regression.*

retropulsion. Running backward, as sometimes seen in parkinsonism.

reversal of affect. *inversion of affect.*

reversal formation. *reaction-formation.*

rhyming mania. *clang association.*

rhypophagy. *scatophagia, -gy.*

rigidity. 1. In the organic sense, physical stiffness, or tension (as in parkinsonism). 2. In psychiatry, an unchangeable pattern of thought, action, or emotion.

Riley-Day syndrome. A neuropsychiatric disorder marked by various muscular and neurological features (loss of deep reflexes, insensitivity to pain, incoordination, difficulty in swallowing, inability to produce tears, etc.) and mental retardation often accompanied by personality changes. The disease is familial (not hereditary) and is noticed soon after birth (the patient seldom lives beyond childhood).

ritualism. The pattern of the obsessive-compulsive reaction. An example of psychoneurotic compulsive ritualism is the *hand-washing complex.*

rivalry, sibling. See *sibling rivalry.*

Rorschach Psychodiagnostic Method. A projective technique, commonly known as the "Rorschach Test" or the "inkblot test," devised by Herman Rorschach, Swiss psychiatrist (1884-1922). It is based on the characteristic differences in perception and interpretation of pictorial form by normal persons and by persons suffering hysteria, schizophrenia, and other mental disorders;

and on the theory that the subject's responses to the forms peculiar to each of the inkblots serve to place him in one or another of these groups. The ten inkblots, of which five are in black-and-white, three in black-and-red, and two multicolored, are shown to the subject, who is asked to tell what he sees in each. Replies are scored as to: universality of response; whether the response is to the whole image or only to parts of it; how the subject reacts to color, shading, shape, and location of elements of the inkblot; whether he sees movement; and whether he projects more complex interpretations (such as the aims and emotional patterns of figures he sees). Scoring involves the total number of replies and their interrelationships, in terms of prescribed norms. The black-and-red and multicolored inkblots usually stimulate responses that indicate the patient's emotional reaction to his daily life. An excessive number of responses to black-gray forms may indicate depression. Bizarre responses may merely indicate capriciousness or creative talent on the part of the patient, or they may indicate autistic thinking and a schizoid tendency. The method has proved to be sufficiently reliable and selective to uncover signs of brain damage and neurologic pathology; this is valuable in differentiating psychogenic and organogenic conditions. See also *Piotrowski's signs.*

Rubenstein-Taybi syndrome. A form of moderate mental retardation (I.Q. 20-60), first described in 1963 by J. H. Rubenstein and H. Taybi, American pediatricians. Physical characteristics include excessively wide thumbs and great toes and, in severe cases, split or reduplicated digits and a thumb which does not oppose the fingers properly; a peculiar facies with beak-like nose, eyes which appear to slant downward toward poorly developed cheeks, and many other signs of imperfect development. Except for split or reduplicated digits, these manifestations are usually so mild in early childhood as to go unnoticed or do not cause great alarm until as late as adolescence.

rumination. Voluntary regurgitation and reswallowing of stomach contents, sometimes observed in psychotic individuals. Syn. *merycism.*

"running fits." *cursive epilepsy.*

Rush, Benjamin. American hospital administrator (1745-1813), regarded as the father of American psychiatry for his insistence on a medical approach to mental illness and his pioneering in the development of mental hospitals.

sadism. Specifically, the impulse to derive satisfaction by inflicting pain. The motivation is usually sexual, though this may be masked. In a more general sense, the word refers to the psychic force behind any act or pattern of behavior by which the individual derives pleasure from the psychic pain (fear, sense of indignity, embarrassment) which he causes in another. It accounts for aggression and for hate and hostility. Sadism may or may not be pathologic. It is commonly observed in the audience of a prize fight, a debate, or other contest where the spectator vicariously "punishes" the loser. See also *anal sadism, oral sadism.* Cf. *masochism.*

sadomachism. The coexistence in the individual of both sadistic and masochistic tendencies.

Saint Vitus' dance. *Sydenham's chorea.*

Sakel, Manfred. Austro-American psychiatrist (1900-1957) who introduced into the U. S. in 1936 the use of insulin shock therapy for mental disorders.

saltatory spasm. Irregular movements of the lower limbs giving rise to jumping or skipping seen occasionally in hysteria.

saphism. *lesbianism.*

satisfaction. In psychiatry, release of tension. Mentally ill persons, both psychotics and psychoneurotics, often achieve satisfaction in perverse ways. Indeed, the mental illness, even when accompanied by extreme distress, may itself be the patient's method of gaining satisfaction. Satisfaction through illness is common in psychosomatic conditions, in which it is called *secondary advantage.*

saturnism. *plumbism.*

satyriasis. Excessive sexual drive in the male. Syn. *gynecomania, lagnosis.* Cf. *nymphomania.*

scanning speech. Slow, laborious speech, with pauses between syllables, as seen in multiple sclerosis.

scaphocephalia, -ly. A malformation of the skull, which is shaped like the frame of a boat, with a keel-like ridge; seen in certain mentally retarded persons.

scatophagia,-gy. Eating of feces. Not regarded as abnormal when an occasional occurrence in infants; it is sometimes observed in deteriorated and regressed schizophrenics. Syn. *coprophagy, rhypophagy.*

scatophilia. *coprophilia.*

scatophobia. *coprophobia.*

Scheerer, Martin. Contemporary American psychologist.

Schilder's disease. A type of brain tissue degeneration described by Paul Schilder, German-American psychiatrist (1886-1940). This neurologic affliction of children and youths is marked by paralysis, visual changes, and mental deterioration. Syn. *encephalitis periaxialis diffusa.*

schizoaffective disorder or **reaction.** An emotional and mental reaction manifesting elation or depression as the dominant symptom. The term represents a growing tendency among psychiatrists to regard depressive reaction as early emotional manifestations of schizophrenia.

schizoid, schizothymic. Resembling schizophrenia.

schizoid personality. A personality that has some of the features of schizophrenia, principally extreme introversion and occasional bizarre behavior. It is usually, but not always, a harbinger of psychosis.

schizophrenia, schizophrenic reaction. The commonest psychosis, characterized by withdrawal, regression, infantilism, asocial (possibly antisocial) behavior, hallucinations, delusions, and aberrant ideas. The term was introduced by Bleuler in 1911 to replace an old term "dementia praecox" ("early dementia") because the condition is found in adults as well as younger persons and because it more clearly describes the outstanding feature of the disorder, i.e., the apparent "splitting off" of elements of the personality (especially those concerned with distinguishing reality from unreality). The clinical varieties are: *catatonic, hebephrenic, paranoid, simple,* and *mixed* (the last indicating coexistence of two or more of these types). See also *autism, nicotinamide adenine dinucleotide, pseudoneurotic schizophrenia, schizoaffective disorder.*

schizophrenia, infantile. See *autism.*

schnauzkrampf. Pouting, a grimace frequently seen in catatonic states.

schrecktherapie. ("fright treatment") Freud's derogatory term for the use of hypnosis as practiced by Charcot in the treatment of hysteria. Freud declared that such treatment, while removing overt symptoms, did not affect the unconscious conflict behind the psychoneurosis.

scissors gait. A type of walking in which the knees come close together and may actually cross, as seen in Little's disease. Cf. *marche à petits pas.*

sclerencephalia, -ly. Sclerosis (hardening) of the brain.

scopolagnia. *voyeurism.*

scopophobia. Morbid fear that one is being stared at.

scotophilia. Preference for the dark. Cf. *phengophobia.*

scotophobia. Morbid fear of the dark.

screen memory. In Freudian psychoanalysis, recollection by the analysand of insignificant experiences or ideas instead of the associated significant ones which the unconscious is striving to conceal.

scrupulosity. Overconscientiousness that is anal-erotic in motivation, as typified by many obsessive-compulsive persons, and is a socially acceptable means of draining off unconscious guilt. See *anal erotism.*

secondary advantage or gain. Emotional satisfaction achieved through illness or damage to an organ or a system of organs which is involved in an unconscious conflict. See *organ language.* Cf. *epinosis.*

SDS. *Self-rating Depression Scale.*

secondary elaboration. A mental mechanism by which a person in relating a dream fuses elements of the *manifest content* into a more or less logical and sequential dream story without being aware that these elements which he has reconstructed and re-arranged are fragments of the *latent content.* See *dream.*

Séguin, O. Edouard. French-American psychiatrist (1812-1880) known for his pioneering work in establishing the first state school for the mentally retarded in the United States. He was also the first professor of psychiatry in the United States.

selaphobia. Unreasoning or exaggerated fear of flashing light.

self-analysis. Self-probing to uncover one's psychodynamic mechanisms. It is regarded as relatively unproductive, tending to deal only with superficialities. Rarely can the individual reach deeply enough into his unconscious, owing to the activity of his ego and superego. Although a person may realize that he is emotionally disturbed and with this knowledge at his command achieve adjustment, his deeper conflict remains unknown to him. Freud arrived at his principles of psychoanalysis in part through efforts in self-analysis. Cf. *autocatharsis, bibliotherapy.*

Self-Analysis Scale. A personality inventory devised by Raymond B. Cattell, Anglo-American psychologist. It consists of a series of questions that the subject answers while alone. The aim of the procedure is to reveal the motivation and directive course of an individual's personality. Cf. *Minnesota Multiphasic Personality Inventory.*

self-hypnosis. *autohypnosis.*

self-mutilation. Masochistic, often compulsive activity seen in psychoneurotic individuals who pick at their skin, pull out their hair, etc., and in regressed schizophrenics who may gouge their skin with fingernails, cut off their genitalia, or blind themselves.

Self-rating Depression Scale (SDS). A self-administered psychiatric inquiry to assess depressive disorders. The questions, twenty in all, vary from "I feel down-hearted and blue" and "I still enjoy sex" to "I feel that others would be better off if I were dead." The patient checks each statement as "yes" or "no." Diagnostic analysis is divided into three main groupings: pervasive affect, physiological equivalents, and psychological equivalents.

semantic aphasia. Loss of the ability to understand the meaning of words, due to organic brain damage.

senile psychosis. A diagnostic category of mental disorders associated with the degenerative processes of advanced age (but *not including* cerebral arteriosclerosis). Senile psychosis is manifested in four types: delirious and confused, depressed and agitated, paranoid, and presbyophrenic. The following table differentiates between psychosis due to cerebral arteriosclerosis and that due to senility.

Cerebral Arteriosclerosis	*Senility*
Occurs early in old age.	Seen in the later years.
Of brief duration.	Slightly longer duration.
The onset is apt to be abrupt and stormy.	The onset is gradual.
Intellect confused.	Intellect normal.
Depressive and hypochondriacal states are common.	Depressive and hypochondriacal states are unusual.
Paranoid states are present but not marked.	Paranoid states are very common.
Headaches, dizziness, stroke, fainting, convulsions are present.	These symptoms are rare.
Capricious defects of memory: "patchy."	Orderly, retrograde defect of memory.
Blood pressure may be elevated.	Blood pressure not elevated *per se*.
Personality is fairly well preserved.	Personality is not well preserved.

sensorimotor. Involving both the motor and the sensory functions.

sensorium. The total awareness (judgment, orientation, clarity of thinking, logicalness, and similar features of thinking) of the individual.

sensory. Pertaining to the function of nerves that receive stimuli from within and without the body.

sensory aphasia. A condition, due to brain damage or disease, in which a person who formerly possessed the ability to understand written words, symbols, or gestures, or spoken words, has lost this ability. In the former instance it is called *word blindness;* in the latter, *word deafness.* In neither instance is the visual or auditory apparatus impaired. Syn. *receptive aphasia.* Cf. *motor aphasia.*

sensory apraxia. Inability to use, or to name the uses of, objects with which the subject has been thoroughly familiar, such as a pencil, a knife, or a cigarette. The condition is frequently observed in psychosis associated with cerebral arteriosclerosis and in certain other types of organic brain damage.

sensory center. See under *cerebral cortex.*

sensory epilepsy. Unconsciousness, with or without convulsions, resulting from sensory stimuli, such as flashes of light (*photogenic* epilepsy), certain types of music (*musicogenic* epilepsy), etc. It is not, however, the light or the music *per se,* but the associated emotions that trigger the attack. The cause is unknown.

serotonin. A substance naturally present in the blood, brain, and cerebrospinal fluid which impedes the passage of nerve impulses at synapses. Serotonin production is decreased by the action of certain tranquilizers.

serum protein-bound-iodine test. A laboratory test for measuring the amount of thyroid hormone (thyroxin) in the blood in order to establish the rate of thyroid activity. It is useful in determining whether or not an excitable, overactive person is suffering from hyperthyroidism or from a psychiatric disorder such as manic-depressive psychosis. On the other hand, a lowered rate of thyroid activity in a phlegmatic, indifferent person would indicate that the problem has a glandular rather than a psychologic basis. See also *basal metabolism.*

sexoesthetic inversion.   *effemination*

sexual deviation.   A sociopathic disturbance the chief manifestation being abnormal sexual behavior, such as active homosexuality, pederasty, voyeurism, etc. Syn. *psychopathia sexualis.*

sexual inversion.   Selection of another of one's own sex as a love object; the choice may or may not progress as far as overt homosexual practice. See *infantile sexuality.*

shaking palsy.   *parkinsonism.*

Sheldon, William.   American psychologist (1899-   ) whose system of matching body type with temperament, along with Kretschmer's, enjoys wide acceptance. See *somatotypes.* Cf. *habitus.*

"shell shock."   This World War I term (replaced by "combat fatigue" or "combat neurosis" in World War II) lacked validity even when it was current. Many service men said to be suffering from "shell shock" had never been in the vicinity of an exploding shell. All these terms merely describe transient situational personality disorders. See also *traumatic neurosis.*

shock.   In psychiatry, deep mental depression in response to sudden emotional trauma. Also, a popular shorter term for electric shock therapy and insulin shock therapy.

shock therapy.   See *electric shock therapy, insulin shock therapy.*

sibling rivalry.   Competition among children of the same generation in a family for love, approval, recognition, and affection. Although a child's relationships with his parents constitute the most significant emotional factor in his early years, his relationships with his siblings are also extremely important as regards his personality development. If he acquires deep-seated feelings of hostility, inferiority, and jealousy as a child in his association with brothers and sisters, it is likely that he will encounter difficulty, if not abysmal failure, in the interpersonal relationships of later life.

"sick headache." *migraine.*

siderophobia. *astrophobia.*

sign. A manifestation of pathology objectively determined (by relatives, friends, physicans). Cf. *symptom.*

simple schizophrenia. Schizophrenia marked by extreme indifference to environment and society, introversion, and general listlessness. The advent of hallucinations and/or delusions indicates that regression to hebephrenia has occurred.

singultus gastricus nervosis. Hiccough due to "nervous stomach."

situational disorders. See *transient situational personality disorders.*

skin-writing. *dermatographia.*

sleeping sickness. *epidemic encephalitis.*

sleepwalking. *somnambulism.*

smudging. A speech defect marked by the omission of some consonant sounds.

social worker, psychiatric. A social worker who has had special training in abnormal psychology and in the techniques of dealing with individuals and families afflicted with emotional disturbances. The principal functions of the psychiatric social worker are: field visits, preparing life histories of patients, and assisting patients and their families to adjust to each other and to life in the community.

socialization. 1. The process of adjustment that begins in early childhood as the individual becomes aware of the need to accommodate his inner drives to the demands of reality. 2. In psychotherapy, the transition from insight into one's emotional conflicts to modification of one's behavior in interpersonal relationships in accord with that insight. 3. A nonmedical procedure of directive psychotherapy, championed by Adolf Meyer and others, designed to help the patient to readjust to society and to shift libido from himself to others in the environment. In institutions this program includes dances, parties, picnics, motion pictures, and various excursions outside the hospital. See also *education, re-education.*

sociopath. One who suffers from a *sociopathic personality disturbance.*

sociopathic personality disturbance. A group of personality disorders primarily expressed through inability or unwillingness to conform to prevailing mores. It has replaced the term "psychopathic personality." The sociopathic personality disturbances are *antisocial reaction, dyssocial (amoral) reaction,* and *sexual deviation.* Syn. *sociopathy.*

sociopathy. *sociopathic personality disturbance.*

sodium amytal. Trade name for a preparation of amobarbital (a barbiturate) which is a sedative sometimes used in the initial stage of hypnoanalysis and hypnotherapy.

sodium pentothal. *pentothal sodium.*

sodomy. 1. Sexual intercourse (usually between males) per anum. Cf. *pederasty.* 2. Sexual intercourse between a man and an animal. Syn. *bestiality.*

softening of the brain. *encephalomalacia.*

"soldier's heart." *effort syndrome.*

soma. Body structure and function as distinguished from the psyche. *adj.* somatic.

somatogenic. Originating in the body or its processes.

somatopsychic. *psychosomatic.*

somatotonia. A somatotype described by Sheldon that is marked by aggressive temperament and comparative independence, along with a large body frame.

somatotypes. Sheldon's term for his body types which he pairs with types of temperament: *endomorphy* = *viscerotonia, mesomorphy* = *matotonia, ectomorphy* = *cerebrotonia.* Cf. *habitus.*

somnambulism. Sleepwalking. Though it occurs normally in childhood, if it persists it may be symptomatic of the earlier stage of profound emotional disorder, even a budding psychoneurosis. It may be an attempt to act out symbolically some unconscious conflict. Syn. *hypnobasia, noctambulism.*

somnifacient. Inducing drowsiness or sleep.

somniloquence, -quism. Talking during sleep.

somnipathy. Hypnotic somnambulism.

somnolism. *hypnosis.*

somnovigil. Obsolete. Somnambulism. Cf. *coma vigil.*

sophomania. A psychotic belief in the profundity of one's own wisdom.

Souque, Alexandre Achilles. French neurologist (1860–1914). See *kinesia paradoxa.*

spasm. A sudden involuntary, violent, rigid contraction of muscle. See *clonic spasm, habit spasm.*

spasmophemia. *stammering.*

spastic. Related to or of the nature of a spasm.

spastic diplegia. *Little's disease.*

spastic gait. A manner of walking observed in cases of damage to motor pathways or their centers in the brain, in which the leg is extended at the knee, the hip and thigh are turned inward, and the heel is raised, causing the limb to be swung in an arc.

spastic paralysis. *Little's disease.*

special symptom reactions. A subcategory of *personality disorders,* comprising learning and speech disturbances, enuresis, sleepwalking, and other abnormal conditions.

spheresthesia. *globus hystericus.*

spinal canal. The central passageway running through the vertebrae (individual bony segments) which encloses the spinal cord and its meninges. Syn. *vertebral canal.*

spinal cord. The continuation of the medulla oblongata within the spinal column, constituting, with the brain, the cerebrospinal axis. Its nerve pathways bring motor impulses from and sensory impulses to the brain. The spinal cord is the link between peripheral organs and the brain. It also provides a passage for cerebrospinal fluid to and from the brain.

spinal fluid.   See under *cerebrospinal fluid.*

spinal tap.   Hypodermic drainage of cerebrospinal fluid for diagnostic examination, relief of intracranial pressure, and induction of spinal anesthesia.

"split personality."   See *multiple personality.*

stammering.   Hesitant, spasmodic speech, with interruptions in which no sound is produced. It is regarded as psychoneurotic in origin, with strong environmental influences. Still undergoing investigation is the use of amphetamines in the treatment of stammering and stuttering. These drugs have been effective with mentally retarded children who stammer, but conclusions have not yet been possible as to the benefit for adults and mentally normal children. Syn. *anarthria literalis, ischonophonia.*

stamper.   A colloquialism for one suffering tabes dorsalis; the word refers to the gait in this condition, in which the feet are raised high then stamped on the ground.

Stanford revision, Stanford-Binet Scale.   See under *Binet-Simon Scale, Tests.*

stasibasiphobia.   A pathologic distrust of one's ability to stand or walk.

stasiphobia.   A morbid fear of standing still lest one lose his balance, a conscious manifestation of an unconscious feeling of insecurity. It is also observed in parkinsonism.

status convulsivus.   *status epilepticus.*

status epilepticus.   A severe form of epilepsy in which the patient suffers a series of grand mal seizures without regaining consciousness between convulsions. Syn. *status convulsivus.*

Stekel, Wilhelm.   German psychoanalyst (1868-1940), who stressed the need for a more active role by the analyst in the re-education of the patient. See *direct psychoanalysis.*

stereognosis. Ability to identify objects by the sense of touch. Cf. *astereognosis.*

stereotaxia. Surgical destruction of a small area of the brain by the application of an electrical current to alleviate unmanageable emotional reactions in persons suffering such disorders as parkinsonism and epilepsy, and in irritable mentally retarded persons.

stereotype. Thinking, speaking, or acting in an unvaried pattern. It is common in schizophrenia, (especially the catatonic form), but many normal persons may show some degree of stereotype in action and speech. Syn. *perseveration, rigidity.* See also *obsessive-compulsive reaction.*

stiff man syndrome. A sudden and severe contraction of muscles of the lower half of the body occasionally observed in neurotic individuals, usually precipitated by an emotional shock. It may be so severe that fracture of the hip occurs.

stimulant therapy. Treatment directed toward accelerating retarded metabolism, glandular activity, and insufficiently functioning organs and organ systems, and rousing emotionally depressed and psychotically indifferent and introverted persons to activity and renewed interest in their environment. Syn. *irritation therapy.*

Storch, Alfred. Swiss lay analyst, born in Hamburg, Germany, 1888.

strephosymbolia. A reading disability in children attributable to mixed motor dominance in the cerebral hemispheres; the visual apparatus is intact. The principal feature is inability to distinguish between letters that resemble each other, such as *o* and *e, b* and *d, p* and *q, n* and *u,* etc.

stridor dentium. *bruxism.*

stroke. An acute, sudden, and severe seizure or attack, as of paralysis or apoplexy.

structured environment. Any prescribed continuous interaction of people, circumstances, and patterns of thinking. It is the aggregate of all the external conditions and influences affecting the life and development of a person or group of persons. In an institutional milieu, structured environment is part of the "total push" program. The concept is applied chiefly in treatment-planning of emotionally and mentally disturbed children. See also *interpersonal relationships.*

stupidity, neurotic. See *neurotic stupidity.*

stupefacient. *adj.* Causing stupor. *n.* Any chemical agent or other influence that causes stupor.

stupor. 1. Partial consciousness. 2. In psychiatry, mutism in a psychotic person whose sensorium is unimpaired.

stuttering. Uncontrollable repetition of certain consonant sounds in rapid succession. The term is also used synonymously with stammering. Syn. *logoclonia, logospasm.*

subacute combined degeneration of the spinal cord. A progressive disease of middle life, due to untreated anemia and certain wasting disorders, in which the posterior and lateral columns of the spinal cord degenerate. Signs and symptoms include various neurological manifestations and, sometimes, mental disorder. Syn. *combined degeneration.*

subconscious. *preconscious.*

subcortical. 1. Relating to the white matter of the brain lying beneath the cortex. 2. Describing mental activity in which the cortex, or gray matter of the brain, is not involved. The term refers to crude, often instinctual or involuntary responses, in which reasoning and complex emotional patterns are not brought into play. Included is behavior motivated by the phylogenetic elements of the personality.

subdelirium. Mild or discontinuous delirium.

subdural hemorrhage. Hemorrhage in one of the meninges interior to the dura mater (i.e., in the arachnoid or the pia mater). See also *cerebrovascular accident.*

subject cathexis.   See under *cathexis.*

subject libido.   *ego libido.*

sublimation.   A defense mechanism whereby consciously unacceptable instinctual demands are channeled into acceptable forms for gratification. For example, aggression can be converted into athletic activity.

subliminal.   Taking place below the threshold of sensory perception or of consciousness. Cf. *liminal.*

substantia grisea.   *gray matter.*

substitution.   In psychoanalysis, one of the mental mechanisms in the dream that serve to conceal the true motivation for the dream. Persons, scenes, objects, and actions acceptable to the ego are substituted for traumatic experiences in the subject's background.

subthalamus.   A part of the brain lying just beneath the thalamus. It is concerned with the control of emotional activity.

succinylcholine chloride.   A chemical agent that causes complete muscular relaxation. It is used with electric shock therapy to prevent excessive muscular rigidity, which might otherwise lead to bone fractures. Trade name: Anectine.

sucking period.   According to Freud, the earlier period (prior to dentition) of the oral stage of psychosexual development. Cf. *biting period.*

suggestion.   A form of psychotherapy in which the therapist suggests an idea to a patient and urges him to accept it in place of another (usually socially unacceptable) one which hampers his adjustment. Cf. *autosuggestion.*

suicide, psychoanalytic interpretation of.   In the dynamic sense, suicide is believed to be motivated by unconscious feelings of guilt and unworthiness, regardless of the precipitating circumstances. Freud pointed out that the person whose superego stands between him and his love object and obliterates it (i.e., the parent of the opposite sex) can reach the love object only by destroying the superego. Thus, suicide is in effect homicide.

Occasionally a catatonic schizophrenic patient kills himself or attempts to kill himself because he has incorporated someone he hates into his own unconscious and identifies himself with the hated person. If the attempt is unsuccessful, the patient usually recovers from his mental-emotional disorder and there is no recurrence of the psychiatric condition. Penetrating interview of such patients following their suicidal attempts tends to substantiate the foregoing theoretical approach to motivation in suicide.

sulcus. (*pl.* **sulci**)   One of the furrows of the surface of the brain; the sulci mark the outlines of the brain's convolutions.

Sullivan, Harry Stack.   American psychiatrist and psychoanalyst (1892-1949) who defined psychiatry as "the science of interpersonal relationships" and summed up his ideas on personality with the word "acculturation." He felt that man's personality emerges out of the personal and social forces acting on him from birth, and that the final personality pattern is the product of interaction with other human beings. Cf. *Horney, Meyer.*

superego.   According to Freud, one of the three basic unconscious components of the personality (see *ego, id*). It is roughly synonymous with conscience, from which it differs in that it does not depend for its development upon the learning of moral codes; it is inherent in the personality. The superego takes on form and force as the id expresses primitive demands and the ego, which has to face reality, must modify these demands according to the dictates of society. The superego acts as a guide-and-check mechanism, a "censor."

superiority complex.   A popular, incorrect term for *inferiority complex.*

suppression.   Conscious muffling of feelings or ideas that induce psychic "pain" in the individual. Cf. *repression.*

suprarenal-genital syndrome.   *adrenogenital syndrome.*

suprarenal gland.   *adrenal gland.*

surrogate.   A substitute. In psychiatry, any person to whom the subject ascribes a role as a substitute for a parent (hence, father surrogate or mother surrogate). Such a person may be another member of the individual's family, a teacher, an employer, or an older friend. Syn. *parent figure*. See also *parent image*.

Sydenham's chorea. A condition seen principally in children marked by spasmodic twitching (chorea) accompanied by emotional changes and not infrequently by mental retardation. It is suspected by some authorities to be of toxic-infectious origin. Syn. *Saint Vitus' dance*.

syllabic utterance. A type of dysphrasia in which each syllable is uttered as if it were a separate word. The disorder is often seen in general paresis and multiple sclerosis. Cf. *scanning speech*.

symbiosis. In psychoanalysis, the mechanism by which the ego incorporates a psychotic or psychoneurotic symptom into the personality. The personality pattern and the symptoms fortify one another (e.g., delusions of grandeur strengthen the individual's narcissism which in turn strengthens the delusion).

symbolism. In psychiatry, an unconscious mental mechanism by which the individual substitutes other objects, thoughts, and persons for those that lie at the core of an emotional problem. It is active in normal mental functioning and in psychoneuroses and psychoses; the mentally retarded are relatively incapable of symbolic thinking. It is a principal factor in the framework of dreams, in which the manifest content is usually rich in symbols for elements of the latent content. See also *phallic symbol*.

sympathetic nervous system. The division of the autonomic nervous system which mobilizes the body's organs and systems to cope with emergencies. Cf. *parasympathetic nervous system*.

sympatheticomimetic. *sympathomimetic.*

sympatheticotonia. Domination of the body's functions by the sympathetic nervous system; manifested by flushed, hot skin, dilated pupils, rapid rates of breathing and heart action, elevated blood pressure, depressed digestive activity, and overexcitability. See also *gastrointestinal reactions*. Cf. *vagotonia*.

sympathetonia. *sympatheticotonia.*

sympathin. A hormone produced at sympathetic nerve endings. It has two forms: SE (excitatory form) which causes blood vessels to constrict, and SI (inhibitory form) which causes them to dilate. It is therefore, like epinephrine, a vital factor in emotional response.

sympathism. The state of being readily susceptible to hypnosis.

sympathomimetic. Acting or causing to act in the manner of the sympathetic nervous system.

symptom. A manifestation of disease that gives rise to a patient's complaint. Cf. *sign.*

syncope. Temporary loss of consciousness most usually due to lowered blood supply to the brain. Syn. *fainting spell.*

syndrome. The complex of symptoms observed in a disease or disorder.

syndrome of approximate answers. *Ganser's syndrome.*

synesthesia. A sensory response in an area other than that to which a stimulus is applied, as a visual sensation evoked by an auditory stimulus.

synkinesia, -sis. Voluntary and involuntary movements occurring simultaneously. This is seen, for example, in a partly paralyzed muscle, which may move in conjunction with the voluntary movement of an unaffected muscle.

syntactic aphasia. Aphasia in which the patient's comprehension of, and ability to use, syntax (sentence structure) is impaired. It is due to brain damage or disease.

syntonic personality. Said of an individual who enjoys harmonious emotional adjustment.

syntropy. Meyer's term for a state of satisfactory interpersonal relationships.

Szondi test. A projective inquiry in which forty-eight pictures of psychiatric patients are presented to a subject; he is asked to arrange the pictures according to his personal preference, which may be based on the sex, attire, or facial expression of the patient.

The choices are said to have value in disclosing unconscious motivations.

T

tabes dorsalis. A late neuropsychiatric manifestation of syphilis. Psychiatric symptoms include hallucinations, delusions, disorientation, and gradual mental deterioration; neurologic signs include acroagnosis, distortion of sensation (e.g., allocheiria), amyostasia, ataxia, and various crises. Syn. *creeping paralysis, motor ataxia, myelopthisis.* Cf. *pseudotabes.*

tabetic gait. *ataxic gait.*

taboo, tabu. In Freudian psychoanalysis, a restriction arising out of superego influence; it is regarded as a phylogenetic heritage.

tache cérébrale. A red stripe made by drawing the fingernail across the skin. It persists for several minutes. It is a sign of several brain lesions and nervous disorders (e.g., meningitis).

tachyglossa. *tachylalia.*

tachygraphia. Compulsive rapid reading, as seen in the manic phase of manic-depressive psychosis.

tachylalia, tachylogia. Compulsive rapid speech, commonly encountered in the manic phase of manic-depressive psychosis. Syn. *oxylalia, tachyglossa, tachyphrasia.* Cf. *logoclonia, logorrhea.*

tachyphagia. Compulsive rapid consumption of food, even of substances that are not foodstuffs; frequently observed in regressed schizophrenics and some mentally retarded persons.

tachyphrasia. *tachylalia.*

tachyphrenia. Abnormally rapid mental activity, observed pathologically in conditions such as the initial stage of cocainism.

tactile agnosia. *astereognosis.*

taedium vitale. Morbid disgust with life and living, a common characteristic of depressed persons.

talion. Retribution. In psychoanalytic doctrine it is regarded as a form of self-punishment, originating in the unconscious and manifested in consciousness. Thus, the guilt that is unconsciously aroused by an "evil" action or thought involving the eyes (e.g., looking at something forbidden or in a wicked fashion, or thinking sinfully about something one has seen) is "punished " by visual disturbances up to and including blindness. Cf. *masochism.*

tantrum. An outburst of violent activity, often occurring intermittently in a maladjusted child. The tantrum is usually not directed at one individual, but indiscriminately toward the environment. It is a tool through which the frustrated child attempts to control his surroundings.

taphephobia, taphophobia. Morbid fear of being buried alive.

tarantism, tarantismus. Chorea of southern Italy, allegedly caused by the bite of the tarantula and supposedly cured by dancing.

taste blindness. *ageusia.*

TAT. *Thematic Apperception Test.*

Tay-Sachs' disease. Blindness accompanied by severe mental retardation occuring at birth and seen almost exclusively in Jewish infants, sometimes in several children of the same family. Other manifestations include: muscle and brain degeneration, decerebrate rigidity, and the appearance of a cherry-red spot on the retina. Formerly known as *amaurotic family idiocy.* A test to detect carriers among prospective parents probes for *aldolase,* an enzyme which normally participates in sugar metabolism. If it is not present in the blood or found only in minute quantity, the subject is regarded as a carrier of Tay-Sachs' disease.

teichopsia. A transient disturbance of vision in which the subject may see images such as *fortification figures;* it is a symptom of migraine.

temper tantrum. See *tantrum.*

temperament. See *Sheldon.*

tension. In psychiatry, emotional strain manifested in the irritability that accompanies anxiety.

tension headache. Headache precipitated by a stressful situation which generates an emotional crisis. These headaches may be psychogenic or they may come from conditions causing contractions of muscles of the back of the neck and of the scalp, experienced chiefly as occipital headache or a "bandlike" sensation. See *headache.* Cf. *migraine.*

Terman Revision. The Stanford Revision of the Binet-Simon Scale by Lewis M. Terman, American psychologist (1877-1956).

testosterone propionate. A hormonal extract obtained from the testes of bulls and also synthetically prepared, used with benefit for children with mental retardation due to malnutrition.

tetraplegia. *quadriplegia.*

thalamic syndrome. A disturbance of sensation accompanying hemiplegia, in which both pleasant and unpleasant feelings are exaggerated.

thalamus. A collection of gray matter at the base of the brain. It is referred to as the "great sensory platform." Impressions reaching the thalamus along sensory pathways from the periphery via the spinal cord and brain stem are interpreted crudely as painful or pleasurable. Thus, the thalamus is deeply involved in emotional experiences and response to them.

thalassophobia. A morbid fear of the sea.

thanatomania. Preoccupation with thoughts of death, as in the case of a psychotic who is convinced that he is under a "spell" that will kill him, Cf. *death wish, Eros and Thanatos.*

thanatophobia. Morbid, persistent fear of death.

Thanatos. See *Eros and Thanatos.*

Thematic Apperception Test (TAT). A projective diagnostic technique which, through the presentation to the subject of 31 pictures depicting problems in interpersonal relationships, seeks to uncover the dynamics of his personality. The subject is asked to tell a story about what he sees and observations are made and recorded of his responses in fourteen areas, such as main theme, hero or heroine, fixing of blame, and his main character's expression of aggressive feelings toward persons and objects.

thematic paralogia. See under *paralogia.*

theomania. A psychotic state marked by religious delusions, especially that of being God.

theophobia. Morbid fear of God. Cf. *hadephobia, hierophobia.*

thermophobia. Morbid aversion to heat.

three-paper test. See *Marie Three-Paper Test.*

thymergasia, thymergastic reaction. Meyer's term for the affective reactions.

thymoleptic. Any agent, usually a drug, which stimulates the emotions or mental processes. Syn. *psychostimulant.*

thymopsyche. The emotional processes of the mind. Cf. *noöpsyche.*

thyroid gland. An endocrine gland situated in front of and partially surrounding the windpipe. It has several functions, principally the control of metabolism and emotional reactions. See *hyperthyroidism, hypothyroidism.*

thyrotoxic crisis, thyrotoxic storm. A sudden and violent increase in all the signs and symptoms of hyperthyroidism, occurring after severe mental stress or thyroidectomy (surgical removal of the thyroid gland). It is felt that this postoperative complication is caused by inadequate preoperative preparation of the patient and probably aggravated by flooding the circulation with large quantities of thyroxin during the operation. As radioactive iodine treatment continues to replace thyroid surgery, the incidence of thyrotoxic crisis is diminishing.

thyrotoxicosis. *hyperthyrodism.*

thyroxin. The chief hormone secreted by the thyroid gland. A synthetic form of it is used to relieve hypothyroidism.

tic. A sudden, repetitive, purposeless movement (blinking, twitching, nodding, jerking, shrugging) not to be confused with the painful spasm associated with certain organic disorders. Most frequently (but not exclusively) seen in children before puberty, tics are regarded as psychogenic, probably due to anxiety. They usually disappear spontaneously; if they persist, the treatment of choice is psychotherapy. Cf. *habit spasm, mannerism.*

tocomania, tokomania. Any affective reaction that accompanies or follows childbearing.

tocophobia, tokophobia. Morbid fear of pregnancy or childbearing.

toilet training. Training of the infant in bladder and bowel control, an element of habit training believed by psychoanalysts to have long-range effects on the formation of the personality. According to Freud, it takes place during the anal-erotic period. See also *anal character, anal erotism, anal sadism, anal stage.*

tokkoni. See *latah.*

tonaphasia. Loss of ability to carry a tune, owing to a brain lesion.

tone. Responsivity, said of the emotions. Cf. *tonus.*

tonitrophobia. Pathologic fear of thunder. Cf. *keraunophobia.*

tonus. A state of tension in an organ or limb due to contraction of its muscles. *adj.* tonic.

topagnosis. Loss of the sense by which one can localize touch or pressure on his body.

topectomy. In psychosurgery, removal of a portion of the cerebral cortex, undertaken to modify the behavior and mental processes of a psychotic person who has not responded to other forms of treatment. Its use rapidly decreased after the introduction of chemotherapy for mental disorders.

topophobia. Morbid dread of a particular place.

torticollis. A condition marked by spasmodic twitching of the muscles of the neck, believed by some psychiatrists to have, in certain cases, a psychogenic background. Syn. *wryneck.*

"total push." The combined effect of all measures taken for the care and treatment of a psychiatric patient: psychotherapy, chemotherapy, treatment of nonpsychiatric illness, contact with doctors, nurses, and psychiatric aides, the advantage of regularity of institutional routine, and freedom from the environmental influences that may have precipitated the mental illness.

toxic psychoses. See *poisoning, psychoses due to.*

toxicomania. A compulsive urge to swallow poisonous substances.

toxicophobia. Morbid fear of being poisoned, often expressed by paranoiacs and by persons suffering a senile psychosis of the paranoid type.

trance. 1. A degree of lowered consciousness achieved through hypnosis, in which the subject's responses to stimuli and commands are controlled through suggestion by the hypnotist. 2. A form of catalepsy marked by prolonged sleep from which the subject cannot be roused; vital functions are diminished (respiration is almost imperceptible) and there is no response to sensory stimuli.

tranquilizer. A substance—natural or synthetic—that soothes a disturbed, excited person or alleviates the mood of depression. The principal difference between tranquilizers and sedatives (such as barbiturates) is that the former are selective in their action while the sedatives have a general effect and depress all somatic and psychic activity. Tranquilizers are rapidly replacing the various kinds of shock treatment, because they render patients cooperative and amenable to psychotherapy. More patients can now be treated without institutionalization, and hospitalized patients can, after a brief period in which maintenance dosage is established, be released for treatment as outpatients. Syn. *ataractic, psycholeptic.*

transference. In psychoanalysis, unconscious displacement of libido, whereby the patient shifts his antagonism and libidinal attachments from the disturbing "characters" in his underlying emotional conflict to the psychiatrist. Cf. *abreaction, countertransference.*

transference neurosis. Freud's original classification of a psychoneurosis that is marked by strong erotic attachment to another person. Cf. *narcissistic neurosis.*

transient situational personality disorders. A category of pathologic mental and emotional reactions in which an individual whose personality is basically stable displays, in a situation of stress, symptoms similar to those seen in the more serious psychiatric conditions. They are acute responses involving temporary maladjustments which clear up when the stressful conditions no longer prevail.

transvestism. Pursuit of sexual excitement by dressing in the attire of the opposite sex. See *homosexual, sexual inversion.*

trauma. In psychiatry, trauma is a violent emotional shock that may produce permanent emotional pathology.

traumatic neurosis. A psychoneurotic reaction provoked by a physical injury, particularly concussion, though the injury may be at a site remote from the brain. The dominant symptom is anxiety over social, economic, or other misfortune, which may be real or imagined. The psychoneurosis commonly occurs weeks to months after the injury. Individuals with inadequate personalities will respond to injury in the same fashion. Hypochondriacal complaints are common; often these persons use the injury (which may not be serious) as an excuse for their deficiencies and failures (see *secondary advantage*), and malingering is not uncommon. The term "posttraumatic neurosis" applies when considerable time has elapsed after the injury before the neurosis is manifested. Cf. *traumatic psychosis.*

traumatic psychosis. A severe mental disorder caused by an injury to the brain, most often seen as a delayed reaction. The manifestations—paranoid, manic-depressive, etc.—are determined by the patient's personality type prior to the injury. As with traumatic neurosis, because of the lapse of time between the injury and the onset of psychotic symptoms, the term "post-traumatic psychosis" is often used.

tremor. Trembling, an involuntary movement involving one or more parts of the body, caused by rapid alternating contractions of opposing muscles or muscle groups (i.e., flexors and extensors). Tremors may be coarse or fine, transient or persistent. They are classified as transient, intention, or rest tremors. A *transient* tremor is a normal response to extreme physical exertion, hunger, cold, emotional shock, etc. An *intention tremor* appears when the affected part is moved voluntarily, as in multiple sclerosis. A *rest tremor,* seen in disorders such as parkinsonism, appears when the involved part is not in motion.

triakaidekaphobia. Obsessive fear of the number 13. Syn. *triskaidekaphobia.*

tribade. A lesbian who acts the role of the male.

trichlorethylene. An anesthetic used in brief surgical procedures. Swallowed in excessive doses, it produces unconsciousness followed by a transient psychotic state resembling paranoid schizophrenia.

trichoclasmania. Compulsion to break off hairs.

trichokryptomania. *trichorrhexomania.*

trichologia, -gy. Plucking out one's hair. Syn. *autodepilation.*

trichomania. *trichotillomania.*

trichopathophobia. Morbid fear of touching hair.

trichorrhexomania. Obsessive headscratching sometimes observed in regressed schizophrenics and in compulsive neurotics.

trichopathophobia. Morbid aversion to the sight or touch of hair. Syn. *trichophobia.*

trichophagia, -phagy. Biting, chewing, or swallowing hair.

trichophobia, *tricopathophobia.*

trichotillomania. A compulsive pulling of one's own hair—in some emotionally and mentally disturbed persons, to the extent of pulling it out.

trimethadione. An anticonvulsant drug used effectively in the treatment of petit mal epilepsy.

triskaidekaphobia. *triakaidekaphobia.*

tromomania. *delirium tremens.*

"truth serum." *pentothal sodium* or *sodium amytal.*

tuberous sclerosis. A congenital condition characterized by multiple nodules throughout the body, accompanied by convulsions and mental retardation.

tumor. See *brain tumor, phantom tumor.*

twilight state. *fugue.*

Ucs. *unconscious.*

uncinate fits. Hallucinations of smell and taste accompanied by spasmodic clamping of the jaw and smacking of the lips, occurring at irregular intervals; due to disease or damage of the temporal lobe of the brain.

unconscious, the. In psychoanalysis, that portion of the psyche which is the repository for primitive and repressed memories and impulses and is rarely subject to awareness. See also *collective unconscious, personal unconscious.*

unconscious mistake. See *Freudian slip.*

unconsciousness. The state of complete or partial unawareness of one's surroundings or reduced sensibility to stimuli. It is physiologically normal only in sleep. Among the causes of pathologic unconsciousness are: acute alcoholism, severe anemia, cerebrovascular accidents (such as stroke), diabetic acidosis, heart failure, shock, and thyrotoxic crisis. States of various degrees of unconsciousness are: *catalepsy, coma, dream state, fugue, hypnolepsy, stupor.*

undoing. A defense mechanism generated by the unconscious and leading the subject to act or speak in a manner reflecting the reverse of some act or wish for which he feels guilty.

$\mathcal{U}$

vaginismus. Painful contraction of the muscles of the vagina which renders sexual intercourse unsatisfactory, if not impossible. The causative background may be psychogenic.

vagotonia. A condition marked by hyperactivity of the vagus nerve (a nerve with many branches throughout the body which dominates the parasympathetic nervous system). Along with several physiological signs and symptoms, general apathy and decreased sexual activity are seen. Cf. *sympatheticotonia.*

vasovagal attack. *carotid sinus syndrome.*

vegetative nervous system. *autonomic nervous system.*

venereophobia. Morbid fear of contracting or having contracted a venereal disease.

ventilation. The patient's "airing" of his emotional problems during a psychotherapeutic session or in a conversation with someone in whom he has confided. Cf. *catharsis, desensitization.*

ventricle. A small pouch or cavity as in the brain or in the heart.

ventriculogram. An X-ray of the brain, taken after cerebrospinal fluid has been withdrawn from the ventricles and air has been introduced in place of it. Through ventriculography, pathologic lesions within the brain can be observed.

verbal agraphia. *motor aphasia.*

verbigeration. Incoherent compulsive repetition of certain words or phrases. Cf. *paralogia.*

vermiphobia. *helminthophobia.*

vertigo. Dizziness. It may be psychic or organic in origin.

virilism. The development of male personality traits in a female.

visceratonia. A personality type described by Sheldon that is hedonistic in drive and marked by concentration of comfort, luxury, eating and drinking, and sociality. It is associated with the endomorph body type.

visual aphasia. *alexia.*

visual center. See under *cerebral cortex.*

Visual Motor Gestalt Test. *Bender Visual Motor Gestal Test.*

voyeurism. The practice of deriving sexual gratification from surreptitiously watching others cohabit or from viewing a naked or disrobing person. Syn. *mixoscopia.* Cf. *gymnomania.*

W

war neurosis. *combat fatigue.*

water on the brain. *hydrocephalus.*

waxy flexibility. *flexibilitas cerea.*

Wechsler-Bellevue Scales. Intelligence tests devised by David Wechsler, American psychologist, to evaluate the intelligence of persons in the adolescent and adult ranges; an additional scale measures the intelligence of children. The Wechsler-Bellevue Scales, which differ in several respects from the *Stanford-Binet* Scale, produce significant material for diagnostic evaluation along with the measurement values. A "per cent of population" factor is assigned to each level of intelligence.

weight at birth. A study conducted in 1965 at Johns Hopkins University on 992 single births from the cradle to the fourteenth year indicates that the child whose weight is low at birth frequently gains normal weight and stature as he develops but often does not "catch up" in intelligence. Flaws in comprehension and abstract reasoning, lack of perseverance, poor gross motor development, immature speech, and impaired I.Q. significantly identify low-birth-weight children. Overly concrete or overliteral thinking and lessened perceptual-motor responses are most commonly observed. This finding is another suggestion that metabolic disorders at birth (see under *metabolism*) play a prominent causal role in mental retardation.

Wernicke's disease. *acute hemorrhagic polioencephalitis.*

Weltschmerz. Extreme pessimism as seen in the melancholic phase of involutional psychosis.

white matter. The portion of the brain and the spinal cord which contains nerve fibers that maintain communication between the various control centers in the gray matter of the cerebral cortex and the rest of the central nervous system. Syn. *substantia alba.* Cf. *gray matter.*

Wide Range Achievement Test. (WRAT). An achievement test that measures an individual's ability to read, write, and use arithmetic. The results are matched with criteria for the subject's intelligence-rating group.

will to power. Adler's term for psychoneurotic aggressiveness, which he interpreted as a compensation for unconsciously motivated feelings of insecurity and inferiority.

Wilson's disease. *hepatolenticular degeneration.*

wishful dream. See under *dream.*

wish-fulfillment. According to Freud, a primary motivation for dreams; fear is another. The wish, arising from the subject's unconscious, is usually unacceptable to the ego (owing to social taboos and the subject's guilt feelings) and his superego will not permit it to emerge into consciousness during the waking state.

withdrawal. Extreme introversion, as seen in schizophrenic regression.

withdrawal syndrome. A series of somatic and psychic reactions that accompany the denial of a drug to a narcotic addict. Some of the somatic features are alternating chills and "hot flashes," a sensation of suffocation, abdominal cramps, and "dragging" pains in the legs. The patient pleads for "just one more shot," alternately begs and threatens, and eventually collapses; this reaction may continue for two or three days after the withdrawal regimen has begun. The accompanying exhaustion may result in death. Syn. *amorphinism, "cold turkey."*

Witzelsucht. Silliness in an individual who has suffered damage to the frontal lobe of the brain.

word association test. See *association, controlled.*

word blindness. *alexia.*

word deafness. An auditory aphasia due to damage of the auditory center in the brain. The subject hears words and sentences but is unable to make sense out of them, even if he has pronounced them himself. Syn. *anacroasia, acousmatagnosis, logokophosis.* Cf. *mind deafness.*

word salad. An outpouring of speech, seen most often in schizophrenia, and characterized by jumping word order or words coined by the patient (neologism). Cf. *asyndesis, cluttering, glossolalia.*

"working through." In a psychoanalysis, the interpretive phase wherein the analyst attempts to probe the source of the patient's resistance.

wryneck. *torticollis.*

X

xenophobia.   Pathologic fear of strangers. Cf. *neophobia*.

xylophobia.   Morbid fear of trees or other wooded plants.

Z

zoanthropy.   Delusion that one has assumed the physical form and/or behavior characteristic of an animal.

zonesthesia.   *girdle crisis.*

zoophilia, -philism.   Erotic fondness for animals.

zoophobia.   Morbid fear of animals.

The Appendix

Appendix

absence, unauthorized. Most health agencies are adopting this term to designate the status of patients who leave an institution without official approval. Included in the newer term are escape, refusal of patients to return voluntarily after a trial home visit, and unapproved retention of patients at home by relatives. The terms "escape" and "elopement" are still used in some quarters to distinguish the act of a patient who leaves a locked ward without authorization from that of one who leaves an open (unlocked) ward. The military designation "A.W.O.L." is also used, though rarely, to refer to unauthorized absences. Most authorities feel that the older terms carry a penal or correctional connotation. See also *open-door policy.*

accidents to patients. Despite the protective environment of a hospital, some psychiatric patients, by the very nature of their condition or that of patients about them, are prey to accidental injury or other mishap. Confused, senile persons and those suffering from impairment of coordination tend to fall; overactive, excited, disturbed patients may become engaged in altercations, collide with objects, or mutilate themselves. In earlier days, under less enlightened management of mental patients and lower standards for procurement of hospital personnel, there was also the possibility of indifferent or rough handling by ward attendants.

A rigorous system of reporting and investigating all serious accidents and injuries has long been mandatory in psychiatric institutions. If there is any question of negligence on the part of hospital personnel or if death results or there has been an attempt at suicide or homicide, the local district attorney or appropriate law enforcement officer must be notified (and, in case of death, the coroner or medical examiner). This provides the opportunity for an impartial outside authority, at his own discretion, to investigate the circumstances surrounding the occurrence. The same procedure is followed in cases of sudden, unexpected death even if there is no apparent injury, or if suicide or homicide is suspected.

acquittal on ground of mental disorder.   A person charged with a crime may offer a plea of "not guilty" on ground of mental illness or mental retardation. When the defense is mental illness or retardation, the judge or justice must instruct the jury that if they acquit the defendant on that ground they must state the fact in their verdict. If he is acquitted, the judge must order such person to be confined in an appropriate institution. In some states such institutions are under the control of a department of mental hygiene or mental health; in others, a department of correction, and in still others, a department of social (or public) welfare.

Should a patient admitted under the aforementioned circumstances recover sufficiently to warrant his release, approval for release must first be obtained from the court that ordered the admission and, depending on the law of the particular state, the approval may be granted with or without review by a qualified psychiatrist. Some states provide that if such a person, within a specified time after release (usually five years), proves to be unsuitable to be at large, he may be recertified to an appropriate institution by the original certifying court without recourse to other admission procedures.

addict.   According to federal law, "any individual who habitually uses any narcotic drug so as to endanger the public morals, health, safety, or welfare, or who is so far addicted to the use of such narcotic drugs as to have lost the power of self-control with reference to his addiction."

administrative record.   That portion of the case record comprising certain official papers, such as the documents covering the patient's admission to the institution, accident and injury reports, and other non-clinical papers.

admission procedures.   Persons to be admitted to a civil or licensed private institution or a division of a general or proprietary hospital for the diagnosis and treatment of mental disorder òr retardation are classified as "willing" or "unwilling." In the former group are those who voluntarily seek institutional assistance or those who do not object to institutionalization when someone in their behalf seeks such admission for them (e.g., a parent for a minor, a relative or friend for an elderly patient). All others are "unwilling" patients. Directors of psychiatric institutions are encouraged by mental hygiene authorities to convert the status of "unwilling" patients to that of "willing" whenever possible.

Appropriate institutions can be found easily by consulting a private physician or psychiatrist; the police; a local hospital; the local departments of health, social welfare, hospitals, or community mental health;

an outpatient psychiatric service maintained by an institution; a religious group; a philanthropic or charitable organization; or an aftercare clinic.

Most states are turning from judicial procedures to mostly medical provisions, recognizing that mental illness and retardation are medical problems, not legal matters. Means of admission are as follows (each one explained under its individual heading):

For willing patients	For unwilling patients
nonstatutory admission	community, county, or municipal
voluntary admission	agency certificate
	court certification (commitment)
	one-physician certificate
	two-physician certificate

admission rate. A statistical index stating the number of patients admitted to a hospital or group of hospitals, or within a geographic area per 100,000 of the general population. It is usually broken down into first admissions and readmissions. The most accurate picture of the incidence of mental disorder in the general population is obtained from the rate of first admissions rather than from the number of beds occupied. The latter figure can be misleading because of the long-continued residence of some patients and the tendency of others to suffer relapses and to be readmitted.

adult. In some jurisdictions, a person is legally considered an adult at age 21; in other jurisdictions, at age 18; and in others, it varies for the sexes. For the purpose of signing an application for voluntary or nonstatutory admission to a psychiatric hospital, the applicant must be an adult.

after-care. Treatment of a patient following release from a psychiatric institution may be with the patient's private psychiatrist or at a psychiatric clinic. Modern after-care is as all-inclusive as the program of treatment in the institution. The patient may receive individual or group therapy on a daily, weekly, or monthly basis; he may receive free medication (as in some civil clinics); he may be given vocational guidance, training, and assistance in job placement; and he may participate in various types of occupational and recreational therapy programs. In general hospitals that maintain outpatient and in-hospital facilities, the practice is to have the same resident psychiatrist who treated the patient in the hospital treat the patient in the after-care setting.

alcoholic intoxication, determination of. In most jurisdictions, determination of a state of alcoholic intoxication is accomplished by observation and appraisal of a subject's appearance, deportment, clarity of mental faculties, and command of muscular coordination, particularly in balance and walking. Various laboratory devices and tests may also be used to determine alcoholic content of the blood. A driver is usually considered to be intoxicated if the alcoholic content of his blood is 0.15 percent by volume; a content of 0.10 and up to but not including 0.15 percent may elicit a judgment of "driving while impaired." See also *alcoholics, hospitalization of*.

Alcoholics Anonymous. A voluntary association organized in the United States in the late 1930's with the objective of assisting sufferers from alcoholism to conquer their addiction. The core of its "self-treatment" program (supplemented when necessary by medical participation) is a group therapy setting, in which members mutually, openly, and frankly discuss their personal failings and lend encouragement to one another in an effort to achieve and maintain complete abstinence.

alcoholics, hospitalization of. Practically every psychiatric institution cares for and treats people suffering from alcoholism. The person who is arrested for "drunk and disorderly conduct" and is taken to the observation ward of the local mental hospital or psychiatric division of a general hospital is treated there for the acute phase of alcoholic intoxication. He is discharged unless found to be suffering a major psychosis, in which case he is retained for further therapy or transferred to a civil or Veterans Administration hospital. In most jurisdictions, a chronic alcoholic who needs institutional care and psychotherapy but does not voluntarily seek it may be judicially certified to a civil or licensed private institution for the treatment of alcoholism. The certification is made upon petition by a relative or close friend and examination by two physicians who certify that the person is chronically addicted to alcohol and requires institutional care. Such petition and examination, supported by a signed statement by the director of the private institution to which it is proposed to have the person admitted, declaring the director's willingness to receive such person, are presented to a judge of a court of record. The judge may thereupon order the admission effected, directing that the patient remain in the institution for a specified period of time or (as in some jurisdictions) until he is regarded as clinically fit to be released. If an alcoholic is to be sent to a civil institution, no written statement of willingness is required of the director.

alcoholism, prevalence of. By sheer numbers, alcoholism is one of the gravest of public health problems. It is believed that in the United States there are about 4.25 million men and 0.75 million women alcoholics, i.e., 1 in every 36 adults. From the socioeconomic point of view, the picture is appalling; an estimated million alcoholics have reached the point where serious physiologic and mental problems have developed, and many of them are found among the denizens of "Skid Row" districts and among persons who run afoul of the law.

According to the World Health Organization, the national distribution of alcoholism is as follows:

Rank	Country	Per 100,000 Adults
1	United States	4,300
2	France	2,850
3	Sweden	2,580
4	Switzerland	2,385
5	Denmark	1,950
6	Canada	1,630
7	Norway	1,560
8	Chile	1,500
9	Finland	1,430
10	Australia	1,100
11	England-Wales	1,100
12	Italy	500

Some investigators believe that factors such as climate and terrain may influence the drinking habits of a country and consequently the prevalence of alcoholism. It will be noted that countries in the temperate and colder latitudes dominate the above table and that no completely tropical nation is listed. Perhaps the rugged life of colder and/or mountainous regions is a factor; there is support for this in the fact that "hard liquor" appears to be preferred in colder countries.

alien patient, return to homeland. There are two procedures by which a mentally ill or retarded alien may be removed from the United States: repatriation (optional) and deportation (compulsory).

Repatriation. Any noncitizen in an institution in the United States because of mental illness or retardation may, on his own request or that of a relative or friend, be returned to his homeland or to any country, if a visa can be obtained. Expenses may be borne by the federal government. Some states also subsidize the expense of return, particularly if it is clear that the patient will require extended hospitalization.

Deportation. The basic elements for deportation are a congenital psychiatric disorder or a disorder occurring within five years after the last entrance into the United States, with the patient having become a public charge. Alien patients receiving treatment in private licensed institutions, or for whom statutory maintenance charges are being paid in civil hospitals, are not subject to deportation.

American Boards. A physician is said to be "boarded" when he has received the approval of the governing authority that certifies practitioners of his specialty. With regard to psychiatrists that authority is the American Board of Psychiatry and Neurology, composed of representatives from the American Medical, American Psychiatric, and American Neurological Associations. A practitioner so certified is known as a "diplomate" (i.e., he holds a diploma awarded by the board) or a "certified specialist." In medical directories, diplomates in psychiatry and/or neurology are listed as: D-N (diplomate in neurology), D-P (diplomate in psychiatry), and D-PN (diplomate in both psychiatry and neurology). Diplomates may be certified in such sub-specialties as mental hospital administration, child psychiatry, etc.

anamnesis.   The assembled information regarding a patient's personal and family history, plus accounts of his illness derived from his own complaints and reports of family, friends, and associates—all having been acquired prior to the current admission to the institution or acceptance as a private patient.

annulment.   See *marriage, dissolution on ground of mental illness.*

APA.   American Psychiatric Association, American Psychoanalytical Association, American Psychological Association.

attending staff.   See *consulting and attending staff.*

A.W.O.L.   See under *absence, unauthorized.*

bequests to mental patients.   Most states have statutory provisions whereby individuals or agencies may make a bequest or establish a trust fund for a given patient or group of patients or for all patients in a civil institution. Such funds are administered by the commissioner of mental hygiene or social welfare, the state comptroller, or by the institution's board of visitors or managers. States having antidiscrimination laws will not accept donations earmarked for a specific religious, racial, or ethnic group. However, places of worship for a specific religious group may be erected on institution grounds, and bequests for this purpose may be accepted.

births to patients in psychiatric institutions.   Infants born to institutionalized women may be removed by the mother's relatives. If relatives do not take the child, it is placed with a social welfare adoption agency. No child of a mental patient is retained in an institution beyond a fixed period (usually 14 days).

board of governors, managers, or visitors.   Every state and county civil institution for the mentally ill or retarded or epileptic in the United States has a group of citizens variously referred to as governors, managers, or visitors (sometimes, overseers) whose duty is to observe the operation of the institution through periodic visits, to meet regularly with the director (usually once a month), and to render monthly and annual reports to the cognizant state officer (the governor or the commissioner of mental hygiene or welfare). The board members serve without pay and are customarily appointed by the governor; they are usually residents of the district from which patients are admitted to the institution.

"boarded." See under *American Boards.*

boarding out. See *family care.*

case history. That portion of the case record comprising the anamnesis, reports of results of examination on admission, notes on the patient's progress at the hospital, opinions given at staff meetings, and other nonadministrative information. Syn. *clinical record.* Cf. *administrative record.*

case record. The complete record of a patient, encompassing the *case history,* and the *administrative record.*

certificate, certification. See *community, county, or municipal agency certificate; court certification; one-physician certificate; two-physician certificate.*

certified specialist. See under *American Boards.*

clinical psychologist. See *psychologist, clinical.*

clinical record. *case history.*

clothing and money supplied to patient upon release. A patient, upon release from a civil institution (discharge, convalescent status, conditional release, etc.) is entitled to be furnished with suitable and seasonal clothing and sufficient funds to defray his expenses until he reaches his relatives or obtains employment.

colony. See *residence house.*

committee. A person, group of persons, or an institution appointed by the court to safeguard the material interests (e.g., moneys, real estate) of a patient confined in a psychiatric institution, public or private. The committee (in the Veterans Administration and in some states referred to as a "guardian") may be a relative, friend, attorney, the commissioner of public welfare or mental hygiene, or the director of the institution in which the patient is confined. Ordinarily the committee is required to post a bond equal to not less than the total of the incompetent person's property and his probable income from any and all sources for the following two years. A small stipend is usually paid the committee, always from the interest accruing to the patient's estate and never from the principal. The usual full legal title for such person acting in the patient's behalf is "committee of the person and property of (patient's name)." Cf. *conservator, limited committee*.

common law power of a court.   The authority of a court to intervene in the business affairs of a mentally ill or mentally retarded person rests on the established principle that it is the duty of the state to protect from the consequences of his own acts any person not "under the guidance of reason" (a legal phrase proposed and accepted at the turn of the century). In the exercise of this power, a contract will be declared voidable if one of the parties was "unable to form an intelligent purpose deliberately to execute the matter in question." The protected party, or his legal representative, may accept or reject the contract as his best interests determine. In order to uphold the testament of a person alleged to have been mentally ill at the time of its execution (see also under *legal papers*), it is necessary to show that the testator had sufficient capacity to comprehend perfectly the condition of his property, his relations to the persons who were or should or might have been heirs to his estate, and the scope and bearing of the provisions of his will. Similarly, a marriage will be annulled (see *marriage, dissolution of*) if incapacity to consent for want of understanding can be proved.

In all these instances, the court must be persuaded that the alleged incapacity involves lack of comprehension of the specific act in question. In other words, if a litigant's attorney raises the issue of lack of understanding, he must prove that his client was unable to perform intelligently the act at issue; the mentally ill person has an obvious advantage if he is attempting to avoid performing the act. The fact that the person involved was a certified patient in a mental hospital during the time in question apparently has the effect of shifting the burden of proof to the person who is claiming against the patient. Mere presence in such a hospital would probably have the same effect even without the certification (as in the case of patients admitted on nonjudicial status or on the certificate of one or two physicians, etc.).

A practical difficulty with this kind of court intervention is that it comes after the fact, sometimes long after. In business affairs third parties must often be assured of the legal competence of the party with whom they are dealing at the time of the particular transaction. Furthermore, the court cannot preserve the business position of a person confined in a mental hospital, who is as a consequence physically unable to handle his affairs. It was for these reasons that the various states and the Veterans Administration long ago made statutory provisions for legal guardians and committees.

community mental health. The united efforts of a local community to make psychiatric diagnostic and treatment facilities available to those who cannot afford them, and to enhance and encourage research, outpatient services, and inpatient accommodations. In most instances, supplementary financial assistance is obtained from state and federal resources.

community, county, or municipal agency certificate. Upon the written request of a county or municipal commissioner of health (or social or public welfare), local health officer, director of a community mental health service, or a physician duly designated by any of them, the director of a civil psychiatric institution may receive for care and treatment any person regarded by the aforementioned officials as dangerous to himself, to others, or to the community, or who, in their opinion, requires immediate care and treatment because of mental illness or retardation. Under such a certificate the patient may be retained for a specified period of time (from 10 to 60 days in various states). At the end of the given period, unless the patient has signed a voluntary application for retention, or a nonstatutory admission form, he must be either returned to the agency involved or admitted to the institution under the provisions of a more binding instrument such as a court certification, one- or two-physician certificate, etc.

competence, -cy. A legal term describing the ability of a person to function with mental clarity, reasonable logic, and relatively unimpaired judgment. In its most practical application it refers to the capacity to participate in ordinary legal matters which may concern the individual's welfare: the making of a will, control of real property, management of a business, etc.

A judge may decide that a person was (at the time in question) incompetent to manage his own affairs or unable to carry out properly a particular transaction, for one of a number of reasons: chronic alcoholism, senility, or mental illness or retardation. See also *criminal responsibility, M'Naghten rule.*

confidential nature of information about a patient. Information provided by a patient or by someone in his behalf and the documents and records in which it is recorded are regarded as confidential. In fact, a physician (or anyone else who has access to the information) is forbidden by law to disclose any such information acquired in attending or treating a patient. Exceptions are: instances wherein a patient who is regarded as competent (see *competence*) gives written permission for revelation of the confidence, and situations in which the revelation would not be inimical to the best interests of the patient.

conservator. In many jurisdictions persons are appointed by the courts to assist patients in psychiatric institutions who are unable to care for themselves or their property. When a judge designates someone to act as a conservator, the appointment is on an informal basis; for example, the designee does not have to post a bond to cover the patient's income and property. Otherwise, the duties and qualifications of a conservator are the same as those of a committee.

consulting and attending staff. All civil and many licensed private institutions have consulting and attending physicians in the various branches of medicine. Such physicians are certified by the American boards of their specialties (e.g., internal medicine, gynecology, surgery) and their subordinates are either similarly certified, or are "board-eligible" (i.e., they have the necessary professional qualifications but lack the number of years of experience required before admission to the board's examinations). *Attending* physicians visit the institution at regularly scheduled intervals; they make rounds, teach the resident staff, and review unusual cases for the purpose of establishing or verifying diagnosis and/or treatment programs. *Consultant* physicians perform similar duties, but only when called to the institution. Other attending and consulting staff members include such nonmedical specialties as podiatrists and orthodontists.

convalescent care, convalescent status. In the 1940's these terms began to replace "parolee" and "parole" as designations for the administrative status of a patient who, although released to the community, was regarded as still in need of some psychiatric attention and who called at the institution's outpatient clinic for "check-ups" or was visited at home by a psychiatric social worker. Under the Interstate Mental Health Compact it is now legally permissible to place a patient on convalescent status in a state other than the one in which he resides. Cf. *trial visit.*

county agency certificate. See under *community, county, or municipal agency certificate.*

court certification. This legal procedure, formerly called "commitment," is being employed less frequently as the trend toward nonstatutory admission grows. It is a means whereby a person is adjudged to be mentally ill or retarded and in need of treatment, possibly in a psychiatric institution. The document supporting the action comprises: 1) a *petition* made by a spouse or other relative, a close friend, a health or welfare official, or the landlord or person with whom the alleged mentally ill or retarded person resides; 2) the *medical certificate*, a record of an examination by two physicians qualified by the state or under statutory standards to conduct such an examination; and 3) the *certification* itself, in which a judge orders that the patient be placed in the care or custody of a relative, friend, or guardian (see *committee*), or, in some states, in the custody of the commissioner of mental hygiene, who then assigns the patient to an institution. In some jurisdictions the court directs that the patient be admitted to a specific institution. The certification document also provides for a hearing, or review of the past proceedings, subsequent to the making of the order of certification. This review may be undertaken at the request of the patient or someone in his behalf, or by order of the judge.

court of record. A court of record is one whose actions and judicial proceedings and judgments are permanently preserved and hence can be verified through the record. Magistrates' and police courts, whose records are discarded after a stipulated lapse of time, are not courts of record.

crimes committed by the mentally ill. Whenever a crime, especially one of violence, is committed by a person who has been hospitalized in a psychiatric institution, there is a hue and cry in the news media about negligence on the part of the hospital staff or mental health authorities, ranging from charges of "faulty diagnosis" and "lax control of patients" to "unwise and precipitate release of dangerous persons." It should be reassuring to an anxious public, however, to know that the American Psychiatric Association's Blaine Report of 1954, based on a nationwide survey, showed that among former mental patients the rate of crime is one-fourth that of the general population.

It must be borne in mind that mental institutions are not prisons, but places for the care and treatment of sick people. It is inevitable that a large number of persons with criminal records will turn up in mental hospitals. When such a patient has recovered from his psychiatric illness, he *must* be released; if he is to be retained, this is a responsibility of the courts and public authorities. With expansion of the open-door policy in mental institutions, some risks are bound to be incurred, though the aforementioned statistics indicate that they are minimal. To cite an example from the clinical viewpoint: more than half of all patients in mental institutions have paranoid tendencies in varying degrees, but a mental hospital cannot retain a patient for life merely because of his paranoid and potentially destructive inclinations.

One fact remains to be considered. Not infrequently relatives of a disturbed, potentially violent patient, usually in remorse or with feelings of guilt, demand his release and, armed with a writ of habeas corpus, are able to override the objections of the hospital director.

criminal responsibility.   In February, 1966, the United States Court of Appeals, Second Circuit, discarded the M'Naghten rule of criminal responsibility and adopted for its jurisdiction a new standard formulated by the American Law Institute. The new standard provides that:

'A person is not responsible for criminal conduct if at the time of such conduct as a result of mental disease or defect he lacks substantial capacity either to appreciate the wrongfulness of his conduct or to conform his conduct to the requirements of law.'

This definition goes considerably further than any state statute by adding the phrase "or to conform his conduct to the requirements of the law." This embodies the concept that even though a defendant may be aware of the wrongfulness of his act, he may lack the substantial capacity to control his actions.

The same court rejected the concept of "irresistible impulse" which, it said, as a "test, has become encrusted on the laws of several jurisdictions. . . . We find the 'irresistible impulse' test to be inherently inadequate and unsatisfactory. Psychiatrists have long questioned whether 'irresistible impulses' actually exist; the more basic legal objection to the term . . . is that it is too narrow and carries the misleading implication that a crime impulsively committed must have been perpetrated in a sudden and explosive fit. Thus . . . it excludes the far more numerous instances of crime committed after excessive brooding and melancholy by one who is unable to resist sustained psychic compulsion or make any real attempt to control his conduct. . . . The criminal act may be the reverse of the impulse; it may be coolly and carefully prepared yet nevertheless the result of a diseased mind. The 'irresistible impulse' test is . . . little more than a gloss on M'Naghten. . . ." See also *competence, M'Naghten rule.*

criminality and mental illness or retardation.   When an alleged criminal has been arrested and it appears to the judge that he is mentally ill or retarded, the judge may direct that the accused be admitted to an appropriate institution for a specified period of time (usually thirty or sixty days) for observation. The director of the institution is ordered to render, at the end of that time, a written opinion as to the individual's psychiatric status. The director may also be called upon to testify in court. If the alleged criminal has been arrested, confined, and indicted, and it appears to the district attorney or the judge that the person may be mentally ill or retarded, the foregoing procedure is usually followed. The defendant's counsel may also ask that the accused undergo psychiatric examination, or he may notify the judge that a plea of "mental illness" (in some jurisdictions, "insanity") or "mental retardation" (or "deficiency") will be entered by the defendant. If in either instance it is shown that the mental illness or retardation is of such degree that the defendant cannot be held criminally responsible for his act, he cannot be sentenced, imprisoned, or punished for his crime. (See *criminal responsibility, M'Naghten rule.*) The judge then certifies the defendant for admission to an institution for mentally ill or retarded criminals, ordering that he be confined therein until such time as his condition has improved sufficiently for him to stand trial. Even if the defendant is regarded as competent to stand trial, the judge may still certify him for care and treatment in a mental institution, if he believes such action to be in the defendant's best interests.

As time passes, a patient in an institution for mentally ill or retarded criminals may no longer show criminal tendencies but continues to be mentally impaired. In many states he may be transferred to a civil mental institution.

If an inmate of a correctional institution becomes mentally ill, he may be transferred to a suitable institution. Upon recovery from the mental illness, he is returned to prison to complete his sentence, unless he has been pardoned. Time spent in the mental institution is counted as time spent in prison.

day care center. A community facility for the treatment of mentally retarded or emotionally disturbed children, operated as an adjunct of a psychiatric institution or independently as a clinic by a state or local mental hygiene agency. The stress is on preventive psychiatry, with parents and child receiving counsel and needed therapy and training.

de lunatico inquiriendo. A legal phrase describing the function of a body appointed by the court to determine the mental condition of a person whose competency has been challenged.

deportation. See under *alien patient, return to homeland.*

diagnosis in mental illness. The diagnostic approach in psychiatry is becoming increasingly holistic, bringing into play any procedure that may facilitate understanding of the patient's condition. Among the routine measures are: history-taking (which itself permits the exercise of observation and interpretation), physical examination as for any medical condition (including laboratory and x-ray studies), and a broad range of psychologic inquiries, among them the Wechsler Adult Inventory Scale, Rorschach Diagnostic Method, and Minnesota Multiphasic Personality Inventory. In contrast to former approaches, the effort is made not so much to fit the patient into a standard diagnostic category as to learn the internal and external stresses to which he has been subjected and the form of his reaction to them.

diplomate.   See under *American Boards.*

discharge of patient.   See under *release of patient from institution.*

drug addict, admission to psychiatric institution.   Traditionally, psychiatric institutions have not accepted drug addicts as patients unless a clear-cut mental disorder coexisted with the addiction. However, some states have statutes which provide that a person arrested for possessing and using narcotics or charged with a crime committed while under the influence of drugs may be remanded to a mental institution for medical treatment and psychotherapy. (Admission to a federal institution for narcotism is on a voluntary basis.)

elopement.   See *absence, unauthorized.*

emergency admission.   In most jurisdictions, when a person's mental condition warrants his immediate hospitalization, statutory provisions permit admission to a civil or licensed private psychiatric facility solely on the petition and medical certificate portions of the document described under *court certification.* Within ten days from and inclusive of the date of such admission, the director of the institution must either discharge the patient or arrange for his retention for further care and treatment under another of the admission methods enumerated under *admission procedures;* often this has to be a court certification. See also *peace officers' responsibilities.*

epilepsy and the community.   Once regarded with apprehension in the community, and denied certain privileges and refused employment, epileptic persons have won acceptance and cooperation. For example, many states have declined to grant them licenses to drive motor vehicles, but with the advent of effective anticonvulsant drugs that enable many epileptics to continue symptom-free, a campaign was initiated in 1963 to liberalize motor vehicle statutes in this respect. From the economic point of view, the United States Department of Health, Education, and Welfare has announced that between 80 and 90 percent of the nation's 1.5 million epileptics are capable of normal employment.

escape. See *absence, unauthorized.*

family care. A system of outpatient care originating in Belgium and instituted in New York State in the 1930's. A patient suitable for release but having no relatives or friends to whom he can go or who could provide appropriate quarters and supervision is placed with a family that has expressed willingness to accept him. Prior to the patient's release, the foster home is inspected by a psychiatric social worker from the institution, who interviews the family. After placement, the social worker visits the patient at regular intervals. The family is reimbursed by the state or county, and a specified amount is given to the patient for spending money whether or not he is gainfully employed. Syn. *boarding out.* Cf. *halfway house, residence house.*

FANA. Fellow of the American Neurological Association.

FAPA. Fellow of the American Psychiatric Association, American Psychoanalytical Association, or American Psychological Association,

fingerprinting of patients. See *photographing and fingerprinting of patients.*

follow-up treatment. See *after-care.*

foster care of children. While it may be assumed that any normal child develops a more rounded personality in the milieu of a family than under institutional care, there are no statistics to show how the normal foster child fares in comparison with the normal child raised by his own family. However, with regard to disturbed children in foster care, an intensive research program conducted in 1963 clearly established that a total-treatment outpatient program does not substantially improve the condition of the disturbed foster child nor preclude his reinstitutionalization. The study revealed that while foster care might have brought about improvement in overt behavior, there were no basic changes in the child's personality. Comparisons between normal foster children and emotionally disturbed foster children indicate that foster home care is ineffectual as a method of treatment for the seriously disturbed child.

governors.   See *board of governors, managers, or visitors.*

ground parole.   An earlier term for *honor privileges.* See also *open-door policy.*

guardian.   See *board of governors, managers, or visitors.*

habeas corpus, writ of.   A judicial order the objective of which is to bring before a judge or court a person who is alleged to be detained or imprisoned against his will or unlawfully. The director of a psychiatric institution is required to release a patient to the custody of a court in response to such a writ.

halfway house.   A dwelling, usually in a city or large town, where patients from civil mental institutions who have no relatives or immediate prospects for employment or self-support are sent upon their release (discharge or on convalescence). A halfway house enables the former patient to return to urban life on a gradual scale (i.e., he is not thrust into the hubbub of the city directly from the comparatively sheltered milieu of the institution). It also provides a dignified home where the patient may help in the housework and enjoy the company of others in his age bracket and life situation, and from which he can make occasional probing excursions into the center of the community. Such facilities are supported by the local (usually municipal) government, in some cases with state aid, or under the aegis of private or religious welfare and mental hygiene agencies. Cf. *boarding out, family care, residence house.*

health officer's certificate.   See under *community, county, or municipal agency certificate.*

home visit.   See *trial visit.*

homicidal tendencies.   The tendency to homicide in mentally ill persons is not nearly so prevalent as many laymen believe, the incidence being about one-quarter that in the general population. The rare instance of homicide within a psychiatric institution or committed by a patient who has left the institution with or without permission is usually described so dramatically by news media that public reaction and anxiety are stronger than they need to be. A minority of mental patients who commit homicides have shown homicidal tendencies in their past histories. In most states patients who manifest such tendencies and who are regarded as overtly or potentially dangerous to others may be transferred to an institution for mentally ill criminals. See also *crimes committed by the mentally ill.*

honor privileges. Mental patients whose condition has improved to the extent that they no longer require continuous observation are accorded complete freedom of the institution's grounds and/or the privilege of unrestricted visits in the surrounding community during daylight hours. See also *open-door policy.*

imprisonment of mentally ill persons. See *peace officers' responsibilities.*

incompetency. See *competence.*

informal admission. *nonstatutory admission.*

information about mental patient. See *confidential nature of information about a patient.*

insanity, acquittal on ground of. See *acquittal on ground of mental disorder.*

inspection of psychiatric institutions. Inspection of conditions in public and private psychiatric institutions is a continuous process, conducted at prescribed intervals and at various levels. It encompasses not only the efforts of institution directors and their department heads but outside agencies, such as local municipal fire departments and health, welfare, and sanitation authorities. In addition, institutions are inspected at least twice a year by officials of the controlling state department of mental hygiene, health, or welfare. All patients admitted and remaining since the last inspection by a state official must be privately interviewed, and their complaints heard and investigated. The environment, treatment program, and dietary of the institution are reviewed systematically. See also *board of governors, managers, or visitors.*

institutions, kinds of. Psychiatric institutions are designated as either civil (public) or licensed private; civil institutions are categorized as either federal, state, county, or municipal. Some are engaged principally in psychiatric and neurologic research. State institutions for the mentally retarded are often called "state schools." Those who have run afoul of the law are usually cared for and treated in institutions for defective delinquents or hospitals for mentally ill criminals.

Interstate Mental Health Compact. An agreement among states to accept in transfer, regardless of their statutory restrictions, psychiatric patients who would benefit by the transfer. Criteria of residence and citizenship are replaced by economic, social, and therapeutic considerations; for example, opportunity for employment or the presence of sympathetic relatives in another state may justify the transfer. The first signatory to this agreement was Connecticut (1955), followed by New York (1956). By 1964 more than half the states had joined the compact.

irresistible impulse.   See under *criminal responsibility*.

judicial certification.   *court certification.*

juvenile delinquency. Crimes and misdemeanors committed by juveniles are generally accorded greater leniency by the courts than the same antisocial acts committed by older persons. The assumption is that the younger person is relatively less well equipped to exercise judgment and is therefore less responsible for his misdeeds. The problem is complicated by the differences in age stipulations of a "juvenile." Statutes give the level as 16, 18, or 21 years, depending on the character of the delinquency and the jurisdiction. In the latter half of this century both the incidence and the severity of juvenile delinquency have increased by leaps and bounds throughout the western world, and even in Soviet Russia, where behavior is rigidly controlled. More and more the courts are "unloading" juvenile delinquents on psychiatric clinics and hospitals rather than committing them to correctional institutions. The one feature common to most cases is emotional instability in the home, and it is generally believed that therapy which does not encompass the family constellation brings few changes in the delinquent's behavior. Economic stress is not regarded as a determining factor since delinquency is evident at all social and economic levels. Few delinquents are found to be suffering from severe psychotic or neurotic reactions; they usually fall within the category of transient situational personality disorders, if indeed there is any question of mental illness.

legal papers, signing and serving of.   Except upon an order of a judge, a patient in a psychiatric institution may not be served with any legal paper or process. The only exceptions are: citations for probate of wills; letters of administration or application for intermediate or final settlement of accounts of committees of patients; final accountings of committees in designated courts; and papers dealing with appointment of committees. The director of the institution or his designated officer must be present. A note of the event must be made in the patient's record. Copies of the legal paper served are filed in the case record and with the state departments of law and mental hygiene (or social welfare). A copy is also sent to the patient's committee or nearest relative, and a copy is given to the patient.

No mentally ill, retarded, or epileptic patient is permitted to sign a check or other evidence of indebtedness, to make a will, or to execute a deed, mortgage, contract or other legal conveyance, except upon permission of the commissioner of mental hygiene (or public welfare) or by order of a judge of a court of record. Ordinarily this does not apply to a patient hospitalized under nonstatutory conditions (voluntary patient), though the institution director must be informed of the circumstances. A patient may, however, endorse a check if the money is to be deposited to his account in the institution and made available for his own use. Most states allow a patient to draw or endorse checks when the sum involved does not exceed a specified amount.

Whenever a psychiatric patient is permitted to execute or issue a legal instrument, he must (1) have sufficient mental capacity to understand the transaction and the nature and consequences of his act and (2) be willing to sign and execute the instrument.

In the making of a will, in addition to the aforementioned requirements, the named beneficiaries must exist and have a reasonable association or relationship with the patient; if a philanthropic or charitable cause is designated as an heir, it must be a reputable one and acceptable to the court.

The above restrictions normally apply only to persons who have been judicially certified to be mentally ill or retarded, and in some jurisdictions, epileptic. Patients in institutions on voluntary application or under nonstatutory types of admission are not denied such liberties of action unless they show signs of irresponsibility at the time.

limited committee. The interests of a patient in a psychiatric institution are protected by a court-appointed committee or conservator. However, most jurisdictions provide also for a limited committee. In such circumstances, the law provides that the commissioner of mental health or hygiene or public or social welfare may authorize directors or superintendents of mental institutions to receive or obtain funds or other personal property (except jewelry) due or belonging to a patient who has no committee—up to a specified amount or value—without taking proceedings for the appointment of a committee. Such funds and the proceeds of the sale of other personal property so received are placed to the credit of the patient for whom received, and disbursed, on the order of the director or superintendent, to provide luxuries, comforts, and necessities for the patient. A director or superintendent may, on behalf of the patient, also give receipts, execute releases and other documents required by law or court order, endorse checks and drafts, and convert personal property (except jewelry) into cash by sale for adequate consideration. Cf. *committee, conservator.*

mail to and from patients. Patients in civil institutions for the mentally ill and retarded are permitted and encouraged to write as often as they like; if they cannot afford stationery and postage, these are supplied. The institution may censor all such outgoing mail, and if a relative requests in writing that a patient's mail to another person be stopped because of the disturbing effects of its contents or of profane or obscene language used by the patient, such a request may be honored. Mail adjudged by the censoring officer to be objectionable is returned to the patient, along with the reason for refusing to post it. However, all letters addressed to the governor or attorney general of the state, officers of the department of mental hygiene (or welfare), judges of courts of record, district attorneys, and attorneys licensed to practice in the state must be posted without any examination of their contents. All incoming mail is delivered unopened to the patient. However, packages are opened in his presence and dangerous materials (e.g., razor blades) and alcoholic beverages are removed and retained for return to the patient's relatives.

marriage, dissolution on ground of mental illness. Throughout the United States, statutes hold that a marriage may be dissolved if one of the parties has been "incurably" mentally ill for a period of five years or more prior to the commencement of the action. Contrary to popular belief, it is not necessary that the mentally ill partner have resided in an institution during the stated period. A husband who institutes such action must, before the dissolution is granted, provide a security prescribed by the court, for the wife's care and maintenance for life. Should she remarry, this obligation ceases. See also under *common law power of a court.*

McNaughton rule. See *M'Naghten rule.*

mechanical restraint. See *restraint, protective.*

medical services in psychiatric institutions. All civil and many private licensed institutions for the mentally ill and retarded have general hospital facilities (for internal medicine, surgery, obstetrics, etc.) and their staffs are provided with consulting and attending physicians.

The term "medical service" in this framework refers to nonpsychiatric medical services. See also *consulting and attending staff.*

mental age and criminal trial. Several jurisdictions have statutory provisions whereby a mentally retarded adult defendant is regarded as a minor with a chronologic age the same as his mental age. That is, if his mental age is eight years, ten months, he is tried as if he were a child eight years, ten months old.

mental health information service for the court. Several states have begun to enact legislation whereby each appellate court district is afforded access to the services of psychiatrists, social investigators, and other specialized personnel who, when the need arises, may be directed to study the circumstances surrounding a patient's admission to or retention in a psychiatric institution, as well as to inform the patient of his rights before the law. The service is made available only to patients already in institutions under other than voluntary or nonstatutory arrangements (i.e., court certification, community or county agency certificate, etc.)

mental hygiene. This term was used in psychiatric literature as early as the middle of the nineteenth century. The concept is based on the belief that preventive measures can be developed and applied for mental illnesses as they are for other health problems. The term first gained wide recognition and use in the name of the National Committee for Mental Hygiene, established in 1909. It was the forerunner of several present-day lay organizations which encourage and subsidize research, new and improved community facilities, and institutional programs, and support progressive legislation concerning the mentally ill and retarded. The principal such organizations are:

> Mental Health Foundation of America, Inc.
> > 2 East 86th Street, New York, N.Y. 10028
> National Association for Mental Health, Inc.
> > 10 Columbus Circle, New York, N.Y. 10019
> National Institute of Mental Health
> > National Institutes of Health, Public Health Service
> > U.S. Department of Health, Education, and Welfare
> > Bethesda, Maryland 20014
> Association for the Help of Retarded Children
> > 200 Park Avenue South, New York, N.Y. 10016
> United Epilepsy Association, Inc.
> > 111 West 57th Street, New York, N.Y. 10019
> World Federation for Mental Health
> > 124 East 28th Street, New York, N.Y. 10016

M'Naghten (M'Naughten) (McNaughton) rule. A guiding principle in law which still wields considerable influence on juristic attitudes in cases of crime where the mental competency of the accused is in question. It requires proof that the accused (1) did not know the nature and quality of the act, and (2) did not know that the act was wrong. Many attorneys and psychiatrists favor revision of this to read: A person is not responsible for criminal conduct if, at the time of such conduct, as a result of mental disease or retardation, he lacks substantial capacity

(1) to know or appreciate either the nature and consequence of such conduct or that such conduct was wrong, or

(2) to conform his conduct to the requirements of the law. As used here the term "mental disease or retardation" does not include an abnormality manifested only by repeated criminal or otherwise antisocial conduct. See *competence, criminal responsibility.*

municipal agency certificate.   See under *community, county or municipal agency certificate.*

Narcotics Anonymous.   An organization formed in the 1950's with the objective of helping individuals to overcome drug addiction. By its own statement, it is "an informal group of addicts banded together to help one another renew our strength in remaining free of drugs. Our precepts are patterned after those of Alcoholic Anonymous. . . . We claim no originality . . . but since we believe that the causes of alcoholism and addiction are basically the same, we wish to apply to our lives the truths and principles which have benefited so many otherwise helpless individuals. We believe by so doing we may regain our health and sanity. It shall be the purpose of this group to foster means of rehabilitation for the addict and to carry a message of hope for the future of those who have become enslaved by the use of habit-forming drugs."

National Association for Mental Health.   A nonprofit organization composed of professional and lay persons devoted to the propagation of informative and educational material and guidance on mental health matters; the fostering of research in all fields of psychiatric endeavor; and the development of improved facilities for handling the public health aspects of mental disease and retardation.

National Institute of Mental Health.   The division of the National Institutes of Health (the research arm of the United States Public Health Service) that is devoted to research in psychiatry and related disciplines.

nonjudicial medical admission.   This type of admission procedure includes: one-physician certificate, two-physician certificate, and county or municipal agency certificate.

nonstatutory admission.   An informal type of hospital admission in which the patient (in the case of a minor, a parent or guardian of the patient) requests hospitalization because of emotional or mental disorder and simply signs an agreement to abide by the rules of the institution.

Beginning early in 1963, many states enacted legislation making it possible for a person to enter a civil or licensed private mental institution on the same basis as for a general hospital. That is, the statute permits a psychiatric institution to admit persons suitable for treatment therein without having recourse to any formal or written application and allows them to leave the hospital at their own discretion. Informal admission obviates the stigma of legal (judicial) commitment and its implications. In addition, the simplified procedure of the informal admission expedites hospitalization without unnecessary delay. Syn. *informal admission.* See also *voluntary application for admission.*

ombudsman.   In Denmark and Sweden, an official whose function is "protector-at-large" for the citizenry vs. the state. Anyone who believes himself to be the victim of an injustice may appeal to the ombudsman. Though he has no judicial status, he is empowered to bring grievances to public attention, and it is his duty to do so. Any Dane or Swede placed in a mental institution has the right to appeal in writing to the ombudsman directly, without censorship.

one-physician certificate.   Many states provide for the admission of a mentally ill or mentally retarded person (or an epileptic) upon a petition made by the nearest relative and an examination by one physician (in some states a duly qualified psychologist may conduct the examination). In all instances the patient must express willingness to be admitted at the time of admission. The patient may be retained only for a stated period (usually 60 days) under such an arrangement. At any time he or someone in his behalf may make written application for his discharge. The director of the institution has a specified period of time (usually 15 days) in which he must either comply with the request or, if he believes further hospitalization is needed, begin proceedings to have the patient judicially certified as requiring continued hospitalization.

open-door policy. Mental health authorities have long recognized that a majority of patients can best adjust in the environment of the community, but it is also known that in some cases it is these very environmental forces that precipitate or aggravate the mental illness. Further, the safety of the patient and the community must be borne in mind. The practice of allowing institutionalized psychiatric patients freedom of movement within and away from the hospital is by no means new. More than a century ago selected "inmates" of "lunatic asylums" attended picnics and river-boat rides, took walks "downtown," and engaged in outdoor recreation, often with minor supervision or none at all. In the 1950's, however, this practice was expanded considerably, only the most disturbed, withdrawn, or hallucinative patients being restricted in their activities. Advances in therapy, in particular the use of energizing and tranquilizing drugs, have played an important role in this progress, by making patients more accessible to psychotherapy.

The term "open door" also refers to the growing practice of eliminating most of the "locked-door" wards of psychiatric institutions.

parole.   See *convalescent care, ground parole.*

pastoral psychiatry.   It has been inevitable, and highly desirable, that the clergy should play a significant role in the mental hygiene field. Ministers, priests, and rabbis have long served as either full-time or part-time staff members at psychiatric institutions. In the mid-1950's, however, there was a vigorous movement toward a closer rapprochement between psychiatry and religion, evidenced in a growing number of courses in mental health problems being added to the curricula of seminaries.

peace officer's responsibilities.   Public safety authorities are becoming more enlightened in matters that involve psychopathology. Most police departments give their personnel some training in the recognition of abnormal behavior, management of the mentally ill person, and legal aspects of psychiatry pertinent to their duties. In an emergency, a peace officer is empowered to act on his own judgment in the interest of the public and for the benefit of the individual who may, for example, be acting destructively or creating a disturbance. Where appropriate facilities are available, he arranges for prompt admission of a mentally disturbed person to the observation department of a general hospital or to a psychiatric hospital. Only where facilities do not exist, or are remote, may a mentally ill person be confined temporarily in another kind of institution and then only pending execution of proper documents directing admission to a psychiatric institution. In most communities detention of an alleged mentally ill person in a jail or lockup is positively forbidden. See also *emergency admission, psychiatric emergencies.*

personal property of patients. Upon admission of a patient to a psychiatric institution, all of his personal property that accompanies him (apparel, money, jewelry, dentures, etc.) is immediately inventoried and listed, the list attested to, and the record preserved. Valuables are locked in the institution's vault and kept there until the patient is released or until they are surrendered to the nearest relative upon request. If a patient dies in the institution his personal property is turned over to the nearest relative or the patient's committee. If the patient has made a will, the property is retained at the institution until claimed by the executor. In the absence of relatives, committee, or heirs, personal property is customarily distributed to needy patients.

photographing and fingerprinting of patients. In most public (and some private) mental institutions, patients over the age of sixteen (in some jurisdictions, eighteen) are photographed and fingerprinted. These records, retained at the institution, are not available to anyone except by consent of the commissioner of mental hygiene or social welfare or upon an order made by a judge of a court of record. Such order is to be issued with sufficient notice given to the director of the institution so that he may offer the court reason why such confidential material should not be released. The practice is, however, being gradually abandoned.

prisoner under sentence of death. If a prisoner awaiting execution of a death sentence appears to be mentally disturbed, his sentence is held in abeyance while qualified psychiatrists, appointed by the sentencing court, examine him to determine whether he is malingering or genuinely ill. In the latter instance he is remanded to an institution for mentally ill criminals where he remains until he is regarded as recovered. He is then returned to the prison and execution is carried out unless he has been pardoned or his sentence has been commuted.

property of mental patient. See *personal property of patient.*

protective restraint. See *restraint, protective.*

protective seclusion. See *seclusion.*

public welfare, certificate of the commissioner of. See under *community, county, or municipal agency certificate.*

psychiatric aide. The currently accepted term for "ward attendant."

psychiatric services. Facilities for the treatment of mentally ill, retarded, and epileptic persons include both in-hospital and out-patient services.

In-hospital psychiatric services include civil and private institutions. These are also spoken of as "inpatient facilities." Private facilities may be exclusively devoted to psychiatry or they may be part of a large general hospital or sanatorium or separate buildings on the grounds of a religious organization.

Outpatient services are civil or private facilities licensed or approved by federal, state, county, or municipal agencies (departments of health, mental hygiene, mental health, public welfare, social welfare). Outpatient services include clinics, day and night care services, after-care and rehabilitation centers, residential treatment centers for children, day care centers, special day schools for emotionally disturbed children, facilities for alcoholic and narcotic addicts, and round-the-clock walk-in psychiatric emergency centers.

psychiatric social worker. The psychiatric social worker is a case-worker who has had special instruction in the psychology of abnormal persons and whose professional activities are concerned principally with the family and community relationships of the mentally ill or retarded or epileptic. He may be responsible for service to patients resident in a psychiatric hospital or to those on community status from the hospital or both; or he may act in behalf of a mental health (hygiene) clinic. The psychiatric social worker usually contributes considerable material to the anamnesis with regard to family history, personal history, health background, and mental and emotional difficulties, as well as significant facts about the patient's environment and his reactions to it. Later, the social worker is responsible for surveying the environment to which the improved or recovered patient may be returned, and for evaluating facilities and milieu of foster homes, family care homes, etc.

psychiatrist. In the strictest sense, a physician who is certified as a specialist in psychiatry by the American Board of Psychiatry and Neurology. In courts of law, a noncertified psychiatrist is seldom qualified as an expert witness. See *American Boards.*

psychologist, clinical. The practice is growing whereby statutes require that an individual possess his doctorate (Ph.D.) in psychology before he can be permitted to list, describe, or advertise himself as a psychologist. Property qualified psychologists may conduct examinations for certain classes of certifications leading to the admission of a mentally ill or retarded person to a psychiatric institution.

Scope of Practice. The practice of psychotherapy by a psychologist who is not a physician has been a bone of contention between psychiatrists and psychologists since the 1950's. At the core of the dispute is the question whether or not psychotherapy is medical therapy. In the holistic approach to mental-emotional disorder, psychic and organic considerations become inextricably interwoven. This impasse has been further aggravated by the advances in pharmacologic knowledge and its application in psychopathology. In the hands of a psychologist, whose training and experience in pharmacology, physiology, and anatomy are usually limited, a patient would be denied the benefit of this area of treatment, since a nonmedical practitioner is forbidden by law to prescribe medication.

In general, the psychiatrist regards the clinical psychologist (who holds a doctorate) as being qualified to assist in diagnosis (as in the administration and interpretation of intelligence tests and personality inquiries) and in uncovering the dynamics of the patient's personality through interview. Paradoxically, it is in the psychologist's interest for his range of activity to be defined, for there is no law that prohibits anyone with less training than a psychologist (or no training at all) from calling himself a "therapist" under whatever guise. Psychotherapy undertaken by a psychologist is best conducted under the prescription, guidance, and supervision of a psychiatrist, and this is the procedure followed in hospitals or clinics that have psychologists on their staffs.

readmission. See under *return of patient to institution.*

reimbursement for care in a public psychiatric institution. There is a system of reimbursement for the care and treatment of mentally ill persons in most civil mental institutions. Whether the charge will be levied, and the amount of the charge, depends on the family's finances or the income from the patient's estate (income, property, moneys in banking institutions, securities, pension, social security benefits, etc.) as certified in the annual accounting rendered by the patient's committee. Generally the maximum statutory rate is the estimated average per-patient cost as expressed in the institution's budget for the ensuing fiscal year.

Recovery, Incorporated. A system of self-help for former mental patients, developed by Abraham Low, contemporary Chicago psychiatrist, based on continued psychotherapy after institutionalization. At regular meetings, under the guidance of a "mediator"—also a former patient—the group conducts a group therapy session. The stated objectives of the organization are "to prevent relapses and to avoid chronicity in mental disorders." Meetings may be held in civil mental institutions and clinics, schools, churches, etc. The national headquarters of Recovery, Incorporated is in Chicago, Illinois. Branches are located in all large cities.

release of patient from institution. A psychiatric patient is released from an institution under either of two general circumstances: he may be released outright (discharged), in which case he is no longer counted in the hospital's census of patients and his current case record is closed; or he may be released under one of several conditions which are in essence intermediate stages, in which case he is still carried on the institution's books.

Discharge may be deemed suitable because (1) the patient has made a complete recovery and requires no further follow-up study or therapy; (2) his family has moved to another state, or to another country (see *alien patient, return to homeland*); (3) he is being transferred to another institution in the state, usually a veterans' hospital or to an institution in another state, or to a licensed private institution (see *transfer of psychiatric patients*); or (4) his discharge has been ordered through habeas corpus proceedings or by the commissioner of mental hygiene or public welfare or, in some jurisdictions, by the director of the institution because he deems the patient not mentally ill or retarded or not suitable for detention in the institution.

Intermediate stages of release include convalescent status, family care, and trial visit.

repatriation. See under *alien patient, return to homeland.*

residence house. Formerly known as a "colony." A dwelling principally used to accommodate mentally retarded patients who are being considered for final release from the parent institution. Such houses are customarily located in residential areas of urban communities and provide rooms accommodating two patients each. The residents are usually those capable of filling positions such as maid, clerk, launderer, etc. who, when they attain sufficient clinical improvement and vocational efficiency, may work in the community and return to the residence house for the evening meal and to sleep. Residence houses are particularly effective in the case of retarded persons (most always mildly retarded), who, by this intermediate live-in, work-out arrangement, can be "eased" into the outside world, whereas direct release might be too much of a challenge to be borne by their limited intelligence. Cf. *family care, halfway house.*

restraint, protective.   The oft-mentioned "strait jacket" has practically vanished from the psychiatric scene in the United States. The advent of tranquilizers has to a great degree obviated the use of mechanical restraint and seclusion in institutions for the mentally ill. Most civil and private institutions use only the camisole (which restricts arm and hand movements) and restraining sheet (which allows body movement while the patient is confined to bed). See also *seclusion.*

return of patient to institution.   When a patient returns to an institution after a prior admission and subsequent release, his statistical classification as a returnee depends on the conditions of his release. A person who is discharged and subsequently returns to the institution (whether it is the same day he leaves or many years later) is a readmission. A patient who left the hospital on convalescent status and returns after one day or several years is a return from convalescent status. In the case of readmission, new documents must be executed to accept the patient; the convalescent patient continues on his original status. Since 1955, coincident with the advent and use of tranquilizers, returns of patients to civil and private institutions have been steadily decreasing. Prior to this time, the average rate of return was 25 to 40 percent; since then it has fallen as low as 15 percent. It is believed that the return rate could be lowered still further but for two factors: (1) the inability in many instances to have the responsible relative or friend see that the patient regularly takes medication as prescribed and reports for after-care treatment; and (2) the inability of many underprivileged patients to afford to purchase prescribed medication, since some social welfare laws do not permit the use of funds for this purpose.

right-and-wrong test.   See *M'Naghten rule.*

sanitorium.   A privately operated profit or nonprofit institution for the care and treatment of mentally ill or retarded persons or persons suffering from chronic physical diseases is known as a sanatorium, and should not be confused with a sanitarium, which is a health resort.

sane, sanity.   Legal terms referring to mental state, and applied with regard to the individual's competence. The words have no significance in psychiatry.

seclusion, protective.   The practice of placing disturbed patients in seclusion or isolation is gradually being abandoned. Technically, a patient is considered to be "in seclusion" either in daytime or night-time, when in a room alone with a closed door that cannot be opened from the inside. The rules of most mental hospitals stipulate that no patient may be kept in protective seclusion for more than three hours in the daytime and he must be visited every hour, day and night, and that seclusion, like restraint, can be carried out only upon the written order of a physician. A ward nurse or psychiatric aide must maintain a complete record of all periods of protective seclusion.

sex offender.   Sex offenders present a legal and psychiatric dilemma. State legislatures have frequently provided funds and passed implementing laws for the treatment of sex offenders in hospitals because it has been generally agreed that a prison term does not bring improvement. However, a nation-wide survey in the United States showed that sex offenders who are sent to treatment centers show little or no improvement; only 7 percent of these institutions reported that hospitalization was effective, another 7 percent that it was of "some help." Intensive research is needed in this field, both in psychodynamics and in therapy; otherwise, the pendulum of legal opinion may swing back to stress on custodial care.

social security benefits.   Psychiatric conditions are included among the conditions warranting payment of disability benefits under the social security system in the United States. Because proof of any disability is the responsibility of the afflicted person, and the severely mentally ill person usually lacks the capacity to undertake the required action, in most states application for benefits is made by the institution, though a relative or friend may initiate the application on the patient's behalf.

social worker, psychiatric.   See *psychiatric social worker.*

state school.   An institution for the care, treatment, and training of mentally retarded persons. The term "state hospital and school" is now gaining favor.

statistics of mental illness.   Appreciation of the significance of mental illness as a public health problem depends in large measure on the availability of meaningful statistics. The principal areas of interest are reflected in the following basic yardsticks (which do not include figures for the mentally retarded):

ratio of hospitalized mentally ill to the general population
    (414 per 100,000, or 1 in 240 persons)
expectancy of mental illness
    (It has been estimated that 1 person out of every 10 in the United States
    will at some time in his life require treatment for some form of mental
    illness.)

percent of all hospital beds occupied by psychiatric patients
> (about 50 percent of all hospital beds [about 1,800,000] in the United States)

net change in number of patients discharged vs. number admitted to psychiatric hospitals
> (In New York State, with about one-eighth of the hospitalized psychiatric patients in the United States, discharges since 1955 have exceeded admissions to such an extent that the resident patient population continues to drop at an average annual rate of 3.5 percent; this occurs despite an increase in admissions during the same period.)

percent of beds in psychiatric hospitals occupied by patients of advanced age, for whom continued hospitalization is anticipated
> (In 1931, patients 60 years and older comprised 10 percent of patients resident in New York State psychiatric hospitals and their average life expectancy was 2.1 years; since 1963 such patients constitute 40 percent of the resident patients and their life expectancy is over 10 years.)

suicide.   Among hospitalized mental patients the incidence of suicide is much lower than in the general population, and it is continually decreasing. This is believed to be due in great measure to the broader use of the tranquilizing drugs, which either reduce deep depression or render the patient more amenable to effective psychotherapy.

The suicide (or attempt at suicide) of a patient in a psychiatric institution is immediately investigated by the institution's director or by a senior officer designated by him. The details are reported to the coroner or medical examiner of the community in which the institution is located, and to the commissioner of mental hygiene (or social welfare).

suicide, prevention of.   The International Association for Suicide Prevention was established in Vienna, Austria, March 10, 1965. The association has among its goals the establishment of an organization in which individuals and agencies of various disciplines and professions from different countries can find a common platform for interchange of experience, literature, and information about suicide. The association aims to disseminate information on suicide prevention to professional and public groups, to arrange for specialized training of selected persons in suicide prevention, and to encourage, facilitate, and carry out programs and research, especially those which can be pursued through international joint cooperation.

Synanon Foundation.   A nonprofit national organization providing residential assistance for the basic character problems of narcotic addicts. It was founded in 1959 at Santa Monica, California, under the leadership of Charles Diderich; there are branches throughout the United States.

transfer of psychiatric patients. A patient may be released from a civil psychiatric institution on transfer status to go to a Veterans Administration facility, to another state (under a reciprocal agreement between the states involved or in accordance with the provisions of the Interstate Mental Health Compact), or to a nonpsychiatric institution for special medical care (e.g., a hospital for the treatment of cancer).

trial visit. A psychiatric patient who shows clinical improvement may, prior to actual release, be permitted to visit relatives or friends when called for by them, for periods of time from part of a day to several days, to determine how he adjusts to life outside the institution. Syn. *home visit*.

two-physician certificate. A medical certificate executed by two licensed physicians (or two psychiatrists or one psychiatrist and one physician) recommending that a person believed to be mentally ill or retarded be received by a suitable psychiatric institution for care and treatment. The certificate is given upon petition by a relative, friend, person with whom the mentally ill individual resides, or by a local health official. Most jurisdictions require that the certificate be completed within a specified time (usually ten days) after the petition is made. Some states accept certificates that have been completed by the two physicians simultaneously; other states require that such medical examination be made by each physician in the absence of the other. In some states, the two-physician certificate is valid indefinitely or until the patient or someone in his behalf makes written application for release or until the institution discharges him or places him on convalescent status; in other states, such a patient may be retained only for a specified period of time at the expiration of which he must either be discharged or a new form of admission arranged.

visits to psychiatric patients. Psychiatric institutions have varying schedules of visiting days and hours, but under ordinary circumstances any patient who is critically ill may be seen at any time, providing his condition will not be aggravated by the visit. Visits by young children are generally discouraged. Visitors are usually prohibited from bringing food that is excluded from a special diet and implements, such as can openers, paring knives, and other objects, which may lead to accidents. Money brought for patients is deposited with a designated representative of the institution, who issues a receipt for it. Such money is made available to the patient for modest purchases at the hospital store. Gratuities to hospital personnel are forbidden by law.

visitors. See *board of governors, visitors, or managers.*

voluntary application for admission. Provision is made for an individual to request treatment in a psychiatric institution. His request, in writing, remains in force for a stated period of time (usually from 10 to 30 days), at the conclusion of which he may request in writing to be released. Such request is granted unless, upon advice of the hospital director, a more binding arrangement (e.g., court certification) has been made to provide continued hospital treatment.

will made by patient. See under *legal papers.*